SCHOLASTIC

100 MATHS LESSONS

Terms and conditions

IMPORTANT – PERMITTED USE AND WARNINGS – READ CAREFULLY BEFORE USING

Recommended system requirements:

- Windows: XP (Service Pack 3), Vista (Service Pack 2), Windows 7 or Windows 8 with 2.33GHz processor
- Mac: OS 10.6 to 10.8 with Intel Core™ Duo processor
- 1GB RAM (recommended)
- 1024 x 768 Screen resolution
- CD-ROM drive (24x speed recommended)
- 16-bit sound card
- Adobe Reader (version 9 recommended for Mac users)
- Broadband internet connections (for installation and updates)

For all technical support queries, please phone Scholastic Customer Services on 0845 6039091.

Book End, Range Road, Witney, Oxfordshire, OX29 0YD
www.scholastic.co.uk

© 2014, Scholastic Ltd

1 2 3 4 5 6 7 8 9   4 5 6 7 8 9 0 1 2 3

British Library Cataloguing-in-Publication Data
A catalogue record for this book is available from the British Library.

ISBN 978-1407-12776-7
Printed by Bell & Bain Ltd, Glasgow

Due to the nature of the web we cannot guarantee the content or links of any site mentioned. We strongly recommend that teachers check websites before using them in the classroom.

Author
John Davis, Sonia Tibbatts and Caroline Clissold

Series Editor
Ann Montague-Smith

Editorial team
Emily Jefferson, Jenny Wilcox, Roanne Charles, Vicky Butt and Sara Wiegand

Cover Design
Andrea Lewis

Design Team
Sarah Garbett, Shelley Best and Andrea Lewis

CD-ROM development
Hannah Barnett, Phil Crothers, MWA Technologies Private Ltd

Typesetting and illustrations
Ricky Capanni, International Book Management

MIX
Paper from responsible sources
FSC® C007785

Contents

Introduction

About the series

The *100 Maths Lessons* series is designed to meet the requirements of the 2014 National Curriculum, Mathematics Programme of Study. There are six books in the series for Years 1–6, and each book contains lesson plans, resources and ideas matched to the new curriculum. These six titles – along with the accompanying *100 Maths Planning Guide* – have been carefully structured to ensure that a progressive and appropriate school curriculum can be planned and taught throughout the primary years.

About the 2014 Curriculum

The curriculum documentation for Mathematics provides a yearly programme for Years 1 to 6 (ages 5 to 11).

The new curriculum goes further than the previous version with times tables to 12 x 12 by Year 4, an early introduction to long division and an increasingly complex understanding of fractions and decimals. The new curriculum also has a strong focus on varied and frequent practice of the fundamentals of maths – mastery of number facts and times tables should be developed throughout the primary phase.

There is a renewed emphasis on reasoning mathematically and solving problems with particular emphasis on multi-step problems and problems in the context of measurement, money and time. The main coverage of the use and application of mathematics however can be found in the aims of the curriculum:

> *The National Curriculum for Mathematics aims to ensure that all pupils:*
> - *become fluent in the fundamentals of mathematics, including through varied and frequent practice with increasingly complex problems over time, so that pupils have conceptual understanding and are able to recall and apply their knowledge rapidly and accurately to problems*
> - *reason mathematically by following a line of enquiry, conjecturing relationships and generalisations, and developing an argument, justification or proof using mathematical language*
> - *can solve problems by applying their mathematics to a variety of routine and non-routine problems with increasing sophistication, including breaking down problems into a series of simpler steps and persevering in seeking solutions.*

Terminology

The curriculum terminology has changed; the main terms used are:
- **Domains:** The main areas of mathematical study, such as Number and Geometry.
- **Topics:** These are identified in each weekly planning grid and drill the domains down into 'Place value', 'Addition and subtraction' and so on.
- **Curriculum objectives:** These are the statutory programme of study statements or objectives.
- **Appendix:** Any reference to an appendix refers to the Mathematics Apendix 1 'Examples of formal written methods for addition, subtraction, multiplication and division.'

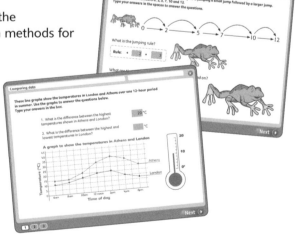

■ SCHOLASTIC

About the book

This book is divided by term and week with a summary heading giving an indication of the week's work. Each week follows the same structure:

Weekly overview

At the start of each week you will find a summary of what is covered, which includes:

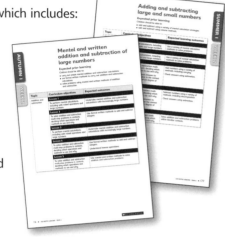

- **Expected prior learning:** What the children are expected to know before starting the work in the chapter.
- **Weekly planning grid:** A lesson-by-lesson breakdown of the coverage of each week – by 'topic', 'curriculum objectives' and 'expected outcomes'.
- **Oral and mental starters:** Suggested activities that might be used from the bank of starters that follow each half-term's lessons.
- **Overview of progression:** A brief explanation of the expected progress that children should make through each week's work.
- **Watch out for:** Possible mathematical misconceptions with ideas for addressing them.
- **Creative context:** How the week's work could link to other 2014 curriculum areas.
- **Vocabulary:** Key vocabulary to introduce or consolidate. (Words in bold also appear in the glossary, see CD-ROM notes on page 7.)
- **Preparation/You will need:** A full list of resources required from book and CD, as well as any general class resources requiring preparation. (A full resource list is given on page 256.)
- **Further practice:** Ideas for consolidating learning using additional resources or practical activities.

Lessons

Each half term contains six weeks' work. Each week contains five lessons. Each lesson includes the following:

- **Curriculum objectives:** A list of the relevant objectives from the Programme of Study.
- **Success criteria:** Expected outcomes for the lesson written as 'can do' statements.
- **You will need:** List of required resources.
- **Whole-class work:** Ideas for working together as a class.

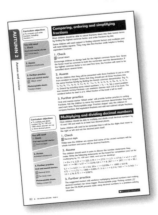

- **Group/Paired/Independent work:** Teaching notes for paired, groups or independent work.
- **Differentiation:** Ideas to support children who are not sufficiently fluent with concepts or to challenge children to apply their understanding (see 2014 National Curriculum aims for further information on the approach to differentiation).
- **Progress check:** 'Mini-plenaries' to enable teachers to check progress throughout the lesson.
- **Review:** Opportunity to reflect on children's learning, and address any misconceptions.

Assess and review

At the end of each half term are activities designed to assess children's understanding or mastery of key curriculum objectives. These can be conducted during the half-term's lessons or at the end, in an 'assess and review week'.

There are four curriculum objectives covered in each half–term. Each section includes ideas to:

- Check progress using appropriate starter activities.
- Assess children's learning using a mix of activities, problems and puzzles.
- Provide further practice activities to consolidate their understanding.

Oral and mental starter activities

In each half term a bank of oral and mental starters is provided. These can be used flexibly to address particular requirements, though suggestions are made within each weekly overview as to which starters might be used across a week's lessons. Each starter includes modelled teacher questions to probe children's ability to recall facts, rehearse strategies or apply learning.

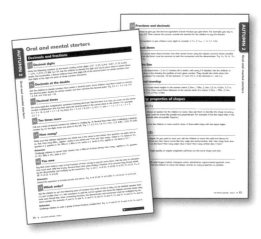

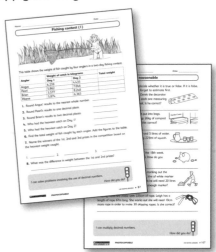

Photocopiable pages

At the end of each chapter, you will find a bank of photocopiable pages linked to the 'Assess and review' section. These sheets offer an 'I can...' statement at the bottom to allow self-assessment of pupil progress towards a particular curriculum objective. Ask the children to colour in the traffic lights next to each statement green, amber or red to reflect their confidence with the objective. There is also space for comments. Additional sheets, linked to the lessons, can be found on the CD-ROM (see page 7 for further information).

Equipment list

This provides an overview of all of the classroom resources required to teach each year's lessons. The resources are broken down by mathematics topic.

Vocabulary list

This provides a list of all key vocabulary to introduce or consolidate over the course of the year. Words appearing in bold type also appear in the glossary (see page 7 for further information).

■ SCHOLASTIC

About the CD-ROM

The CD-ROM contains:

- Printable versions of the photocopiable sheets from the book and additional photocopiable sheets as referenced in the lesson plans.
- Interactive activities for children to complete or to use on the whiteboard.
- Interactive teaching resources such as 'Number grids' and 'Pattern squares', designed to support whole–class teaching.
- Printable versions of the lesson plans and the oral and mental starters.
- Digital versions of the lesson plans with the relevant resources linked to them.

Getting started

- Put the CD-ROM into your CD-ROM drive.
    - For Windows users, the install wizard should autorun, if it fails to do so then navigate to your CD-ROM drive. Then follow the installation process.
    - For Mac users, copy the disk image file to your hard drive. After it has finished copying, double-click it to mount the disk image. Navigate to the mounted disk image and run the installer. After installation the disk image can be unmounted and the DMG can be deleted from the hard drive.
- To complete the installation of the program, you need to open the program and click 'Update' in the pop-up. **NB** This CD-ROM is web-enabled and the content needs to be downloaded from the internet to your hard-drive to populate the CD-ROM with the relevant resources. A web connection is only required on first use, after which you will be able to use the CD–ROM without any connection. If at any point any content is updated you will receive a pop-up message upon start–up when you are next connected to the web. You will then have the option to update the content as required.

Navigating the CD-ROM

There are two options to navigate the CD-ROM, either as a Child or as a Teacher.

Child

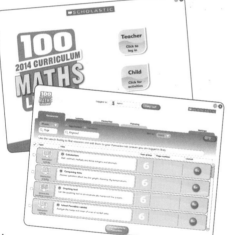

- Click on the 'Child' button on the first menu screen. In the second menu click on the relevant year group (please note only the books installed on the machine or network will be accessible. You can also rename year groups to match your school's naming conventions via Teacher > Settings > Rename Books area.)
- A list of interactive activities will be displayed; children need to locate the correct class or year group and click 'Go' to launch.
- There is the opportunity to print or save a PDF of the results of each activity on completion.

Teacher

- Click on the 'Teacher' button on the first menu screen and you will be taken to a menu showing which of the *100 Maths Lessons* titles you have purchased. From here, you can also access the credits and 'Getting started' information
- To enter the product, click 'Next' in the bottom right of the screen.
- You can then enter a password (the password is: login).
- On first use:

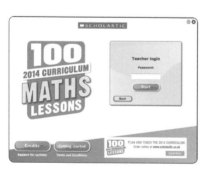

    - Enter as a Guest by clicking on the 'Guest' button.
    - If desired, create a profile for yourself by adding your name to the list of users. Profiles allow you to save favourites and to specify which year group(s) you wish to be able to view.
    - Go to 'Settings' to create a profile for yourself – click 'Add user' and enter your name. Then choose the year groups you wish to have access to (you can return to this screen to change this at any time). Click on 'Login' at the top of the screen to re-enter the CD-ROM with your new profile.
- On subsequent uses you can then select your name from the drop-down list.
- The 'Guest' option will always be available if you, or a colleague, prefer to use this.
- When you have set up your profile, you can then save activities or lessons in 'Favourites'.

For more information about how to use the CD-ROM, please refer to the 'Help' file which can be found in the teacher area of the CD-ROM. It is displayed as a red button with a question mark inside, on the right-hand side of the screen just underneath the 'Settings' tab.

Place value and rounding

Expected prior learning

Children should be able to:

- read, write and order numbers up to 1 million and determine the value of each digit in large numbers
- round integers to the nearest 10, 100 and 1000.

Topics	Curriculum objectives	Expected outcomes
Number and place value	**Lesson 1**	
	To read, write, order and compare numbers up to 10,000,000 and determine the value of each digit.	Read, write, order, compare and convert numerals to words, and vice versa, up to 10 million.
	Lesson 2	
	To read, write, order and compare numbers up to 10,000,000 and determine the value of each digit. To solve number and practical problems.	Determine the value of each digit in a number up to the value of 10 million. Write large numbers using expanded notation.
	Lesson 3	
	To read, write, order and compare numbers up to 10,000,000 and determine the value of each digit. To solve number and practical problems.	Identify and compare in numerals and words large numbers found in examples of everyday statistics.
	Lesson 4	
	To round any whole number to a required degree of accuracy.	Round numbers to the nearest 100 and the nearest 1000.
	Lesson 5	
	To round any whole number to a required degree of accuracy. To solve number and practical problems that involve all of the above.	Round numbers in a practical situation, for example to the nearest million pounds or hundred pounds when comparing earnings.

Preparation

Lesson 1: copy 'Right place (1)' for each pair; write six- and seven-digit numbers on the board

Lesson 2: copy 'Digit circles' for each pair; write seven-digit numbers on the board, with single digits circled in different-coloured pens

Lesson 3: copy 'Think big' for each child; try to find examples of very large numbers from newspapers, magazines and web pages

Lesson 5: copy 'Superstars' for each child

You will need

Photocopiable sheets
'Right place (1) and (2)'; 'Digit circles'; 'Think big'; 'Superstars'

General resources
'Number cards 0–9'

Equipment
Number flip books; abacus charts; individual whiteboards; dice (optional); counting blocks

Further practice
'Right place (2)' offers further practice of comparing and ordering numbers to 10,000,000.

Oral and mental starters suggested for week 1
See the bank of starters on page 44. Oral and mental starters are also on the CD-ROM.

1 Place value

2 Digit spotting

3 Roundup

Overview of progression
During this week, children will extend their knowledge of place value to reach 10 million. They will practise converting digits into words and vice versa. There will be the opportunity to register their knowledge of place value by showing numbers on an abacus framework. There are activities in which the children can compare the sizes of numbers and also place them in the correct order, smallest to largest and vice versa. Later, the children will be rounding numbers to the nearest 10, 100 and 1000. To extend this, they will also be asked to round large numbers to the nearest million.

Watch out for
Some children may have problems placing digits in the correct place value columns. Make sure knowledge of six-digit numbers is secure before proceeding to millions. Continue to use the abacus frameworks if children have difficulty knowing where to position zeros as place-holders. If children have problems rounding three-digit numbers to the nearest ten and four-digit numbers to the nearest hundred, make sure they focus on looking for and changing the correct digit(s).

Creative context
Encourage children to look out for and record large numbers in newspaper and magazine stories and in television news reports.

Vocabulary
approximately, approximating, compare, digit, expanded notation, hundred, index, million, nearest, nearly, notation, numeral, order, place-holder, place value, roughly, rounding, thousand

Curriculum objectives
● To read, write, order and compare numbers up to 10,000,000 and determine the value of each digit.

Success criteria
● I can read, write, order and compare numbers up to ten million.

You will need
Photocopiable sheets
'Right place (1) and (2)'
General resources
'Number cards 0–9'
Equipment
Number flip books; abacus charts; counting blocks

Differentiation
Less confident learners
Children should work with a teaching assistant. They would benefit from the use of abacus charts at an early stage, and equipment like counting blocks may also prove useful.
More confident learners
Set a series of word problems involving large numbers. For example:
Write in digits the number which is:
a) a thousand more than a million
b) ten less than a million
c) ten more than a million
d) a thousand less than a million.

Lesson 1
Oral and mental starter 1

Main teaching activities

Whole-class work: Write some six- or seven-digit numbers on the board. Ask the children to say the number in words so you can write these alongside. Repeat the process, but this time start with numbers written as words and ask the children to give you the digits. Remind the children of the importance of the use of zero as a place-holder, for example in: 702,315, 945,004, 1,004,278 and 7,120,507.

Paired work: Ask the children to work in pairs with a set of number flips between them. Challenge one child to make up a six- or seven-digit number using the number flips and the other child has to say the number (as it would be written in words, not just the individual digits). Then ask the partners to switch over. Then change the activity so that the children take it in turns to say a six- or seven-digit number in words that has to be shown in numerals on the number flips chart.

Progress check: Invite children in their pairs to show examples of the six- or seven-digit numbers they have produced. Ask them to explain the methods they use to identify the value of particular digits in a number. Ask: *Is it easier to start with the smaller-value digits or the larger-value digits? Which of the larger-value digits are most difficult to identify and name?* Can the children explain the importance of using the zero digit in our number system?

Whole-class work: Bring the class back together at this point. Show the children an eight-line abacus on the interactive whiteboard. Identify the million column and explain that the column to the left of it will be the ten million column. Ask the children to name the column headings, going up in size from the right-hand side of the abacus and multiplying by 10 each time: 1, 10, 100, 1000, 10,000, 100,000, 1,000,000, 10,000,000. Repeat the process coming down from the left-hand side, this time dividing by 10 each time: 10,000,000, 1,000,000, 100,000, 10,000, 1000, 100, 10, 1. Practise writing some seven-digit numbers for the children to repeat in word form, for example: 5,645,931 and 7,952,070.

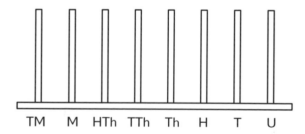

TM   M   HTh   TTh   Th   H   T   U

Paired work: Ask the children to return to their pairs. Provide them with photocopiable page 'Right place (1)' from the CD-ROM. The activities on this sheet offer practice of writing large numbers in both words and digits. Further practice activity 'Right place (2)' involves making the largest and smallest numbers from a given set of seven digits, and placing numbers in order of size.

Review
Go over the work the children have done in converting large numbers from figures into words and vice versa. Look, for example, at 8,213,591 as words, and five million, four hundred and twenty-seven thousand, six hundred and seventeen as figures. Ensure the children are confident about the position of zeros as place-holders in large numbers, such as 4,042,199 and 8,567,004. Ask: *How would you say these numbers?* Show the children a set of seven number cards, for example: 5, 2, 7, 3, 9, 6 and 1. Ask: *What is the smallest number that can be made?* (1,235,679.) *What is the largest number that can be made?* (9,765,321.) Challenge the children to make a selection of some of the other seven-digit numbers possible and place them in order of size.

■SCHOLASTIC

Curriculum objectives
● To read and write numbers up to 10,000,000 and determine the value of each digit.
● To solve number and practical problems.

Success criteria
● I can determine the value of each digit in a large number.

You will need
Photocopiable sheets
'Digit circles'
Equipment
Individual whiteboards

Differentiation
Less confident learners

Children should spend time working on the examples of expanded notation, starting with the lowest numbers.

More confident learners

Move children on to examine even larger numbers. Use 714,389,625, as an example. Ask: *Which digit is in the hundred million place? In which place is the digit 1? Write this number in words.*

Lesson 2 — Oral and mental starter 1

Main teaching activities

Whole-class work: Explain to the children that the purpose of this lesson is to help them identify and name the value of each single digit within a large number. Write a number of examples on the board, for instance, 7,564,370. Circle the 6 and ask: *What is the value of the 6?* (Sixty thousand.)

Demonstrate to the children strategies for either counting *down* the columns on the abacus chart from the largest digit – on the left (million), or counting *up* the columns from the smallest digit – on the right (one).

Go on to explain that writing numbers in full, using a method known as expanded notation, can also show the value of single digits. For example: 6,571,255 can be expanded in full to show
6,000,000 + 500,000 + 70,000 + 1000 + 200 + 50 + 5.

Paired work: Provide each pair with photocopiable page 'Digit circles' from the CD-ROM. They are asked to identify the value of certain digits in seven- and eight-digit numbers and to use expanded notation as a way of developing their digit recognition.

Progress check: Write some seven-digit numbers on the board. Circle some of the digits. Challenge the children to write on their individual whiteboards and show the value of each digit as you circle it.

Review

Discuss some real-life situations in which very large numbers are used. Challenge the children: *How would you say and write the following numbers in full?*

- *A transfer fee of £5.8 million*
- *A distance in space of 230 million kilometres*
- *A city's population of 2¾ million people*

Curriculum objectives
● As lesson 2.

Success criteria
● I can write large numbers in numerals and words.
● I can identify, order and compare large numbers found in everyday life.

You will need
Photocopiable sheets
'Think big'
Equipment
Large numbers given in news stories/web pages; abacus charts and number cards

Differentiation
Less confident learners

Help them to make some of the numbers on abacus charts or number cards.

More confident learners

Ask children to write large numbers including fractions in a different way.

Lesson 3 — Oral and mental starter 1

Main teaching activities

Whole-class work: Tell the children that they are going to discover more about everyday situations in which large numbers are used. From discussion, establish that they are found in newspapers, magazines, reference books, news bulletins and so on. Share some examples if you have them. Explain to the children that, therefore, it is important that they are able to read, write, compare and order such numbers. Give out photocopiable page 46 'Think big'. Go through each of the sections with the children. Revise key fractions of one million with the children such as ½ million = 500,000, ¼ million = 250,000 and ¾ million = 750,000.

Independent work: Ask the children to complete photocopiable page 46 'Think big'.

Progress check: Bring the class together after each section of the photocopiable sheet has been attempted. Share strategies used and review progress. Ask: *Which are the largest numbers you have come across? Which are the smallest? Which numbers are the most difficult to understand? Are there examples where numbers have been rounded off?*

Review

Invite children to read out some of their answers and explain the way in which they were able to decide how to say and record the large numbers given. How did they decide on the number of digits that needed to be used? How did they decide where zeros should be placed?

Curriculum objectives
• To round any whole number to a required degree of accuracy.
Success criteria
• I can round numbers accurately.

You will need
Equipment
Dice and/or number cards

Differentiation
Less confident learners
Check children can work confidently with four-digit numbers and rounding to the nearest 1000 before moving on.

More confident learners
Let children use rounding to find approximate answers to additions and subtractions. For example: 31,205 + 49,854 = 30,000 + 50,000, so an approximate answer is 80,000.

Lesson 4   Oral and mental starter 3

Main teaching activities

Whole-class work: On the board, revise rounding numbers to the nearest thousand. Five hundred is the halfway point. Numbers up to 500, therefore, go back, and numbers of 500 or more go up. Work through some examples: 1302 goes back to 1000; 5720 and 8500 would go up to 6000 and 9000 respectively. Also practise instances where four-digit numbers are rounded to the nearest 10, 100 and 1000. For example: 2674 is 2670 to the nearest 10; 2700 to the nearest 100; and 3000 to the nearest 1000. Repeat with five-digit numbers (halfway point 5000) and six-digit numbers (halfway point 50,000). For example: round 14,237 to the nearest 10 (14,240), to the nearest 100 (14,200), to the nearest 1000 (14,000), and to the nearest 10,000 (10,000). Round 538,652 to the nearest 10 (538,650), ...100 (538,700), ...1000 (539,000), ...10,000 (540,000) and 100,000 (500,000).

Progress check: Ask volunteers to talk through the rules being practised. *How would you round a number to the nearest 100? ...to the nearest 1000? Are there any tips to help remember the rules?* Prompt the children to explain the rules by giving examples.

Paired work: Ask the children to generate five-digit numbers using dice or number cards, then round them to the nearest 100, 1000 and 10,000. They should also generate six-digit numbers for rounding to the nearest 1000, 10,000 and 100,000. Some children should progress to rounding to the nearest 1,000,000.

Review

Work through some of the rounding examples the children have generated with their dice or number cards. Check that the rules for rounding to the nearest 1000, 10,000 and 100,000 are secure. Look through the more confident learners' approximated answers to addition and subtraction calculations. Ask some children to explain how they tackled this activity.

Curriculum objectives

Curriculum objectives
● To round any whole number to a required degree of accuracy.

Success criteria
● I can round numbers accurately in a real-life situation.

You will need

Photocopiable sheets
'Superstars'

Differentiation

Less confident learners

Work with this group to ensure they fully understand rounding numbers to the nearest 100, 1000 and 10,000 before moving on to rounding off larger numbers.

More confident learners

Ask children to investigate the shorthand way of writing very large rounded numbers that are multiples of 1000, 10,000, 100,000 and 1,000,000 using index notation. $1000 = 10^3$, $10,000 = 10^4$, $100,000 = 10^5$, and so on. 400,000 can be written as 4×10^5, and 9,000,000 can be 9×10^6 to the power of 6.

Lesson 5

Oral and mental starter 3

Main teaching activities

Whole-class work: Revise quickly the activities that have been covered already in this week on place value and rounding off numbers. Write some problems on the board for the children to solve and then discuss. Try the following examples to get you started.

● *How would you say this number in words: 8,572,904?*
● *Write this number in figures: four million, two hundred and fifteen thousand, six hundred and two.*
● *What are the values of the two 9s in this number: 7,951,793?*
● *Round this number to the nearest 100, ...1000, ...10,000 ...and 100,000: 496,257.*

Independent work: Explain to the children that they are now going to complete a number-rounding activity individually using a practical problem-solving situation, in this case involving the wages of some of the world's top football players. Say rounding is often done to make it easier to compare players' salaries, especially in a news programme when a general audience is listening and/or watching. Words like about, approximately and roughly have to be used to show that rounding has taken place. Give out photocopiable page 'Superstars' from the CD-ROM. Explain to the children that they will have to round off the annual payments made to players to the nearest million and then the amounts given to the players each week to the nearest £100, £1000, £10,000 and £100,000.

Progress check: Stop the children at intervals as they work through the activities on the sheet. Ask volunteers to come out to the board to give their

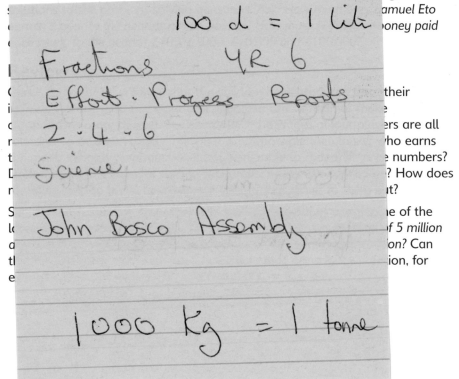

Mental and written addition and subtraction of large numbers

Expected prior learning

Children should be able to:

- carry out simple mental addition and subtraction calculations
- use formal written methods to carry out addition and subtraction calculations
- solve problems using mental and written methods of addition and subtraction.

Topic	Curriculum objectives	Expected outcomes
Addition and subtraction	**Lesson 1**	
	To perform mental calculations, including with mixed operations and large numbers.	Undertake mental addition and subtraction calculations with increasingly large numbers.
	Lesson 2	
	To solve addition and subtraction multi-step problems in contexts, deciding which operations and methods to use and why.	Use formal written methods to add and subtract integers.
	Lesson 3	
	To perform mental calculations, including with mixed operations and large numbers.	Undertake mental addition and subtraction calculations with increasingly large numbers.
	Lesson 4	
	To solve addition and subtraction multi-step problems in contexts, deciding which operations and methods to use and why.	Use formal written methods to add and subtract integers. Understand inverse operations.
	Lesson 5	
	To solve addition and subtraction multi-step problems in contexts, deciding which operations and methods to use and why.	Use mental and written methods to solve addition and subtraction problems.

Preparation

Lesson 1: copy 'Quick-fire' for each pair

Lesson 2: copy 'Down the column' for each child

Lesson 3: copy 'Number pyramids' for each group

Lesson 4: copy 'Inkblots' for each group

Lesson 5: copy 'Checkouts' for each child

You will need

Photocopiable sheets
'Quick-fire'; 'Down the column'; 'Numbers pyramids'; 'Inkblots'; 'Checkouts'

General resources
Interactive teaching resource 'Squared paper'

Equipment
Individual whiteboards; squared paper

Further practice

Where required, demonstrate formal written methods on the interactive whiteboard using the interactive teaching resource 'Squared paper' to highlight how the units, tens, and so on line up. Give children some further 5- and 6-digit addition and subtraction sentences to practice those methods.

Oral and mental starters suggested for week 2

See the bank of starters on page 44. Oral and mental starters are also on the CD-ROM.

4 Add and subtract

5 Five seconds

6 Tell me about it

Overview of progression

The main aim of the activities this week is to ensure that children are able to carry out addition and subtraction calculations competently both mentally and using more formal written methods. A number of strategies are revised for adding and subtracting increasingly large numbers mentally. Standard column methods for addition and subtraction are also taught, with digits placed correctly and lining up underneath each other. Lessons give practice in the decomposition method of subtraction. The close relationship between addition and subtraction is also stressed and the children explore how this can be used for checking answers. Skills focused on during the week are put to use in a practical problem-solving situation.

Watch out for

Discuss the merits and disadvantages of various strategies when looking at ways of adding and subtracting. Help the children with making decisions about when to use mental methods, mental with jottings, or written calculations. Ensure that digits are transferred correctly from a horizontal setting to a vertical setting and that digits are placed in the right columns underneath each other.

Creative context

Encourage the children to make up story-based contexts, situations and scenarios in which the process of correct addition and/or subtraction is vital to the way in which things develop.

Vocabulary

addition, calculation, carry, decimal place, decimal point, decomposition, decrease, difference, digit, double, increase, integer, inverse, less than, minus, more than, numeral, operation, partition, plus, predict, problem, reason, reduce, relationship, solution, strategy, subtract, subtraction, sum, total, unit

Curriculum objectives
● To perform mental calculations, including with mixed operations and large numbers.

Success criteria
● I can carry out mental additions and subtractions using different strategies.

You will need
Photocopiable sheets
'Quick-fire'

Differentiation
Less confident learners
Work with this group to ensure they understand the procedures being used. Let them work with smaller numbers initially and provide support for the more challenging calculations on 'Quick-fire'.

More confident learners
Encourage children to make up problems that are more complicated – using several operational steps instead of just one – and using increasingly large numbers.

Lesson 1
Oral and mental starter 4

Main teaching activities
Whole-class work: Let the children know that the purpose of this lesson is to revise and practise some of the important strategies that can be used when carrying out mental addition and subtraction calculations.

Look first at finding a *difference* between large numbers by counting up through the next multiple of 1000, 10,000 or 100,000. Share some examples on the board. Ask: *What is the difference between 1004 and 989?* (989 to 1000 would be 11 and 11 + 4 = 15) *10,003 and 9985? 100,017 and 99,990?* Then look at partitioning numbers into 100,000, 10,000, 1000 and so on. For example:

$$125,272 + 343,714 = 400,000 + 60,000 + 8000 + 900 + 80 + 6 = 468,986$$

and:

$$120,594 - 74,263 = 46,000 + 300 + 30 + 1 = 46,331$$

Also consider identifying and using near doubles. For example:

$$14,991 + 14,997 = 15,000 \text{ doubled} - 9 - 3 = 29,988$$

and:

$$250,000 + 260,000 = 250,000 \text{ doubled} + 10,000,$$
$$\text{or } 260,000 \text{ doubled} - 10,000 = 510,000$$

Finally, stress to the children the importance of the close relationship between addition and subtraction. Explain that if we know, for example, that $635,247 - 384,293 = 250,954$, then it follows that $635,247 - 250,954 = 384,293$, and $250,954 + 384,293 = 635,247$. Tell children to think about using reverse order, equivalent calculations and inverse operations.

Paired work: Provide pairs of children with photocopiable page 'Quick-fire' from the CD-ROM. This asks them to solve problems by choosing and using appropriate addition and subtraction strategies at each stage.

Progress check: Invite some pairs to tell the other children which method of calculation they used to work out certain answers. Can the children explain to the others exactly what they did? How did they make their choice? Invite everyone to consider if they could have used more than one method.

Review
Check the solutions to the problems given on the photocopiable sheet. What methods did they use to check that their calculations were correct? Did they use reverse order, equivalent calculations or inverse operations? Ask the children what they found. Ask: *Were the addition calculations easier to answer than the subtraction ones, or the other way around?* Ask more confident children to pose new questions for the rest of the children to answer.

Curriculum objectives
● To solve addition and subtraction problems, deciding which operations and methods to use and why.

Success criteria
● I can add and subtract, using formal written methods.

You will need
Photocopiable sheets
'Down the column'
Equipment
Individual whiteboards

Differentiation
Less confident learners
Support this group when they are working and ensure they focus on the first part of 'Down the column', where numbers are smaller.

More confident learners
This group should work through the second part of 'Down the column' as quickly as possible and then concentrate on the third part (the extension) at the end.

Lesson 2 — Oral and mental starter 5

Main teaching activities

Whole-class work: Explain to the children that they are going to revise the standard column methods of addition and subtraction. Write on the board the calculations shown below. Then demonstrate to the children how to add each column, carrying the numbers into the next column, and so on. Remind the children that digits should be placed correctly, with units, ten, hundreds, thousands, ten thousands and so on, lining up beneath each other.

$$473291 + 387293 = 860584$$

$$942895 - 510531 = 432364$$

Now write on the board: 475,216 − 183,542. Explain the decomposition method of subtraction to the children, working it through on the board with them. As you work on the board, the children should also write the working out on their own individual whiteboards.

$$475216 - 183542 = 291674$$

Ensure that the children understand that the bottom row is taken from the top row and not vice versa. Help them to see that 2 away from 6 in the units column leaves 4, but that in the tens column, 4 cannot be taken from 1, so we need to take 1 from the hundreds column and so on. Work through another example with the children, asking them to explain each step in the process.

Independent work: Ask the children to work on photocopiable page 'Down the column' from the CD-ROM.

Progress check: Check at intervals during the independent work to ensure children are using the correct methods for column addition and subtraction. In addition, check which columns are added first. (Units, then tens, then hundreds...). Ask: *What happens to the numbers that are carried to the next column?* (They are added on.) *What is the method of subtraction being used called?* (Decomposition.) Encourage children to suggest why it has this name. (Because the top line is decomposed, or broken down, to allow subtraction to take place.)

Review

Write the following numbers on one line across the board: 25,379, 120, 453,769, 2003 and 75. Challenge the children to find the total on their whiteboards, using the column addition method. Check that they all understand the importance of writing the digits aligned in the correct place. Repeat the process with the calculation 759,264 − 201,769. Ask a confident child to come out to the board and demonstrate how the decomposition column method of subtraction works. Discuss the results with the others.

Curriculum objectives
● To perform mental calculations, including with mixed operations and large numbers.

Success criteria
● I can carry out mental addition and subtraction calculations with increasingly large numbers.

You will need

Photocopiable sheets
'Number pyramids'

Differentiation

Less confident learners
Organise children into mixed-ability groups to receive the support of other children.

More confident learners
When they have completed the pyramids targets of 1000 and 10,000, challenge children to make number pyramids with 100,000 as the target number at the top.

Main teaching activities

Whole-class work: Tell the children that they are going to use mental addition and subtraction calculations to make pairs of numbers add up to 1000 and 10,000. Write the following numbers on the board: 473, 609, 752 and 874. Discuss with the children:

● *What numbers would go with them to make 1000 each time?*
● *What do you think is the best method to use?*
● *Is it easier to subtract from 1000, or add on to reach 1000?*

Encourage the children to explain their choices. Extend this activity by asking the children how to make the following numbers to 10,000: 2307, 4002, 7893, 9276.

Progress check: Collect answers that children have written on individual whiteboards and discuss the methods used. Ask for volunteers to explain to the others how they carried out these mental calculations. Encourage them to use the board to illustrate the steps they took. Prompt as necessary, asking, for example: *How did you decide what method to choose? Was there always a certain method to be used or was there a choice in some cases?*

Whole-class work: Now show the children an example of a number pyramid with three rows of bricks, blank except for 1000 in the top brick. Explain that in number pyramids, the value of each brick is the sum of the values in the two bricks below. Starting with 1000 at the top, ask the children to complete the rest of the pyramid by either adding or subtracting mentally. For example:

	1000	
527		473
382	145	328

Work through other examples on the board, all with 1000 as the target. Move on to show the children an example of a four-row number pyramid, starting with 10,000 in the top brick. For example:

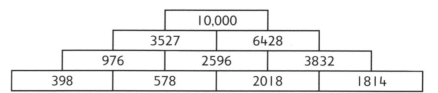

		10,000		
	3527		6428	
	976	2596	3832	
398	578		2018	1814

Group work: Arrange the children into small mixed-ability groups (of three or four children). Tell them that they are going to complete some number pyramids to reach either 1000 or 10,000. Explain that some of the pyramids will already have some numbers in, while others will be blank and will have to be filled in completely. Give out photocopiable page 'Number pyramids' from the CD-ROM to each group.

Review

Check the answers in the children's pyramid bricks. Write some examples on the board to talk through together. Also discuss the methods used each time. Did the children find a difference between a higher brick and a lower brick by counting up? Did they add or subtract a multiple of 100 or 1000 and then adjust? Did they use a partitioning method? How did they check their answers were correct?

Curriculum objectives
● To solve addition and subtraction multi-step problems, deciding which operations and methods to use and why.

Success criteria
● I can use formal written methods to add and subtract numbers.
● I know that addition and subtraction are inverse operations.

You will need
Photocopiable sheets
'Inkblots'
Equipment
Individual whiteboards

Differentiation
Less confident learners
Provide support as children first work through examples using three- and four-digit numbers.
More confident learners
Challenge children to devise additions and subtractions in which random numbers are missing.

Lesson 4
Oral and mental starter 5

Main teaching activities

Whole-class work: Write calculation a), below, on the board. Ask: *How might you find the missing number?* Elicit that you could subtract 14,269 from 74,153. Carry out the calculation, then check it:

a)
$$
\begin{array}{r}
14269 \\
+\ ????? \\
\hline
74153
\end{array}
$$

Try:
$$
\begin{array}{r}
{}^{6}\cancel{7}\ {}^{13}\cancel{4}\ {}^{10}\cancel{1}\ {}^{14}\cancel{5}\ {}^{1}\cancel{3} \\
-\quad 1\ 4\ 2\ 6\ 9 \\
\hline
5\ 9\ 8\ 4
\end{array}
$$

Check
$$
\begin{array}{r}
1\ 4\ 2\ 6\ 9 \\
+\ 5\ 9\ 8\ 8\ 4 \\
\hline
7\ 4\ 1\ 5\ 3 \\
{}_{1}\ \ {}_{1}\ \ {}_{1}
\end{array}
$$

Now try calculation b):

$$
\begin{array}{r}
?????\\
-\ 27418\\
\hline
9542
\end{array}
$$

$$
\begin{array}{r}
2\ 7\ 4\ 1\ 8 \\
+\quad 9\ 5\ 4\ 2 \\
\hline
3\ 6\ 9\ 6\ 0 \\
{}_{1}\ \ {}_{1}
\end{array}
$$

Check
$$
\begin{array}{r}
{}^{2}3\ {}^{1}6\ 9\ {}^{5}\cancel{6}\ {}^{1}0 \\
-\ 2\ 7\ 4\ 1\ 8 \\
\hline
9\ 5\ 4\ 2
\end{array}
$$

Ask the children how the numbers already given can be used to find the numbers that are missing. Remind them that addition and subtraction are inverse operations. Elicit that 27,418 + 9542 should equal the missing number. Ask the children to work through the next calculation on their whiteboards:

$$
\begin{array}{r}
54797 \\
-\ ????? \\
\hline
39651
\end{array}
$$

Check answers. Establish that 54,797 − 39,651 was needed to find the missing number: the inverse operation was not used this time.

Progress check: Check that the children understand the close relationship between addition and subtraction. Sometimes, but not always, the inverse operation can be used to find the solution.

Group work: The children should work on photocopiable page 'Inkblots' from the CD-ROM, on which stains have covered some important missing digits.

Review
Write on the board: 56,429 + 37,005 = 93,434, and 76,942 − 34,496 = 42,446. Ask: *What method would you use to check each answer is correct?* Make sure the children offer correct use of the inverse operation.

Curriculum objectives
● As lesson 4.
Success criteria
● I can solve addition and subtraction problems using mental and written methods.

You will need
Photocopiable sheets
'Checkouts'

Differentiation
Less confident learners
Help children to extract the calculations. Support when column addition and subtraction are needed.
More confident learners
Ask children to use the information on 'Checkouts' to pose other problems.

Lesson 5
Oral and mental starter 5

Main teaching activities

Whole-class work: Quickly revise with the whole class the main topics covered during the week involving adding and subtracting larger numbers both mentally and using written methods. Stress the close links between addition and subtraction and how the inverse operation can often be used to check the accuracy of calculations.

Tell the children they are going to put their skills of addition and subtraction into action in a problem-solving context. Advise them that they can work mentally, mentally with the help of jottings or by using written methods. Suggest that suitable methods of checking should also be used.

Independent work: Ask each child to work on photocopiable page 'Checkouts' from the CD-ROM.

Progress check: Discuss what methods the children have been using so far. Can any of the questions be done mentally or mentally with jottings? Are written methods always needed?

Review
Go through the answers to the photocopiable sheet. Discuss methods used. Ask more confident children to suggest extra questions for the others to answer.

Multiples, factors and prime numbers

Expected prior learning

Children should be able to:

- recall all their tables up to and including 12 × 12
- be aware of the differences between the terms *multiple*, *factor* and *prime number*
- identify some prime numbers
- solve problems involving all four operations.

Topic	Curriculum objectives	Expected outcomes
Multiplication and division	**Lesson 1**	
	To perform mental calculations, including with mixed operations and large numbers.	Recall all multiplication and division tables to 12 × 12. Recognise square numbers.
	Lesson 2	
	To identify common factors, common multiples and prime numbers.	Identify multiples of one-digit numbers.
	Lesson 3	
	To identify common factors, common multiples and prime numbers.	Identify common factors of two-digit numbers. Express numbers in prime factors. Find the prime factors of two-digit numbers.
	Lesson 4	
	To identify common factors, common multiples and prime numbers.	Recognise that prime numbers have only two factors. Identify prime numbers less than 100.
	Lesson 5	
	To solve problems involving addition, subtraction, multiplication and division.	Find multiples, factors and prime numbers. Solve problems involving addition, subtraction, multiplication and division.

Preparation

Lesson 4: copy 'Hundred square' for each child; prepare a large version with all the prime numbers circled

Lesson 5: copy 'Solve it' for each child

You will need

Photocopiable sheets
'Solve it'

General resources
'Hundred square'; interactive activity 'Prime time'; interactive activity 'Prime numbers to 100'

Equipment
Individual whiteboards; squared paper; highlighter pens; tables squares or charts

Further practice
Use the interactive activity 'Prime time' to further consolidate understanding of factors and prime numbers.

Oral and mental starters suggested for week 3

See the bank of starters on pages 44 and 45. Oral and mental starters are also on the CD-ROM.

6 Tell me about it

7 Answers please

8 Family of three

9 Who am I?

Overview of progression

During this week, the children will revise their tables up to 12 × 12, including the identification of square numbers up to 100. They will become aware of the close relationship between multiplication and division. There are activities this week involving multiples and number sequences, finding the factors of two-digit numbers and identifying the prime numbers between 1 and 100. Children will also be introduced to the term *prime factors* and learn how numbers can be reduced to this. The last lesson of the week will provide the opportunity to practise solving problems using all four of the main operations.

Watch out for

Children who do not have a good working knowledge of their tables will have difficulty with all aspects of multiplication and division. Watch out for confusion between the terms *multiple* and *factor*. Multiples are about multiplying (1 × 5 = 5, 2 × 5 = 10, 3 × 5 = 15, 4 × 5 = 20...) and factors are about division – numbers that go into other numbers. Remember to stress that prime numbers are almost always odd numbers (2 is the exception), but that not all odd numbers are prime numbers (15, 21, 39, for example). Some children may be unfamiliar with using indices as a shorthand way of expressing numbers as prime factors.

Creative context

Work on narrative situations where multiples feature strongly, for example numbers going up by the same amount each time. Objects increasing in fives (5, 10, 15, 20, 25 and so on) might work well. Look at how graphs will produce straight lines from zero if the numbers increase in constant proportion each time. Also think about exploring regular patterns in art using multiple blocks to make shapes, for example. Many of the mathematicians of Ancient Greece became fascinated with number patterns, especially Pythagoras and Archimedes.

Vocabulary

common multiple, consecutive, division, factor, factorise, index, indices, inverse, multiple, multiplication, pattern, prime factor, prime number, problem, **product**, **quotient**, relationship sequence, square number, solution

Curriculum objectives
- To perform mental calculations, including with mixed operations and large numbers.

Success criteria
- I can say my tables up to 12 × 12.
- I know the family of square numbers to 10 × 10.

You will need

Equipment
Individual whiteboards; tables squares or charts

Differentiation

Less confident learners
A thorough knowledge of multiplication tables is needed for this lesson. Some children may need to refer to tables squares or tables charts to check they are using the correct combinations of numbers.

More confident learners
Ask children to use larger numbers in their families of three, for example: 12, 300 and 25; 238, 17 and 14; 8400, 350 and 24.

Lesson 1 — Oral and mental starter 6

Main teaching activities

Whole-class work: Introduce the week's lessons by explaining to the children that in this first one they are going to look at the close relationship between multiplication and division and revise their knowledge of multiplication tables up to 12 × 12.

Write on the board some families of three (where a large number is a multiple of two smaller ones). For example, write: 9, 63 and 7; 4, 8 and 32; 4, 100 and 25; 50, 10 and 5. Ask the children to look carefully at the numbers. Say that the three numbers in a group will make *four* multiplication and division facts. If, for example, they choose 9, 63 and 7, they could write: 9 × 7 = 63, 7 × 9 = 63, 63 ÷ 7 = 9, and 63 ÷ 9 = 7. Try out some of the other families you have written on the board.

Move on to include square numbers so that this group of numbers can be revised as well. Point out that with a square number, only *two* statements can be written. For example, considering 36, we can only write: 6 × 6 = 36 and 36 ÷ 6 = 6. Compare this with, for example, 63, above: (9 × 7 = 63, 7 × 9 = 63, 63 ÷ 7 = 9, and 63 ÷ 9 = 7).

Now ask the children to choose their own groups of three numbers and convert them into four statements on their individual whiteboards.

Progress check: Make sure that the children have written two facts for multiplication and two for division for each set of numbers. Can the children start with a division fact and provide the other family members from there? Did they need to do any actual calculating to work out each of the number facts? How quickly could they complete each set?

Paired work: Ask the children to repeat the activity from whole-class work, but this time working together to use larger numbers, especially multiples of 10 and 100. For example: 30, 50 and 1500; 2100, 30 and 70; 50, 4500 and 90; 200, 140,000 and 700; 6000, 400 and 2,400,000.

Review

Ask for volunteers among the pairs who can share some of the groups of three that they have made. Ask all the children: *Is the relationship between multiplication and division clearer now? What other pairs of operations go together in the same way?* (Addition and subtraction.) Challenge the children to demonstrate how a multiplication statement can be used to check a division calculation and how a division statement can be used to check a multiplication calculation. In simple terms, for example: 20 ÷ 5 = 4, so 5 × 4 = 20, and 6 × 8 = 48, so 48 ÷ 6 = 8. What do the children understand now by the terms *inverse operation* and *square number*?

Curriculum objectives
- To identify common multiples.

Success criteria
- I can identify multiples of one-digit numbers.

You will need

Equipment

Squared paper; tables squares or charts

Differentiation

Less confident learners

Some children will be less familiar with some multiplication tables and will need tables squares or tables charts. Provide teaching assistant support for this group too.

More confident learners

Encourage children to use multiples of numbers beyond the 12 × 12 tables, such as 14, 15 and so on. Also ask them to look out for multiples that are common to more than one table list. For example, 8 is a multiple of 1, 2, 4 and 8, while 15 is a multiple of both 3 and 5 as well as 1 and 15. Also examine the term *lowest common multiple* which is important for work on fractions.

Lesson 2   Oral and mental starter 8

Main teaching activities

Whole-class work: Revise with the children their understanding that the *multiples* of a number are the numbers in its multiplication (times) table. Chant through the multiples of one-digit numbers. Try 4, for example, to start with; the multiples being 4, 8, 12, 16, 20... as far as 48. Then look at the multiples of 9: 9, 18, 27, 36, 45, 54... as far as 108.

Now try looking at some multiples of a number in reverse order too. For example, the multiples of 6 in reverse order are: 72, 66, 60, 54, 48... Try to include revision of all the tables including 11 and 12.

Progress check: Check that the children understand exactly what a multiple is by asking a few problem-solving questions. Write the following numbers on the board: 42, 18, 15, 27, 12, 30. Then ask the following questions. Point out that some of the answers will be outside the range of 12 x 12, for example 42 ÷ 3 = 14, though they should still be easy to find.

- *Which of the numbers are multiples of 2?* (42, 18, 12 and 30.)
- *Which of the numbers are multiples of 3?* (All of them.)
- *Which are multiples of 6?* (42, 18, 12 and 30.)
- *Which are multiples of 7?* (Only 42.)
- *Which are multiples of both 2 and 4 (common multiples of 2 and 4)?* (Only 12.)
- *Which are common multiples of 5 and 10?* (Only 30.)

Paired work: Organise the children into pairs and provide them with squared paper. Ask the children to take it in turns within their pairs to choose a one-digit number and to start off its list of multiples. For example, they might choose 5, so: 5, 10, 15, 20. Their partner then has to continue the sequence until they reach 12 times the number, so, from 25 up to 60. Or, they could use the squared paper to make a ladder of multiples with gaps in the sequence for their partner to complete. For example:

		72			
		??			
		??			
		??			
		48			
		42			
		36			
		??			
		??			
		??			
		12			
		6			

Encourage the children to try to include larger numbers if they can, such as multiples of 15, multiples of 20, and multiples of 30.

Review

Check through the work the children have done on making and completing their own and each other's multiple ladders. Pick out some examples of two-digit numbers they have produced, then pose some 'true or false' statements such as the following: *29 is a multiple of 3.* (False.) *36 is a multiple of 4.* (True.) *The multiples of 7 are all even.* (False.) *The multiples of 5 all end in 5 or 0.* (True.) *18 and 81 are common multiples of 3 and 9.* (True.) Ask more confident learners to share their findings on common multiples.

Curriculum objectives
- To identify common factors, common multiples and prime numbers.

Success criteria
- I can find the factors of two-digit numbers.
- I can express numbers in terms of prime factors.
- I can find the prime factors of two-digit numbers.

You will need

General resources
Interactive activity 'Prime time'

Equipment
Individual whiteboards

Differentiation

Less confident learners
Children should focus on finding the factors of one-digit numbers such as 6, 8 and 9 first, before moving on to small two-digit numbers like 12, 15, 24 and 30.

More confident learners
Ask children to demonstrate that the final roots of any factor 'tree' will be the same whichever factors they use. For example: $18 = 2 \times 9 = 2 \times 3 \times 3 = 2 \times 3^2$, while $18 = 3 \times 6 = 3 \times 2 \times 3 = 2 \times 3^2$.

Lesson 3

Main teaching activities

Whole-class work: Revise with the children that the factors of a number are the numbers that divide into it exactly without leaving any remainder. Ask for some examples so that you can write them on the board. The factors of 6, for example, are 1, 2, 3 and 6, while the factors of 14 are 1, 2, 7 and 14. Ask the children to supply you with the factors of other two-digit numbers, such as 16, 28 and 30. Remind them that 1 and the number itself will always be factors of any number.

Move on then to ask the children to find *common factors* of numbers. Remind the children that 5 is a common factor of 10 and 25 because it goes into both numbers exactly. Ask the children to name the common factors of 8 and 12 (1, 2 and 4), 6 and 10 (1 and 2), and 12 and 36 (1, 2, 3, 4 and 6).

Progress check: See if the children can put together their knowledge and understanding about multiples and factors by making up some 'guess the number' puzzles. Explain that the words *multiple* and *factor* must be used, but others can be added as well. Try these examples first:
- *I am a factor of 20. I am a multiple of 2 and 5. The sum of my digits is 1. Who am I? (10.)*
- *I am a factor of 24 and a multiple of 3. I am an even number. Who am I? (12.)*

Then, writing an example on the board, demonstrate how to express a number in *prime factors*. Explain that every whole number can be factored into a product of prime factors – it can be expressed using prime numbers only. Explain, too, that *indices* are used as a shorthand way of keeping statements brief. Write 36 on the board and, for 36, choose two factors such as 9 and 4. Show that you can break 9 and 4 down into their prime factors: 3×3 and 2×2 respectively. Explain that these are the lowest factors and they are both prime numbers. Write them again, using the shorthand method and say that, therefore, 2^2 and 3^2 are the prime factors of 36.

Paired work: Write the following numbers on the board: 8, 10, 20, 24, 32, 40 and 48. Ask the children, working in pairs and recording on their individual whiteboards, to write each number as a product of its prime factors. Stress that all stages in the process should be shown and that indices should be used to show an answer in its most concise form.

Progress check: Stop the children after a short while and work through the first example in detail. $8 = 2 \times 4 = 2 \times 2 \times 2 = 2^3$.

Review

Put a selection of other numbers on the board, perhaps 12, 16, 18 and 33, and some prime factors (2×3^2, 2^4, 3×11, and $2^2 \times 3$). Ask the children to work in pairs to match the numbers to the correct set of prime factors. Share answers, and work together to correct any mistakes and misunderstandings. The interactive activity 'Prime time' on the CD-ROM might also be used at this time to further consolidate children's understanding of prime factors and prime numbers.

Curriculum objectives

● To identify common factors, common multiples and prime numbers.

Success criteria

● I can identify all the prime numbers between 1 and 100.

You will need

General resources

'Hundred square'; interactive activity 'Prime numbers to 100'

Equipment

Highlighter pens; tables squares

Differentiation

Less confident learners

Children may need tables squares. Provide support and work as a group for the Sieve of Eratosthenes activity. Use the interactive 'Prime numbers to 100' with these children.

More confident learners

Children should go on to calculate prime numbers between 100 and 200. Ask them to find out more about Eratosthenes.

Lesson 4 — Oral and mental starter 4

Main teaching activities

Whole-class work: Revise that factors are whole numbers that divide into another number without a remainder. What do the children notice about the factors of numbers like 11, 13 and 17? Elicit that there are only two factors for each: 1 and the number itself. Recall that such numbers are called *prime numbers*. Ask the children for another prime number between 10 and 20. (19.)

Independent work: Tell the children they are going to carry out an investigation to reveal the prime numbers between 1 and 100. The method is called the Sieve of Eratosthenes after the Ancient Greek mathematician who developed it. Provide number squares (use 'Hundred square' from the CD-ROM) and highlighter pens. Stress that your instructions must be followed carefully.

- *Do not cross out 2. Start from 4 and count on in twos, crossing out the numbers.*
- *Do not cross out 3. Start from 6 and count in threes, crossing out every third number.*
- *Do not cross out 5. Start from 10, crossing out every fifth number.*
- *Do not cross out 7. Start from 14, crossing out every seventh number.*
- *Use a different-coloured pen to circle all the numbers that remain.*

Progress check: Discuss why some numbers have been crossed out more than once. Ask: *What name is given to the numbers that have been circled? Why is 1 not included?*

Paired work: Ask: *Is it true that every even number bigger than 6 can be written as the sum of two prime numbers?* (It works for 5 + 7 = 12 and 7 + 13 = 20, but are there others?) *Look at all the prime numbers between 5 and 100. Divide each by six. What is significant about the remainders? Why?*

Review

Display the 1–100 number square with the prime numbers marked so that the children can check their versions. Ask: *Apart from 2, why will there never be a prime number in the 2nd, 4th, 6th, 8th and 10th columns?*

Curriculum objectives

● To solve problems involving addition, subtraction, multiplication and division.

Success criteria

● I can find multiples, factors and prime numbers.
● I can solve problems by adding, subtracting, multiplying and dividing.

You will need

Photocopiable sheets

'Solve it'

Equipment

Tables squares; completed prime-number 100 squares

Differentiation

Less confident learners

Completed prime-number 100 squares will prove useful.

More confident learners

Children find perfect numbers.

Lesson 5 — Oral and mental starter 7

Main teaching activities

Whole-class work: Briefly revise the week. Ask: *What are the multiples of 7 from 7 to 84? What are the multiples of 12 from 144 to 12? What are the factors of 24? What are the common factors of 12 and 20? Express 36 in prime factors. What are the prime numbers between 20 and 40?*

Progress check: Ask the children to define the terms *multiple*, *factor*, *prime factor* and *prime number*.

Independent work: Provide the children with photocopiable page 'Solve it' from the CD-ROM on which there are problem-solving tasks involving multiples, factors and prime numbers.

Review

Pick out a few questions from the photocopiable sheet to check. Then challenge the children to set some missing-number problems for each other using the terms *multiple*, *factor* and *prime number*. For example:

- *I am a factor of 20 and a factor of 48. I am more than 2. Who am I?* (4.)
- *I am the only even prime number. Who am I?* (2.)
- *I am a number between 10 and 20. The total of my factors is 31. Who am I?* (16.)
- *I am a multiple of 12 and 9. I am less than 50. Who am I?* (36.)

Written methods for multiplication and division

Expected prior learning

Children should be able to:

- understand the close relationship between multiplication and division
- use mental and written methods for multiplication and division
- solve problems using all four operations.

Topic	Curriculum objectives	Expected outcomes
Multiplication and division	**Lesson 1**	
	To perform mental calculations, including with mixed operations and large numbers.	Carry out multiplication and division calculations mentally. Understand the relationship between multiplication and division.
	Lesson 2	
	To multiply multi-digit numbers up to four digits by a two-digit whole number using the formal written method of long multiplication. To divide numbers up to four digits by a two-digit whole number using the formal written method of long division. To use estimation to check answers to calculations and determine, in the context of a problem, an appropriate degree of accuracy.	Use formal written methods to multiply two-digit and three-digit integers by a one-digit number. Use formal written methods to divide integers by a one-digit number. Use estimation to check answers, and estimate before using written methods.
	Lesson 3	
	To multiply multi-digit numbers up to four digits by a two-digit whole number using the formal written method of long multiplication. To use estimation to check answers to calculations and determine, in the context of a problem, an appropriate degree of accuracy.	Use formal written methods to multiply two-digit and three-digit integers by a two-digit integer. Use estimation to check answers, and estimate before using written methods.
	Lesson 4	
	To divide numbers up to four digits by a two-digit whole number using the formal written method of long division. To use estimation to check answers to calculations and determine, in the context of a problem, an appropriate degree of accuracy.	Use formal written methods to divide four-digit numbers by a two-digit number. Use estimation to check answers, and estimate before using written methods.
	Lesson 5	
	To solve problems involving addition, subtraction, multiplication and division.	Solve problems involving multiplication and division, and then using all four operations.

See the bank of starters on pages 44 and 45. Oral and mental starters are also on the CD-ROM.

Preparation

Lesson I: make a display chart so that children have easy reference to the key words used in multiplication and division processes; copy and cut out some large blank triangles; copy 'Top triangles' for each pair

Lesson 4: write the problems for individual work on the board

Lesson 5: copy 'Operation time' for each child or pair

You will need

Photocopiable sheets

'Top triangles'; 'Operation time'

General resources

Interactive activity 'Nearest wins'; 'Number cards 0–9'

Equipment

Individual whiteboards; key words display chart (multiplication and division words); squared paper; blank paper triangles

Further practice

Use the interactive activity 'Nearest wins' to further revise written methods of multiplication before going on to teach higher four-digit by one- and two-digit calculations.

Oral and mental starters suggested for week 4

See the bank of starters on pages 44 and 45. Oral and mental starters are also on the CD-ROM.

4 Add and subtract

5 Five seconds

7 Answers please

8 Family of three

Overview of progression

At the beginning of the week, the children revise and develop methods of carrying out simple multiplication and division calculations mentally. They move on to revise the written methods of multiplication and division used in Year 5, sometimes known as short multiplication and short division. They will then learn how to multiply a three-digit number by a two-digit number using the method known as long multiplication, and how to divide a three-digit number by a two-digit number using the method known as long division. In the final session of the week, the children use multiplication and division calculations to solve problems, and then, in other problems, choose which of the four operations are needed.

Watch out for

As in the previous week, children will need a good working knowledge of multiplication tables, and some may find it helpful to refer to tables squares or charts. Both long multiplication and long division require careful setting down in column formation and the use of squared paper should help children ensure that digits are placed in the correct columns. In word-based problems involving all four operations, it will be important that children can convert key words into the correct operations, for example total (+), decrease (−), product (×) and quotient (÷).

Creative context

In problem-solving activities try to include as many 'real life' situations as possible. In multiplication, for example, look at the price of tickets for a family journey and seats in the cinema, while, in division, consider friends sharing the cost of a meal and look at sports events and surveys where the mean (average) has to be found.

Vocabulary

approximate, dividend, division, divisor, decrease, digit, double, estimate, halve, integer, operation, method, multiplication, multiple, multiplier, numeral, partition, **product**, **quotient**

Curriculum objectives

● To perform mental calculations with mixed operations and large numbers.

Success criteria

● I can understand the relationship between multiplication and division.
● I can know key words associated with multiplication and division.
● I can carry out multiplication and division calculations mentally.

You will need

Photocopiable sheets

'Top triangles'

Equipment

Individual whiteboards; multiplication and division key words chart; blank triangles

Differentiation

Less confident learners

Using the display chart (see Preparation, page 27), work with this group so children can check key words with you when choosing between multiplication and division operations.

More confident learners

Set children tasks against the clock, especially when they are trying to recall multiplication and division facts. Challenge them to create their own 'Top triangles'.

Lesson 1 Oral and mental starter 4

Main teaching activities

Whole-class work: See how well the children know their multiplication tables and how quickly they can recall multiplication and division facts. Get them ready with their individual whiteboards, and set them some quick-fire oral problems using key words associated with multiplication and division. Here are some to get them started:

- *Nine eights?*
- *How many 5s in 35?*
- *6 times 7.*
- *Multiply 9 by 6.*
- *Double 26.*
- *Divide 72 by 9.*
- *Halve 74.*
- *What is the product of 12 and 9?*
- *7 multiplied by 0.*
- *What is the quotient of 50 and 5?*

Using the board or flipchart to demonstrate, look at methods of multiplying and dividing mentally. Try the following examples:

Double by partitioning: Double $176 = 200 + 140 + 12 = 352$.

Work out the $16\times$ table by taking the $8\times$ table and doubling it: $16 \times 9 = (8 \times 9) \times 2 = 144$.

To multiply by 50, multiply by 100 and then halve: $24 \times 50 = 24 \times 100 [= 2400] \div 2 = 1200$.

Use factors: $35 \times 18 = 35 \times 6 [= 210] \times 3 = 630$.

Progress check: Revise the key words that are used to indicate the multiplication and division processes, such as *times*, *double* and *multiply*, and *divide*, *halve* and *find the quotient*. Also ensure that the children realise the close relationship between multiplication and division. See, for instance, that if $9 \times 7 = 63$ then $63 \div 9 = 7$, and so on.

Paired work: Organise the children into pairs and provide each pair with photocopiable page 47 'Top triangles'. In each case, the bottom two numbers multiplied together give the top number. When the children have completed the triangles, ask them to write four facts about each triangle, two multiplication facts and two division facts. (These will show inverse operations.) Encourage some children to go on to make up their own 'Top triangles' using increasingly large numbers.

Review

Go over the answers to the photocopiable sheet. Ask volunteers to come out to the board to write up the four number facts they have derived from each triangle. Revise the importance of understanding that multiplication and division are inverse operations, and demonstrate how this fact can be used to check calculations. For example: if $27 \times 56 = 1512$, then $1512 \div 56 = 27$.

Curriculum objectives

- To multiply multi-digit numbers by a two-digit number using long multiplication.
- To divide numbers up to four-digits by a two-digit number using long division.
- To use estimation to check answers and determine accuracy in problem-solving.

Success criteria

- I can multiply two- and three-digit numbers by a one-digit number.
- I can divide two- and three-digit numbers by a one-digit number.
- I can use estimation before writing and to check answers.

You will need

Equipment

Individual whiteboards; squared paper

Differentiation

Less confident learners

Help children to focus on the support section of the calculations on the board, particularly TU × U and TU ÷ U, and work on squared paper. Encourage children to show you their work on individual whiteboards.

More confident learners

Ask children to focus on the core and extension sections of the calculations given, particularly HTU × U, ThHTU × U, HTU ÷ U and ThHTU ÷ U.

Lesson 2

Oral and mental starter 5

Main teaching activities

Whole-class work: Show children how to multiply 194 × 5 and 3298 × 3 using first the partitioning method and then how this leads to the method known as short multiplication. Estimate to get an approximate answer first: 200 × 5 = 1000, and 3300 × 3 = 9900. Clarify that when calculations are set out in columns, ThHTU, the digits must line up under each other. Ask the children to write out each stage of the calculation on their individual whiteboards as you work on the board. Make sure that, in the shorter version, the children understand that the units go directly into the answer box under the number that has just been multiplied. Explain that the tens are 'carried' to be added to the answer at the next stage of multiplication and so on.

$$
\begin{array}{r}
194 \\
\times \quad 5 \\
\hline
100 \times 5 = 500 \\
90 \times 5 = 450 \\
4 \times 5 = \underline{20} \\
970
\end{array}
\qquad \text{leading to:} \qquad
\begin{array}{r}
194 \\
\times \quad 5 \\
\hline
970 \\
{\scriptstyle 4\;2}
\end{array}
$$

$$
\begin{array}{r}
3298 \\
\times \qquad 3 \\
\hline
3000 \times 3 = 9000 \\
200 \times 3 = 600 \\
90 \times 3 = 270 \\
8 \times 3 = \underline{24} \\
9894
\end{array}
\qquad \text{leading to:} \qquad
\begin{array}{r}
3298 \\
\times \qquad 3 \\
\hline
9894 \\
{\scriptstyle 2\;2}
\end{array}
$$

Then revise the short division method using 192 ÷ 6 and 2758 ÷ 7. Again, estimate the answers first: 200 ÷ 5 = 40, and 2800 ÷ 7 = 400. Work through the two examples with the children, asking them to repeat each stage on their individual whiteboards. Explain that, in the first example, 6 into 19 goes 3 times with 1 left over. The 1 is brought down and joins the 2 units. Together they make 12 which, when divided by 6, gives two.

$$
\begin{array}{r}
32 \\
6\,\overline{)\,192} \\
-\underline{18} \\
12 \\
-\underline{12} \\
00
\end{array}
\qquad\qquad
\begin{array}{r}
394 \\
7\,\overline{)\,2758} \\
-\underline{21} \\
65 \\
-\underline{63} \\
28 \\
-\underline{28} \\
00
\end{array}
$$

Progress check: Go through several other examples if necessary until the children are confident using these methods.

Independent work: Write a selection of multiplication and division statements on the board for the children to solve. Put them in support, core and extension sections for groups to work on as appropriate. For example:

- Support: 85 × 6, 59 × 8, 95 ÷ 5, 84 ÷ 3.
- Core: 154 × 4, 372 × 9, 145 ÷ 5, 282 ÷ 6.
- Extension: 3241 × 7, 5708 × 9, 1504 ÷ 4, 3505 ÷ 5.

At this stage, avoid any calculations that produce a remainder or any calculations that include a decimal point.

Review

Review the answers to the calculations. Discuss how useful the estimated answers were. Ask for volunteers to talk through the methods they used. Then challenge the children to suggest their own questions based on practical problems. For example: There are 8 pencils in each box. How many pencils are there in 136 boxes?

Curriculum objectives

● To multiply multi-digit numbers by a two-digit number using long multiplication.
● To use estimation to check answers and determine levels of accuracy.

Success criteria

● I can multiply two- and three-digit numbers by a two-digit number using a formal written method.
● I can use estimation to check answers and before using a written method.

You will need

General resources

Interactive activity 'Nearest wins'

Equipment

Individual whiteboards; sets of number cards (2, 3, 4, 5 and 6)

Differentiation

Less confident learners

Make sure children are really secure first with HTU × U and ThHTU × U. They can get further practice using the interactive activity 'Nearest wins' on the CD-ROM. Work with this group to check stages of long multiplication.

More confident learners

Challenge children to devise word-based problems involving long multiplication. For example: There are 24 tins of soup in a box. How many tins in 250 boxes?

Lesson 3
Oral and mental starter 7

Main teaching activities

Whole-class work: Tell the children you are going to show them how to multiply a three-digit number by a two-digit number using the method known as long multiplication. Work through 352 × 27 on the board. Estimate the answer first: 350 × 30 = 10,500. Explain that, in the compact method being used, 352 × 20 and 352 × 7 can be calculated using the fewest number of steps. Stress that before multiplying by 2 (for 20) a zero should be written down because the number is two tens. Recap that numbers have to be written down in the correct columns, carrying figures should be added on to the next stage of multiplication and both lines of working out should be totalled at the end.

$$
\begin{array}{r}
352 \\
\times \quad 27 \\
\hline
7040 \\
2464 \\
\hline
9504 \\
\end{array}
\qquad
\begin{array}{l}
352 \times 20 \\
352 \times \ 7 \\
\end{array}
$$

Progress check: Work through several other examples with the children. Try: 217 × 34, 209 × 42, 316 × 63, and 243 × 68. Talk through each step of the process, asking leading questions. *What number do we multiply by first? Why did we need to write down the zero? What happens to each carrying figure? What happens to the two lines of working out?*

Paired work: Provide each pair of children with number cards 2, 3, 4, 5 and 6. (No other digits should be used.) Ask them to take it in turns to make a three-digit number and a two-digit number and then multiply the two together. As they make each question, they should look to find the smallest and the largest possible numbers. Remind the children to estimate answers first, to use the method shown in the lesson and to show all of their working out.

Review

Ask children to write on the board some of the long multiplication calculations they made with the number cards. Ask: *Who thinks they have found the largest possible answer? Who thinks they have found the smallest possible answer?* If time allows, look at some of the word problems devised by the more confident learners.

Curriculum objectives
- To divide numbers up to four-digits by a two-digit number using long division.
- To use estimation to check answers to calculations and determine levels of accuracy.

Success criteria
- I can divide a four-digit number by a two-digit number using a formal written method.
- I can use estimation to check answers and before using a written method.

You will need
Equipment
Individual whiteboards

Differentiation
Less confident learners
Ensure children are secure with HTU ÷ U before moving on. Provide adult support to help children work through extra examples.

More confident learners
Expect children to check the accuracy of their calculations by using the inverse operation (multiplication) as well as estimating first.

Lesson 4 — Oral and mental starter 8

Main teaching activities

Whole-class work: Ask the children to estimate 972 ÷ 36. Write some of the estimations on the board to refer to later. Say that you are going to show them how to divide a three-digit number by a two-digit number using the method usually known as long division. Write up the calculation below using a bracket to separate the divisor (the dividing number) and the dividend (the amount to be divided). Stress the importance of keeping the columns correct with units under units, tens under tens and so on. Ask the children to work through the example with you, on their individual whiteboards. Remind them that both multiplication and subtraction are also involved in this division process.

$$\begin{array}{r} 27 \\ 36\overline{)972} \\ -\underline{72} \\ 252 \\ \underline{252} \\ 000 \end{array}$$

Try other examples: 286 ÷ 22, 432 ÷ 24, 342 ÷ 18.

Progress check: Talk through the first example again. *How many times will 36 go into 97? What is the remainder? How many times will 36 go into 252? What is left over?* You may need to reinforce this with several other examples.

Independent work: Tell the children they are going to carry out some practical division calculations. Write the information on the board. Ask: *How many coaches/buses are needed to carry the following groups of people?*

1. 468 people, 36-seater coaches
2. 308 people, 14-seater minibuses
3. 546 people, 42-seater buses
4. 816 people, 48-seater buses

Review

Check the solutions to the passenger/bus problems. How accurate were the estimated answers? How did it help to have this first? Ask more confident children to show how the inverse operation helped them to check their answers. For example, in problem 1: if 468 ÷ 36 = 13 then 36 × 13 should = 468.

Curriculum objectives
- To solve problems involving addition, subtraction, multiplication and division.

Success criteria
- I can solve problems involving all four operations.

You will need
Photocopiable sheets
'Operation time'

Differentiation
Less confident learners
Discuss which operations to use before starting calculations.

More confident learners
When they have finished ask children make up their own word problems.

Lesson 5 — Oral and mental starter 5

Main teaching activities

Whole-class work: Quickly revise long multiplication and long division. Then tell the children that they are going to work on some problem-solving activities. Say that some of the questions will involve multiplication and division, but that others may need addition and subtraction too. Remind them to estimate first and to check afterwards. They must use written methods to find the answers and that all working out should be shown.

Independent/paired work: Decide on the most suitable way for children to work and give out photocopiable page 'Operation time' from the CD-ROM.

Progress check: Stop the children after they have all completed the first two or three problems. Ask: *How are you deciding which operation(s) to use? What methods are you using to check your answers? How does using the inverse operation work? Were the estimated answers helpful?*

Review

Collect answers, discuss the children's methods, and correct errors. Invite confident children to set some of their own word problems for the rest of the class.

Circles and angles

Expected prior learning

Children should be able to:

- draw circles using a pair of compasses
- name the main parts of a circle
- use a protractor
- calculate angles.

Topic	Curriculum objectives	Expected outcomes
Geometry: properties of shapes	**Lesson 1**	
	To illustrate and name parts of circles including radius, diameter and circumference and know that the diameter is twice the radius.	Draw circles accurately using a pair of compasses. Name the main parts of a circle.
	Lesson 2	
	To recognise angles where they meet at a point, are on a straight line or are vertically opposite and find missing angles.	Name and estimate angles and use a protractor to measure and draw them accurately.
	Lesson 3	
	To recognise angles where they meet at a point, are on a straight line or are vertically opposite and find missing angles. To compare and classify geometric shapes based on their properties and sizes and find unknown angles in any triangles, quadrilaterals, and regular polygons.	Measure and calculate unknown angles around a point, on a straight line and vertically opposite.
	Lesson 4	
	To recognise angles where they meet at a point, are on a straight line or are vertically opposite and find missing angles. To compare and classify geometric shapes based on their properties and sizes and find unknown angles in any triangles, quadrilaterals, and regular polygons.	Measure and calculate unknown angles within triangles and quadrilaterals.
	Lesson 5	
	To illustrate and name parts of circles including radius, diameter and circumference and know that the diameter is twice the radius.	Establish practically the relationship between the diameter and the circumference of a circle (pi).

Preparation

Lesson 2: prepare (on screen or on card) one set of large flashcards showing angles of different types and sizes, and another set showing angles about a point, angles on a straight line and angles vertically opposite each other; copy 'Hit out' for each pair

Lesson 3: copy 'About turn' for each pair

Lesson 4: make a large triangle and quadrilateral from sugar paper or thin card; copy 'Shapely angles' for each pair

Lesson 5: get lengths of string ready for measuring the circumferences of circles; collect small round 2D objects, such as rings, hoops, discs, tin and jar lids, wheels and plates

You will need

Photocopiable sheets

'Hit out'; 'About turn'; 'Shapely angles'

Equipment

Classroom protractor (if available); pairs of compasses, protractors, rulers, tape measures, string; sharp pencils, coloured pencils, felt-tipped pens; maths dictionaries; large flashcards (real or digital) showing different kinds of angles; large flashcards (real or digital) showing angles about a point, on a straight line and opposite each other; large paper or card triangle and quadrilateral; selection of small round objects

Further practice

Give children plenty of practical experience drawing a circle and other shapes using a pair of compasses, and measuring using a protractor.

Oral and mental starters suggested for week 5

See the bank of starters on pages 44 and 45. Oral and mental starters are on the CD-ROM.

3 Roundup

5 Five seconds

6 Tell me about it

10 Brackets

Overview of progression

This week starts with the children revising how to draw circles accurately using a pair of compasses when it is set to a radius measurement. There will also be some revision of key circle words including *centre*, *radius*, *diameter* and *circumference*, and the introduction of less familiar ones like *arc*, *sector*, *segment*, *quadrant* and *chord* as well as angle names – *acute*, *obtuse* and *reflex*. The children then estimate the sizes of angles and learn how to draw and measure them using a protractor. Calculations are used to find the sizes of angles around a point, on a straight line and vertically opposite. The children also find missing angles in triangles and quadrilaterals. In the final lesson, the children establish, by practical means, that the circumference of a circle is always a little more than three times the diameter.

Watch out for

Some children may need guidance loading the pencil neatly into the pair of compasses and also setting radius measurements so circles are drawn accurately. Ensure protractors, mainly 180 degrees, are placed correctly on lines when drawing or measuring angles and that the correct scale is used. When measuring angles about a point, it may be easier for the children to measure the small angle between the lines and then subtract from 360 degrees to find the larger angle. Make sure the totals of the internal angles of triangles and quadrilaterals are well known by the children to aid their calculations. Measuring the circumference of circles using string should be done carefully to make sure results are accurate.

Creative context

There are a number of ways in which colourful circles patterns can be produced using media such as coloured pencils, crayons, felt-tipped pens, powder paint, coloured inks. As well as using a pair of compasses to create the circle patterns, experiment with printing from the ends of cardboard tubes of varying sizes. Straight lines meeting and/or crossing at different angles can also produce interesting and colourful artwork. Explore the work of artists like Piet Mondrian, Kasmir Malevich and Wassily Kandinsky for inspiration.

Vocabulary

acute, angle, arc, centre, circle, chord, circumference, degree, diameter, intersecting, obtuse, pi, protractor, **quadrant**, radius, reflex, revolution, right angle, sector, segment, semicircle, straight line

Curriculum objectives

● To illustrate and name parts of circles including radius, diameter and circumference and know that diameter is twice the radius.

Success criteria

● I can draw circles accurately using a pair of compasses.
● I can identify and name the major parts of a circle.

You will need

Equipment

Pairs of compasses; sharp pencils; large board compass; felt-tipped pens; coloured pencils; maths dictionaries

Differentiation

Less confident learners

Provide support so children can ensure they are loading pencils into the pair of compasses correctly. Help them to practise making radius measurements carefully when drawing circles.

More confident learners

Children should research other important terms connected with circles. Provide them with copies of maths dictionaries to check on words. They should become familiar with names like arc, sector, segment and quadrant.

Lesson 1

Main teaching activities

Whole-class work: Tell the children that you are going to revise with them how to draw circles accurately using a pair of compasses. Demonstrate on the interactive whiteboard or with your board compass how to load the pencil, set the radius measurement using a ruler and then draw the circle, keeping the point at the centre steady and firm. Display a large circle and label it with the key words *radius*, *diameter* and *circumference*. Elicit what each of the terms means.

Ask the children to draw circles with radii 4cm, 6cm and 8cm. Ensure that they understand that if a circle needs a radius of 4cm they will need to open their pair of compasses to 4cm. Ask them to find the relationship between the radius and the diameter in each circle by drawing and then measuring a straight line all the way across the centre of the circle from circumference to circumference. Make sure children understand that in any circle $r = d \div 2$ and $d = r \times 2$.

Progress check: Circulate and observe the children while they are drawing the circles to make sure they are using the correct technique and are working carefully and accurately.

Independent work: Ask the children to draw a further selection of circles with radii 3.5cm, 5cm, 7cm and 10cm. Remind them to label the appropriate part of each circle with the words radius, diameter and circumference.

Once these are completed, encourage the children to experiment with their pair of compasses on large sheets of paper to make patterns and designs with circles of different sizes both overlapping and concentric. Let the children add colours to enhance the designs. (This could be done, for example, with sharp coloured pencils loaded in the pair of compasses, or by going over the original pencil circles by hand with felt-tipped pens.)

Review

Make a display of the circle designs the children have created, and discuss the methods that have been used. Encourage the children to talk about the different sizes of circle and the patterns made.

Revise the meanings of the words *radius*, *diameter* and *circumference* and ask more confident learners to explain, making reference to the children's circles artwork where appropriate, other geometric terms, such as *arc*, *sector*, *segment*, *semicircle*, *quadrant* and *chord*.

Curriculum objectives
● To recognise angles where they meet at a point, are on a straight line or are vertically opposite and find missing angles.

Success criteria
● I can estimate the sizes of angles.
● I know the names of different angles.
● I can measure and draw angles using a protractor.

You will need

Photocopiable sheets
'Hit out'

Equipment
Protractors; flashcards showing different kinds of angles; large classroom protractor

Differentiation

Less confident learners
Provide plenty of practice with the use of a protractor.

More confident learners
Challenge pairs to draw extra angles for each other to measure.

Lesson 2
Oral and mental starter 3

Main teaching activities

Whole-class work: Revise work on angles. Ask: *What is an angle? How are angles measured? What different types of angle do you know?* Check the children's understanding of: acute angle (less than 90 degrees), right angle (90 degrees), obtuse angle (between 90 and 180 degrees), straight line (180 degrees) and reflex (between 180 and 360 degrees). Elicit that a complete turn or revolution is 360 degrees. Show some examples of angles on the board, or on the flashcards. Challenge the children to name each angle and estimate its size. Encourage them to explain their reasoning.

Then demonstrate how to measure one or two of the estimated angles, using a protractor. Stress the importance of placing the protractor on the correct line and reading the correct scale. Aim to choose at least one angle where neither line is horizontal. Ask: *How accurate was the estimated answer?* Move on to demonstrate how angles can be drawn using a protractor. Draw a variety of acute and obtuse angles. Point out that angles should be accurate to within one degree.

Paired work: Organise mixed-ability pairs and provide them with photocopiable page 'Hit out' from the CD-ROM.

Progress check: Stop the children when most have completed the photocopiable sheet. Check their results are within the tolerance level (one degree) and that angles are being named correctly. How accurate did the estimates turn out to be?

Review

Revise the names of angles on the flashcards. Check the results of the children's own angle-drawing task. How did the children manage with the 320-degree angle? Go over the steps to measure and draw angles with a protractor.

Curriculum objectives
● As lesson 2.

Success criteria
● I can find unknown angles by measuring and by using calculation.

You will need

Photocopiable sheets
'About turn'

Equipment
Protractors; set of flashcards showing angles about a point; on a straight line and opposite each other

Differentiation

Less confident learners
Provide plenty of practice with the use of a protractor.

More confident learners
Challenge children to draw pairs of intersecting lines of their own and measure the angles formed.

Lesson 3
Oral and mental starter 6

Main teaching activities

Whole-class work: Explain to the children that their focus is now measuring and calculating angles at different positions: around a point, along a straight line and opposite each other on a pair of intersecting lines. Display a selection of these types of angle on the board or on flashcards. Show them how to measure each of the unknown angles. Discuss that, often, a large angle about a point can be found by measuring the small angle instead and subtracting it from 360 degrees (a complete turn). Explain that, in a similar way, missing angles can be calculated if the other angles around them are known. Elicit that angles about a point, for example, total 360 degrees, the angles on a straight line total 180 degrees (two right angles) and that angles opposite each other are equal to each other.

Paired work: Provide pairs with photocopiable page 'About turn' from the CD-ROM and ask them to complete it.

Progress check: Before the children start the calculations in the second section of the sheet, ask them: *What do the angles about a turn always total? What do the angles on a straight line always add up to? What can you tell me about opposite angles when two lines cross or intersect?*

Review

Ask the children some quick-fire questions: *If one of the angles about a turn is 250 degrees, what is the other angle?* (110°.) *If one of the angles on a straight line is 65 degrees, what is the other angle?* (115°.) *If the angles opposite each other where two lines cross are each 85 degrees, what are the other two angles?* (95°.)

Curriculum objectives

● To recognise angles where they meet at a point, on a straight line or are vertically opposite and find missing angles.
● To find unknown angles in any triangles and quadrilaterals.

Success criteria

● I can measure the angles inside triangles and quadrilaterals.
● I can calculate the missing angles inside triangles and quadrilaterals.

You will need

Photocopiable sheets
'Shapely angles'

Equipment
Protractors; large paper triangle and quadrilateral

Differentiation

Less confident learners
Support children to calculate the missing angles.

More confident learners
Encourage children to experiment with several different triangles and quadrilaterals.

Lesson 4
Oral and mental starter 5

Main teaching activities

Whole-class work: Tell the children that in this lesson they will focus on the angles in triangles and quadrilaterals. Remind them that a straight line is made up of two right angles (2 × 90 degrees = 180 degrees) and that a complete turn is made up of four right angles (4 × 90 degrees = 360 degrees). Hold up the large paper triangle. Demonstrate how the three angles can be cut or torn off and arranged on a straight line to show that the angles in a triangle add up to 180 degrees. Repeat the process to show how the four torn angles from the corners of a quadrilateral can be arranged to make a complete turn, 360 degrees.

Now look at calculating to find missing angles in triangles and quadrilaterals. For example: if two angles in a triangle are known to be 120 degrees and 40 degrees, the third angle will be 20 degrees (180 − 160). Similarly, if the three angles in a quadrilateral are 90 degrees, 90 degrees and 70 degrees, the fourth angle will be 110 degrees (360 − 250).

Paired work: Give each pair photocopiable page 'Shapely angles' from the CD-ROM, on which the children calculating missing angles.

Progress check: Stop the children after the first section. Ensure they have been using their protractors correctly.

Review

Ask some quick calculation questions on missing angles in triangles and quadrilaterals.

Curriculum objectives

● To measure and name parts of circles including radius, diameter and circumference.

Success criteria

● I know the circumference of a circle is a little more than three times its diameter.

You will need

Equipment
Rulers; tape measures; lengths of string; pairs of compasses; sharp pencils; selection of small round objects

Differentiation

Less confident learners
Monitor and support children.

More confident learners
Introduce children to the sign for pi (π).

Lesson 5
Oral and mental starter 10

Main teaching activities

Whole-class work: Give out rulers, tape measures, a pair of compasses and string. Have the collection of round objects to hand. Display a circle on the board and ask volunteers to label the circumference, radius and diameter.

Paired/group work: Explain to the children that they are going to explore the relationship between the circumference, radius and diameter of any circle. Ask the children to repeat some of the large circles they drew in lesson 1, for example with their pair of compasses set to 7cm, 8cm and 10cm. For each circle, they should record its radius, diameter and circumference. The circumference should be measured as accurately as possible using string.

Progress check: Check results once these first three circles have been drawn and measured.

Paired/group work: Now ask the children to repeat the process using at least three of the circular objects provided (to measure at least six circles in total). Finally, ask the groups to find the relationships between the radius and the diameter, the radius and the circumference, and the diameter and the circumference. For precise calculations: $d = r \times 2$, $c = r \times 2 \times 3.142$, $c = d \times 3.142$.

Review

Share findings and establish that in all circles: the diameter is twice the radius; the circumference is approximately three times the diameter; the circumference is approximately six times the radius.

Units of measure

Expected prior learning

Children should be able to:

- use standard metric units
- read scales on measuring devices
- carry out problem-solving tasks involving measures.

Topic	Curriculum objectives	Expected outcomes
Measurement	**Lesson 1**	
	To use, read, write and convert between standard units, converting measurements of length, mass, volume and time from a smaller unit of measure to a larger unit, and vice versa, using decimal notation up to three decimal places.	Use, read, write and convert metric units of length.
	Lesson 2	
	To use, read, write and convert between standard units, converting measurements of length, mass, volume and time from a smaller unit of measure to a large unit, and vice versa, using decimal notation up to three decimal places.	Use, read, write and convert metric units of mass and volume.
	Lesson 3	
	To use, read, write and convert between standard units, converting measurements of length, mass, volume and time from a smaller unit of measure to a large unit and vice versa, using decimal notation up to three decimal places.	Use, read and interpret metric scales on different measuring equipment.
	Lesson 4	
	To use, read, write and convert between standard units, converting measurements of length, mass, volume and time from a smaller unit of measure to a larger unit and vice versa, using decimal notation up to three decimal places. To convert between miles and kilometres.	Become more familiar with commonly used imperial units. Read and interpret conversion graphs, converting kilometres to miles, and vice versa.
	Lesson 5	
	To solve problems involving the calculation and conversion of units of measure, using decimal notation up to three decimal places where appropriate.	Solve problems involving metric units of measure and money. Use decimal notation.

Preparation

Lesson 1: organise for some activities to be done outside the classroom; make sure there is a safe working area

Lesson 2: display a range of weighing scales and measuring jugs, containers and cylinders; provide access to water; copy 'Measure by measure' for each child

Lesson 3: enlarge 'Weighing scales' or display it on the CD-ROM; prepare a copy for each child

Lesson 4: enlarge 'Conversion graph' or display it on the CD-ROM; prepare a copy for each pair

Lesson 5: make some enlarged copies of shopping till receipts; copy 'Weekly shop' for each pair

You will need

Photocopiable sheets
'Measure by measure'; 'Conversion graph'; 'Weekly shop'

General resources
'Weighing scales'; interactive activity 'Metric units'

Equipment
Rulers, metre sticks, tape measures, trundle wheels; small plastic containers; measuring jugs, measuring cylinders; weighing scales; centimetre-squared paper; shopping till receipts; a supply of water

Further practice

Interactive activity 'Metric units' offers further practice of reading, writing and converting between standard units of measurement.

Oral and mental starters for suggested for week 6

See the bank of starters on pages 44 and 45. Oral and mental starters are also on the CD-ROM.

5 Five seconds

9 Who am I?

11 Your choice

12 Short measure

Overview of progression

In the first two lessons of the week, the children will be reinforcing their knowledge of metric units of measurement and how these can be written in different ways – converting smaller units into larger units, and vice versa. Units of length will be considered first and then mass (weight) and volume (capacity). The children will also practise reading measurements from a range of scales, become familiar with imperial units that are still in common use, and work specifically on a graph to convert kilometres into miles, and vice versa. During the final session of the week, the children work on a problem-solving situation that involves both metric units and money.

Watch out for

Make sure children are familiar with all the abbreviations used for denoting metric measures. Large display charts in the classroom will help them to remember. Children will need repeated practice to become skilled at writing the same metric measures in a number of different ways. Particular care needs to be taken where decimal points are used in metric measures. Don't move on to more detailed measurement scales until children have mastered basic ones. Make sure too that children can use equipment accurately; measuring from zero, not from the edge of a ruler or tape, for example. When graphs are being used for conversion tasks, provide support while children label axes, decide on scales and mark points.

Creative context

There are a number of practical ways in which children can practise and develop their skills in the use of units of measurement. Measurement plays a key role in shopping, where children should become familiar with units recorded on packaging. Cooking activities require the measurement of ingredients; and in PE, encourage children to collect their own data in running, throwing and jumping events.

Vocabulary

approximate, axis, centilitre (cl), centimetre (cm), constant, conversion, cylinder, division, estimate, foot, gallon, gram (g), imperial, inch, interval, kilogram (kg), kilometre (km), length, litre (l), mass, metric, mile, millilitre (ml), millimetre (mm), ounce, pint, pound, proportion

Lesson 1 — Oral and mental starter 5

Curriculum objectives
● To use, read, write and convert between standard units, converting measurements of length from a smaller unit of measure to a larger unit, and vice versa.

Success criteria
● I can use, read, write and convert metric units of length.

You will need
Equipment
Individual whiteboards; rulers; metre sticks; tape measures; trundle wheels

Differentiation
Less confident learners
Ensure children are confident about using the measuring equipment. Check that they measure from zero, not from the edge of the ruler, for example.

More confident learners
Encourage children to find the perimeters of large objects, like the classroom or the playground, using tape measures and trundle wheels, and then show their results using scale drawing.

Main teaching activities

Whole-class work: Ask the children to list the common units of length. Look for kilometre, metre, centimetre and millimetre. Tell the children that these are all metric measurements. Revise the relationship between them. Remind the children that 1000m = 1km, 100cm = 1m, and 10mm = 1cm. Also explain the details of the vocabulary. Say, for example: *kilo means 1000; centi means* $\frac{1}{100}$. *This helps us to know how big units are.* Go on to say that, a centimetre is $\frac{1}{100}$ of a metre. So, if *milli* means $\frac{1}{1000}$, how many millimetres are there in 1 metre? Carry on by asking some quick-fire questions relating to the conversion of smaller units into larger ones, and vice versa:

- *How many centimetres are there in ¾ of a metre?*
- *How many millimetres are there in 6 metres?*
- *How many centimetres are there in 3.6 metres?*
- *How many millimetres are there in 12.5 centimetres?*
- *How many metres are there in 4.2 kilometres?*

Remind the children too of writing measurements in different ways, including the use of decimal points. For example: 9076m = 9km 76m = 9.076km. Ask the children to write the following measurements in two other ways on their whiteboards: 126cm, 1.3m, 2km 5m. Quickly work through other examples on the board.

Paired work: Provide a range of measuring equipment such as rulers, tape measures, metre sticks and trundle wheels. Let the children measure a variety of small objects in the classroom, such as the height of their table, the length of a book, the circumference of a friend's head. With supervision, some children could take some bigger measurements in other parts of the school. Stress that, first, they all need to choose the right equipment for the task. A 30cm ruler, for example, would not be suitable for measuring the length of the school hall.

Show the children that the measurements should be recorded in two different ways, using the type of chart shown below. Encourage accurate measuring to the nearest millimetre/centimetre, and tell the children that you want them to share thoughts to estimate the length before measuring each object.

Object	Estimated size	Measurement unit 1	Measurement unit 2
Length of Maths book	20cm	25cm	0.25m

Progress check: Check the children at intervals during the activity to assess how they are working. Are they finding enough suitable objects to measure? How good are their estimation skills? Are they choosing the right equipment? Are they recording results correctly on the chart?

Review

Compare children's results, especially those who have measured the same objects. Recap on the relationship between metric units of length and check that the children can convert between the units. Ask questions such as:

- *A table is 1200mm in length. How would this be written in: a) centimetres; b) metres?*
- *A room is 6.2m wide. How would this be written in: a) metres and centimetres; b) centimetres?*

Curriculum objectives
● To use, read, write and convert between standard units, converting measurements of mass and volume.

Success criteria
● I can use, read, write and convert metric units of mass and volume.

You will need
Photocopiable sheets
'Measure by measure'

General resources
Interactive activity 'Metric units'

Equipment
Small containers; measuring jugs; measuring cylinders; weighing scales; water

Differentiation
Less confident learners
Display abbreviations and conversion examples.

More confident learners
Ask children to work with more unusual units.

Lesson 2
Oral and mental starter 9

Main teaching activities
Whole-class work: Revise the common metric units used for measuring mass and volume. Check they appreciate that 1000 grams = 1 kilogram and 1000 millilitres = 1 litre, and that 1000 kilograms = 1 tonne and 100 centilitres = 1 litre. Work together on conversions on the board, for example: Write 3kg 245g in two other ways. Write 5.752 litres in two other ways. Show what happens to the decimal point when changing very small units into larger ones. For example: 200g = 0.200kg, 20g = 0.020kg and 2g = 0.002kg.

Independent/paired work: Working individually at first, ask the children to focus on the first part of photocopiable page 'Measure by measure' from the CD-ROM, where mass and volume measurements need to be converted and then ordered. For the second part, organise pairs to carry out practical measuring tasks.

Progress check: After independent work, check that the children are carrying out conversions successfully. Where measurements have to be ordered, suggest they make all items into the same units before sorting.

Review
Focus on ordering a group of measurements, smallest to largest, by putting them into the same units. Try: Length: 2.45m, 260cm, 2½m, ¾km, 0.76km, 850m. Mass: 1½kg, 1.400kg, 1600g, 1.4800 tonne, 1500kg, 1 tonne 450kg. Volume: 3.800ml, 3l 750ml, 3850ml, 250 cl. Use the interactive activity 'Metric units' on the CD-ROM for further practice.

Curriculum objectives
● To use, read and write standard units of mass and volume.

Success criteria
● I can use, read and interpret metric scales on different measuring equipment.

You will need
General resources
'Weighing scales'

Equipment
A range of mass and volume measuring devices showing a variety of scales

Differentiation
Less confident learners
Use simplified scales initially, where only a small number of large divisions are shown.

More confident learners
Ask children to convert kilogram readings into grams and millilitres into litres.

Lesson 3
Oral and mental starter 11

Main teaching activities
Whole-class work: Emphasise that reading the scale on a measuring instrument is similar to reading a number line. It is important to realise that there are numbers between the main numbers marked. Display the photocopiable page 'Weighing scales' from the CD-ROM. Examine how the measurements are shown; the first three in kilograms; the others in grams. Notice that scales are designed in different ways; they can be horizontal, vertical and curved. Ask the children to work out the value of the interim markers in each case. For example: *If the pointer comes to here, what weight does it show? Where would 2.5kg come on scales 1, 2 and 3?*

Progress check: Ask volunteers to mark the following measurements on scales 1, 2 and 3: 2.7kg, 4100g, 1.8kg, 3300g and 3.4kg. Ask: *Which weights can be shown exactly?* Then ask volunteers to mark these on scales 4 and 5: 60g, 490g, 180g and 325g. Again, see which can be shown precisely and which have to be estimated.

Paired work: Provide each child with a copy of 'Weighing scales'. Ask one child to think of a secret weight and then mark it with an arrow on one of the first three scales. His or her partner should identify the weight and mark it on one of the other scales. Encourage children to check each other's work.

Review
Check the children's work with them. Which scale did they find easiest to read? Which was the most difficult? How did they manage when weights had to be estimated? Show some scales on other equipment; not only on weighing scales, but on measuring jugs, containers and cylinders.

SCHOLASTIC

Curriculum objectives
● To use, read, write and convert between standard units, converting measurements of length, including between miles and kilometres.

Success criteria
● I am familiar with imperial units.
● I can read and interpret conversion graphs converting kilometres to miles, and vice versa.

You will need

Photocopiable sheets
'Conversion graph'

Equipment
Centimetre-squared paper; rulers

Differentiation

Less confident learners
Help children to construct the graph; drawing axes, deciding on scale and marking points.

More confident learners
Encourage children to consider where such graphs are useful.

Lesson 4 — Oral and mental starter 12

Main teaching activities

Whole-class work: Remind the children that metres, kilograms, litres and so on are units in the metric system. Ask the children to name any familiar imperial units, noting them on the board. Write up a range of metric/imperial conversions, stressing that some are only approximate. For example: 8km = 6 miles, 1m = 3 feet 3 inches, 1kg is about 2.2 pounds, 30g is about 1 ounce, 2.54cm = 1 inch, 4.5l is about 1 gallon or 8 pints.

Display photocopiable page 'Conversion graph' from the CD-ROM. Explain that the graph can be used to change one system of units into another. Emphasise that the graph must start at zero as no distance has been travelled at that point. Stress also that the graph forms a straight line because the distances increase by the same quantity each time (constant proportion). Show the children how the points are located as accurately as possible and then connected by a straight line drawn with a ruler.

Paired work: Ask the children to construct the conversion graph from the data. Provide them with centimetre-squared paper and the photocopiable sheet.

Progress check: Ensure that the children are plotting points correctly. Stress that an accurate graph is needed for correct conversions.

Paired work: Write on the board: *How many kilometres are...? 10 miles, 15 miles, 20 miles, 35 miles, 45 miles. How many miles are...? 16km, 28km, 48km, 100km, 115km.*

Review

Ask the children: *What is a conversion graph? What does constant proportion mean?* Ask volunteers to answer the questions given on the board.

Curriculum objectives
● To solve problems involving calculation and conversion of measures, using decimal notation.

Success criteria
● I can solve problems involving metric measurements and money, using decimal points.

You will need

Photocopiable sheets
'Weekly shop'

Equipment
Shopping till receipts

Differentiation

Less confident learners
Give practice at using fractions and decimals.

More confident learners
Encourage children to use till receipts to make up their own questions.

Lesson 5 — Oral and mental starter 12

Main teaching activities

Whole-class work: Tell the children that they will have a problem-solving activity to do which focuses on mass, volume and money.

Paired work: Organise the children to work together on photocopiable page 'Weekly shop' from the CD-ROM.

Progress check: You might want to revise additions involving money, and changing mass and volume amounts into smaller or larger units.

Review

Present a few number statements involving mass, volume and money, and challenge the children to make up problems from them. For example: A 400g tin of beans costs 64p. A 2l bottle of lemonade costs £1.05. Questions could be: *How much do three tins of beans cost? What change would there be from a £2 coin after buying both items?*

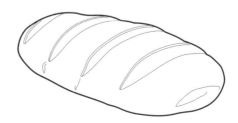

Curriculum objectives
● To read, write, order and compare numbers up to 10,000,000 and determine the value of each digit.

You will need
1. Check
Oral and mental starter
1 Place value

2. Assess
'Number cards 0–9'

3. Further practice
Oral and mental starter
2 Digit spotting

Photocopiable sheets
'Right place (1)'; 'Digit circles'; 'Think big'

Place value to 10,000,000

Most children should be able to make seven-digit numbers using number cards. They should be able to convert numbers into words, and vice versa.

Some children will need practice with five- and six-digit numbers. Focus on place value with an abacus or using expanded notation to break numbers down.

1. Check
1 Place value

Ask the children to write the numbers you say on their whiteboards. Start with five- and six-digit numbers, then extend to seven digits. Include some where a zero is a place-holder.

Present a set of seven digits. *What is the largest number that can be made? What is the smallest number that can be made?*

2. Assess

Children should work in pairs. One child makes up a six- or seven-digit number on number cards for the other child to say out loud. Then they swap. Next, the children take it in turns to say six- and seven-digit numbers to be converted into figures using the number cards. Then ask children to point at individual digits in a number they have made for their partner to identify. For example: *In 7,560,241, what is the value of the 6?* Record the outcomes.

3. Further practice

Use the oral and mental starter 'Digit spotting' to reinforce identification of individual digits within a number. The photocopiable sheets will give practice in securing number making and recognition. Photocopiable page 46 'Think big' includes the use of big numbers in other curriculum areas.

Curriculum objectives
● To identify common factors, common multiples and prime numbers.

You will need
1. Check
Oral and mental starter
6 Tell me about it

2. Assess
Individual whiteboards

3. Further practice
Oral and mental starter
9 Who am I?

Photocopiable sheets
'Solve it'

General resources
Interactive activity 'Prime numbers up to 100'

Multiples, factors and prime numbers

Most children should be able to define the key words *multiple*, *factor* and *prime* and know the important differences between them.

Some children will have trouble making sequences of multiples and finding factors. They may need the support of tables squares or charts. Help them to understand that not all odd numbers are prime numbers.

1. Check
6 Tell me about it

Ensure the children understand what makes a number a multiple, factor and/ or prime. Provide the numbers, then ask for the descriptions. Make sure the descriptions contain one of the three key words. For example: *35 I am the next multiple of 5 after 30; 72 I am the multiple of 9 between 63 and 81; 16 I am a factor of 4 and my digits add up to 7; 7 I am the prime number before 11.*

2. Assess

Write a series of numbers on the board. Ask questions, focusing on the words *factor*, *multiple* and *prime*. For example, write: *13, 24, 9, 18, 47, 36, 5, 50,* and ask: *Which are prime numbers? Which are multiples of 4? Which are factors of 18? Which are multiples of 3?* Extend by asking children to write their own set of numbers and questions. Record the outcomes.

3. Further practice

The oral and mental starter 'Who am I?' lets the children work the other way. This time, clues using *multiple*, *factor* and *prime number* lead to a number answer. Photocopiable page 'Solve it' from the CD-ROM and interactive activity 'Prime numbers up to 100' on the CD-ROM provide more practice in spotting multiples, factors and prime numbers.

You will need

1. Check

Oral and mental starter

8 Family of three

2. Assess

Centimetre-squared paper

3. Further practice

Photocopiable sheets

'Top triangles'

Multiplying and dividing using written methods

Most children should be able to multiply three- and four-digit numbers by one- or two-digit numbers and divide three- and four-digit numbers by one or two digits.

Some children will need practice with TU × U and HTU × U, and TU ÷ U and HTU ÷ U. Support with table charts may be required.

1. Check

8 Family of three

This activity helps children appreciate the close relationship between multiplication and division. Display three numbers and ask the children to create two multiplication and two division statements. Start with two- and three-digit numbers (300, 12, 25), then gradually increase the size (152, 5472, 36). Ask: *Does the order of the numbers matter? Which number comes first in division statements?*

2. Assess

Put these statements on the board: $327 × 45 = 14715$; $2641 × 29 = 76{,}589$; $14{,}688 ÷ 36 = 408$; $71{,}478 ÷ 57 = 1254$. Recall that multiplication and division are inverse operations. Elicit that we could use division to check the first two statements are correct; then multiplication for the next two. Remind the children to use long multiplication and long division, and show their working. Suggest that writing each digit in a square of the squared paper should help them to keep to the correct columns. Record the outcomes.

3. Further practice

Photocopiable page 47 'Top triangles' tests the children's ability to multiply and divide numbers quickly.

You will need

1. Check

Oral and mental starter

12 Short measure

2. Assess

'Match the measures'

3. Further practice

Oral and mental starter

11 Your choice

General resources

Interactive activity 'Metric units'

Converting metric measures

Most children should be able to convert smaller units into larger ones and vice versa, locating the decimal point in the correct place.

Some children may have problems placing the decimal point correctly and knowing when to use zero as a place-holder.

1. Check

Revise that converting units is all about multiplication and division. To convert centimetres to millimetres, you multiply by 10, and to convert millimetres to centimetres you divide by 10. Also consider that a measurement can be written in a number of ways. 136cm = 1m 36cm = 1.36m. Ask: *In what other ways could 2l 320ml be written? How could 1.09kg be written?*

2. Assess

Ask the children to work individually on 'Match the measures' from page 48. Stress that they should think carefully about the location of a decimal point. In measurements including a decimal point, can they give the correct value for each digit? Which conversion is more difficult – larger units into smaller units, or vice versa? Why? Record the outcomes.

3. Further practice

The oral and mental starter 'Your choice', the children decide what kind of equipment they would choose for measuring tasks. The interactive activity 'Metric units' on the CD-ROM offers practice of reading, writing and comparing different standard units.

Oral and mental starters

Number and place value

1 Place value

Revise place value involving six-digit numbers (hundreds of thousands). Ask the children to write the numbers you say on their whiteboards. For example: *fifty-seven thousand two hundred and seventeen* (57,217), *four hundred and thirty thousand nine hundred and forty-six* (430,946). Include some examples where zero is used as a place-holder, such as: *seventy-six thousand and five* (76,005) and *one hundred and two thousand and fifty-eight* (102,058).

2 Digit spotting

Write a selection of five- and six-digit numbers on the board. Circle one digit in each number and invite children to identify the value of the marked digit. For example: 65,**2**13, **4**9,704, 36,97**8**, 1**2**4,563, 448,**4**29.

Extension

Circle two or three digits in the same number. Over time, include seven-digit numbers, such as: 1,752,**3**45, 4,**3**41,2**6**9.

3 Roundup

Revise rounding numbers to the nearest 10. Include three-, four- and five-digit numbers. Remind the children to focus on the final digit. For example: 117 (120), 423 (420), 1237 (1240), 41,306 (41,310) and 58,454 (58,450). Then round to the nearest 100, 1000 and 10,000.

Addition, subtraction, multiplication and division

4 Add and subtract

Consolidate mental addition and subtraction of any two numbers less than 100. Discuss the strategies to use, such as near doubles, near multiples of 10, partitioning, complementary addition. Try: 24 + 23, 63 + 21, 36 − 18, 60 − 29, 61 − 53.

Extension

Increase the size of the numbers to over 100: 109 + 191, 251 + 148, 207 − 94, 351 − 147.

5 Five seconds

Set some word problems. Tell the children that you will say each question twice and they will have five seconds to find the answer. Try: *Find the difference between 150 and 80. How much change do I have from £5 if I spend £3.75? Multiply 26 by 3 and add 12. What is the remainder when 127 is divided by 5?*

6 Tell me about it

Write up some two-digit (and then three-digit) numbers and invite children to say as much as they can about each number, using key words. For example: *34 is an even number. Doubling it equals 68. 17 and 2 are factors of it. It is the total of 18 and 16. 25 is an odd number. It is 5 squared. It is 33 subtract 8. It is half of 50.*

Extension

Add variety by including metric measures and time problems: *How many minutes is it from 19 minutes past 9 to 11 o'clock?*

7 Answers please

Give the children ten seconds to say as many division facts as they can for a target number. For example: for 7, they could say 49 ÷ 7, 70 ÷ 10, 700 ÷ 100 and 56 ÷ 8. Try these target numbers: 3, 5, 6, 10, 20.

Extension
Repeat the process with two-digit and three-digit round numbers, such as: 30, 50, 100, 200.

8 Family of three

Ask the children to make two multiplication and two division statements using the family of three numbers you give them. Allow 20 seconds each time, then collect the four statements in each case. For example: for 45, 9 and 5: 5 × 9 = 45, 9 × 5 = 45, 45 ÷ 9 = 5 and 45 ÷ 5 = 9.

Extension
Repeat with larger numbers, such as: 12, 300, 25, and then decimal numbers: 0.75, 3.4.

9 Who am I?

Play a 'guessing' game where you give some information about a number for the children to work out what (who) the number is. Say the information twice before taking guesses. For example: *I am the next square number after 25. Who am I? I come between 5 and 10 and I'm a factor of 21... I am the product of 5 and 3... I am the sum of the angles in a quadrilateral...*

10 Brackets

Revise that any part of a calculation inside a set of brackets must be done first: (4 × 2) + 3 = 11, 7 + (10 − 5) = 12. Ask the children to do similar problems, including some that include two sets of brackets. For example: (2 + 3) − (10 − 5), (13 − 9) × (4 + 2), (27 + 3) + (5 − 2).

Measurement

11 Your choice

Ask the children to name some common metric units. Then ask the children to choose the appropriate metric unit for: weight of a bus; weight of a child; length of a pencil; width of a postage stamp; distance between two towns; length of a small garden; dose of medicine; volume of a bottle of wine.

Extension
Provide the metric unit and challenge children to name objects to measure. For example: *Name something you would weigh in grams. What could you measure in metres?*

12 Short measure

Revise that to convert cm into mm, you multiply by 10, and to convert mm into cm you divide by 10. Ask the children to convert these measurements into mm: 1cm, 4cm, 7cm, 12cm, 16cm, 8½cm, 15½cm, 6.5cm, 19.5cm. Then convert these into cm: 13mm, 20mm, 27mm, 39mm, 52mm, 109mm, 194mm, 256mm.

Think big

■ Write your answers on a separate piece of paper.

In the news
■ Change the amounts in these newspaper headlines from words into numbers.

£6¾ million robbery

£12 million government cuts

About 20¼ million vehicles use Britain's roads

£2½ million lottery win

Eight hundred thousand pounds spent on swimming pool refit

Space travel
■ Here are some approximate distances of the planets from the Sun. How would you write these distances in words?

Mercury: _____9,000,000km_____   Mars: _____230,000,000km_____

Venus: _____100,000,000km_____   Jupiter: _____770,000,000km_____

Earth: _____150,000,000km_____   Saturn: _____1,400,000,000km_____

City populations
■ Here are population figures for some of the world's largest cities. Make sure you can say these numbers. Put them in order of size, smallest first.

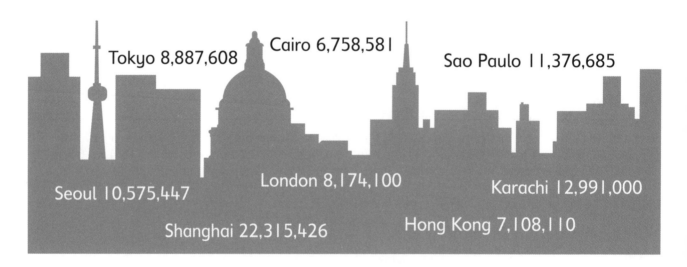

Tokyo 8,887,608
Cairo 6,758,581
Sao Paulo 11,376,685
Seoul 10,575,447
London 8,174,100
Karachi 12,991,000
Shanghai 22,315,426
Hong Kong 7,108,110

I can identify, order and compare large numbers found in everyday life.

How did you do?

Top triangles

- Fill in the missing spaces in these triangles by either multiplying or dividing.

1.
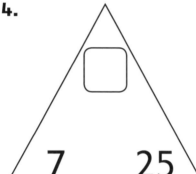

2.
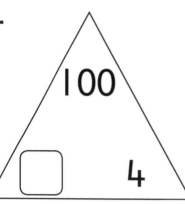

3.
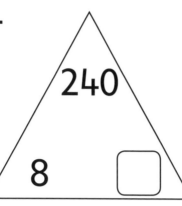

4.
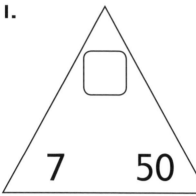

5.
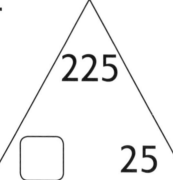

6.
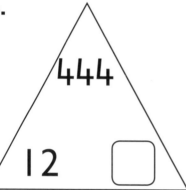

7.
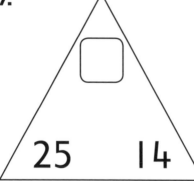

8.
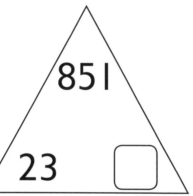

- Now write four facts about each triangle: two multiplication facts and two division facts. For example: 1. $50 \times 7 = 350$; $7 \times 50 = 350$; $350 \div 7 = 50$ and $350 \div 50 = 7$.

I can carry out multiplication and division calculations mentally.

How did you do?

Match the measures

■ Draw lines to match up pairs of the same amounts, one in the left-hand column to one in the right-hand column.

10g	0.770kg
5012g	3kg 270g
4296g	0.006kg
1342g	9.681kg
770g	0.010kg
3270g	4.296kg
9681g	5kg 12g
6g	1.342kg

■ Fill in the missing amounts in these tables.

metres	kilometres
	1.752
2354	
	4.050
64	
	0.002

millilitres	litres
6732	
	1.439
253	
	0.073
5	

I can convert metric measures.

How did you do?

Written methods for multiplication and division

Expected prior learning

Children should be able to:

- understand the close relationship between multiplication and division
- multiply decimal numbers
- divide decimal numbers and recognise remainders
- carry out problem-solving tasks using all four operations.

Topic	Curriculum objectives	Expected outcomes
Multiplication and division	**Lesson 1**	
	To multiply multi-digit numbers up to four digits by a two-digit whole number using the formal written method of long multiplication.	Use written methods to multiply a four-digit number by a two-digit number.
	Lesson 2	
	To divide numbers up to four digits by a two-digit whole number using the formal written method of long division, and interpret remainders as whole number remainders, fractions, decimals or rounding, as appropriate for the context.	Use written methods to divide a four-digit number by a two-digit number.
	Lesson 3	
	To divide numbers up to four digits by a two-digit whole number using the formal written method of long division, and interpret remainders as whole number remainders, fractions, decimals or rounding, as appropriate for the context.	Divide four-digit numbers by two-digit numbers. Represent remainders from division calculations in a number of different ways.
	Lesson 4	
	To multiply numbers with up to two decimal places by whole numbers.	Multiply and divide decimal numbers with up to two decimal places by one-digit whole numbers.
	Lesson 5	
	To solve problems involving addition, subtraction, multiplication and division.	Solve problems involving the four operations and including decimal numbers.

Preparation

Lesson 1: copy 'Number cards 0–9' for each child

Lessons 2 and 4: write up the calculations ready for individual work

Lesson 3: write the word problems on the board; copy 'Rounding up and down' for each child

Lesson 5: copy 'Eating out (1)' for each child

You will need

Photocopiable sheets
'Rounding up and down'; 'Eating out (1)'

General resources
'Number cards 0–9'

Equipment
Individual whiteboards

Further practice

'Eating out (2)' offers further practice of solving decimal word problems.

Oral and mental starters suggested for week 1

See the bank of starters on page 84. Oral and mental starters are also on the CD-ROM.

13 Decimal digits

14 Decimals at the double

15 Decimal times

16 Ten times more

Overview of progression

The beginning of this week builds on work on written methods of multiplication and division. This will be extended so that the children experience multiplying and dividing a four-digit number by a two-digit number. In later division calculations the children learn how remainders can be expressed in different ways. This may also involve rounding. Multiplication and division of decimal numbers is also considered. Finally, the children have the chance to put skills into action in a problem-solving task involving money.

Watch out for

As ever with multiplication and division work, children will need a good working knowledge of multiplication tables. Make sure children fully understand the setting down procedures followed in long multiplication and long division – squared paper may help with recording here. Children need to appreciate that remainders can be shown in different ways. When multiplying and dividing decimal numbers, ensure children understand where decimal points are located in the answer. Estimating answers first should help with this process.

Creative context

There are other methods of multiplication and division that children could explore, making strong connections with the history of mathematics. Investigate a method of multiplying and dividing used by the Ancient Egyptians, for example. It uses doubling, halving and addition. Russian multiplication, as it is often called, is another method to try. This may have originated in Ancient Greece. Also find out about the use of Napier's Bones for multiplying numbers, a system developed in sixteenth-century Scotland.

Vocabulary

approximate, decimal number, decimal point, digit, division, estimate, fraction, inverse, method, multiplication, numeral, operation, **product**, **quotient**, remainder, round down, round up, strategy, whole number

Curriculum objectives

- To multiply multi-digit numbers by a two-digit whole number using long multiplication.

Success criteria

- I can multiply a four-digit number by a two-digit whole number using a formal written method.

You will need

General resources

'Number cards 0–9'

Equipment

Individual whiteboards

Differentiation

Less confident learners

Children should continue to focus on HTU × U and HTU × TU.

More confident learners

Children should make up practical questions where four-digit numbers are multiplied by two-digit numbers.

Lesson 1 — Oral and mental starter 13

Main teaching activities

Whole-class work: Recap long multiplication. Tell them that now they are going to multiply a four-digit number by a two-digit number. Go through this example on the board: 2754 × 38. Estimate the answer first. Explain that we multiply 2754 × 30 and then 2754 × 8 and add the two answers together. Stress that before multiplying by 3, a zero should be written down because the number is 3 tens. Recall that numbers have to be written down in the correct columns, carrying figures should be added to the next stage of the multiplication and both lines of working out should be totalled at the end.

$$
\begin{array}{r} 2754 \\ \times\ \ \ \ 38 \\ \hline 104652 \end{array}
\qquad
\begin{array}{r} 2754 \\ \times\ \ \ \ 30 \\ \hline 82620 \end{array}
\qquad
\begin{array}{r} 2754 \\ \times\ \ \ \ \ \ 8 \\ \hline 22032 \end{array}
\qquad
\begin{array}{r} 22032 \\ +\ 82620 \\ \hline 104652 \end{array}
$$

Work through several other examples with the children.

Progress check: Talk through each stage with the children. Ask: *What number do we multiply by first? Why do we need to write down a zero? What happens to each carrying figure? What happens to the two lines of working out at the end?*

Paired work: Provide each pair with a set of number cards. Ask them to take turns to make a four-digit number and then a two-digit number to multiply by. Remind children to estimate before using the written method.

Review

Invite volunteers to show how they worked out some of their calculations. Ask the class to check the working out is correct.

Curriculum objectives

- To divide numbers up to four-digits by a two-digit whole number using long division.

Success criteria

- I can divide a four-digit number by a two-digit number using a formal written method.

You will need

Equipment

Individual whiteboards

Differentiation

Less confident learners

Give children calculations focusing on HTU ÷ U and HTU ÷ TU before moving on to four-digit numbers.

More confident learners

Expect children to move on quickly to calculations involving four-digits. They should work with larger divisors and check answers using the inverse operation.

Lesson 2 — Oral and mental starter 14

Main teaching activities

Whole-class work: Tell the children they are going to extend their knowledge of the standard written method of division by looking at four-digit numbers. Go through 4256 ÷ 38 on the board, with children repeating each stage on their whiteboards. Estimate first: 4000 ÷ 40 = 100. Explain that 38 into 42 goes once with 4 remaining. Bring down the next digit, the 5, to go with the 4 to make 45. Explain that in this type of division calculation, multiplication and subtraction are also needed. Continue each stage:

$$
\begin{array}{r}
112 \\
38\overline{)4256} \\
-\ \ 38 \\
\hline
45 \\
-\ \ 38 \\
\hline
76 \\
-\ \ 76 \\
\hline
00
\end{array}
$$

Progress check: Go through more examples such as 6084 ÷ 26 and 5396 ÷ 19 until the children are confident. Leave the examples on the board.

Independent work: Write a selection of division sentences on the board for children to solve. Show them in support, core and extension groups for children to work on as appropriate. For example: *Support*: 237 ÷ 3, 425 ÷ 5, 322 ÷ 14. *Core*: 300 ÷ 12, 391 ÷ 32, 1890 ÷ 35. *Extension*: 3375 ÷ 27, 8680 ÷ 35, 27186 ÷ 69. These all give complete whole-number answers.

Review

Share some of the children's calculations. Did the estimate help with checking the answers? In what other way can an answer be checked?

Curriculum objectives
● To divide numbers up to four-digits by a two-digit whole number using long division and interpret remainders as whole numbers, fractions, decimals and by rounding.

Success criteria
● I can divide a four-digit number by a two-digit number.
● I can record a remainder as a whole number, a fraction or a decimal, or by rounding off.

You will need

Photocopiable sheets
'Rounding up and down'

Equipment
Individual whiteboards

Differentiation

Less confident learners

Help children to focus on showing remainders as a whole number and as a fraction before moving on to consider decimal equivalents.

More confident learners

Ask children to focus more on showing remainders as decimal numbers. Also encourage them to make up their own examples of divisions where remainders have to be rounded up or rounded down.

Lesson 3 — Oral and mental starter 15

Main teaching activities

Whole-class work: Write the calculation $433 \div 6$ on the board. Ask the children to complete the calculation as shown:

$$6 \overline{)43^13} \quad 72\ r\ 1$$

Elicit that 6 doesn't go into 433 exactly. There is a remainder. Explain that there are three ways to show the remainder: as a whole number, as a fraction or as a decimal. The simple method above shows the remainder as a whole number (1). Go on to explain that, to show it as a fraction, the remainder (1) becomes the numerator, and the divisor (6) becomes the denominator, giving a fraction remainder of $\frac{1}{6}$. To write a remainder as decimal, we need to continue the calculation by adding a decimal point to both the remainder and the dividend and two zeros to the end of the dividend. The division method then continues. Let the children know that two decimal places will be accurate enough at this level.

$$6 \overline{)43^13.^10^40} \quad 72.16$$

Progress check: Work through some more examples with the children, checking how successful they are at giving the remainder in all three ways each time.

Paired work: Then write the following problem on the board for the children to work on in pairs:

● *A minibus holds 18 passengers. 230 people need to travel to an athletics meeting. How many minibuses will they need?*

Ask the children to work in pairs to solve the problem. Tell them that this time you want them to choose the most appropriate way to show the remainder.

Progress check: Establish that the calculation gives the answer 12 r 14. This means 12 minibuses will be full and there will be 14 people left over. Discuss that therefore another minibus must be hired even though it won't be full, making a total of 13 minibuses. Discuss how remainders sometimes need to be rounded up or down depending on the context. Pose another question:

● *Felt-tipped pens are packed in boxes of 18. There are 230 pens. How many full boxes can be made?*

Establish that we already know the answer to the calculation from the previous question as the numbers are the same (12 r 14). However this time we will need to round *down*. Only 12 full boxes can be made, so the final answer is 12 not 13 as in the previous problem.

Independent work: Ask the children to use photocopiable page 'Rounding up and down' from the CD-ROM to practise working through examples of division problems requiring them to round up or down depending on the context.

Review

Ask: *How many different ways do you now know of showing the remainder in a division calculation?* Choose several questions from the photocopiable sheet to check. Ask volunteers to explain to the others why they rounded their answers up or down.

Lesson 4   Oral and mental starter 14

Main teaching activities

Whole-class work: Start by revising multiplying a small decimal number by a one-digit whole number, for example: 2.7 × 5. Prompt the children to round up or down to estimate the answer first: 3 × 5 = 15. Then complete the multiplication process to produce 13.5.

$$\begin{array}{r} 2.7 \\ \times \quad 5 \\ \hline 13.5 \\ \scriptstyle 3 \end{array}$$

7 × 5 = 35. Put down the 5 units and carry the 3 tens. Then 5 × 2 = 10 and add the 3 that has been carried to make 13. Answer is 13.5, as decimal point should be one place in from the right-hand side.

Explain that, if the children are unsure, the decimal point can be located by referring to the estimated answer. The answer cannot be .135 or 1.35 or 135, only 13.5 because the estimated answer was 15. Also point out that when you multiply a decimal number by a whole number the answer has the same number of digits after the decimal point as the original decimal number. It this case it was one digit.

Then write on the board another example: 5.39 × 6. Again, ask the children to approximate first (5 × 6 = 30), and then demonstrate how the calculation is done. Stress that the answer should be close to the approximation and this time the decimal point will have two digits after it (32.34).

Go on to work through several examples of division calculations including a decimal point, using the long division method taught previously. Try these examples: 21.2 ÷ 4, 17.10 ÷ 6. Use the same checks as outlined above to locate the decimal point in the final answer.

$$\begin{array}{r} 5.3 \\ 4\overline{)21.2} \\ -\ 20 \\ \hline 12 \\ -\ 12 \\ \hline 00 \end{array} \qquad \begin{array}{r} 2.85 \\ 6\overline{)17.10} \\ -\ 12 \\ \hline 51 \\ -\ 48 \\ \hline 30 \\ -\ 30 \\ \hline 00 \end{array}$$

Progress check: Work through several more examples of the same type of questions with the children. Pose key questions throughout the process: *Why is it important to work out an approximate answer first? How do we decide where the decimal point will go in the answer?*

Independent work: Write the following calculations on the board for the children to work through:
- 6.3 × 7, 9.8 × 5, 12.32 × 6, 34.79 × 4
- 13.5 ÷ 5, 31.2 ÷ 8, 40.11 ÷ 7, 86.68 ÷ 4

Stress to the children that they should use the formal written multiplication and division methods practised in this and previous lessons and include all their working out. Also emphasise that they should use both the checks shown to ensure the decimal point is located in the correct position.

Review
Check the children's calculations and work through any difficulties that have arisen. Ask the children to explain the two ways in which they located the place of the decimal point in their answers.

Curriculum objectives
● To solve word problems involving addition, subtraction, multiplication and division.

Success criteria
● I can solve word problems involving addition, subtraction, multiplication and division, including decimal numbers.

You will need
Photocopiable sheets
'Eating out (1)'

Differentiation
Less confident learners

Work with children to focus on some of the earlier questions on 'Eating out (1)' that feature addition and subtraction with decimal numbers.

More confident learners

Expect children to work through the early questions on 'Eating out (1)' quickly so they can move on to the later problems dealing with multiplication and division.

Lesson 5

Oral and mental starter 16

Main teaching activities

Whole-class work: Tell the children that they are going to work on an activity called 'Eating out', which is about a group of people who go to a restaurant for a meal and need to work out how much different things cost. Explain that the problems set could involve adding, subtracting, multiplying or dividing. They will have to decide which operation is needed for each calculation or part of calculation.

Remind the children that when adding and subtracting decimal numbers, the decimal points and decimal places should be lined up under each other. Remind them too about finding the correct place for the decimal point in multiplication and division questions and that after dividing numbers that produce a remainder some rounding off may need to be done.

Independent work: Distribute photocopiable page 'Eating out (1)' from the CD-ROM to each child. Stress that they should clearly show the working out to all their calculations.

Progress check: Stop the children at intervals as they work through the photocopiable sheet, particularly those you wish to assess. Ensure that they are converting key words in the questions into the correct mathematical operations. Have they found, for example, words and phrases like *total*, *difference*, *how much more* and *share*? Check that the correct calculation methods are being used.

Review

Go through the questions from the photocopiable sheet, first identifying the calculations and operations needed. Discuss any difficulties that arose. Ask the children: *How much help was estimating the answers first? Did this make placing the location of the decimal point easier? What methods did you use to check your answers?*

Charlie's Bistro

Starters
Soup £3.50
Garlic Mushrooms £3.75
Goats' Cheese Salad £4.90

Main courses
Beef Hotpot £12.85
Chicken Kiev £10.95
Salmon Salad 13.20

Desserts
Strawberry Cheesecake £4.90
Vanilla Ice Cream Sundae £2.80
Chocolate Fudge Cake £3.15

Comparing and ordering fractions

Expected prior learning

Children should be able to:

- understand the terms *mixed number* and *improper fraction*
- compare and order fractions
- convert a fraction into a decimal number
- add and subtract simple fractions.

Topic	Curriculum objectives	Expected outcomes
Fractions (including decimals and percentages)	**Lesson 1**	
	To compare and order fractions, including fractions >1.	Convert mixed numbers into improper fractions, and vice versa.
	Lesson 2	
	To compare and order fractions, including fractions >1. To use common factors to simplify fractions; use common multiples to express fractions in the same denomination.	Compare and order fractions. Use common multiples to put fractions into the same denomination.
	Lesson 3	
	To associate a fraction with division and calculate decimal fraction equivalents for a simple fraction.	Convert fractions into decimal numbers using division.
	Lesson 4	
	To use common factors to simplify fractions; use common multiples to express fractions in the same denomination.	Put fractions into their lowest terms using common factors (cancelling down).
	Lesson 5	
	To add and subtract fractions with different denominators and mixed numbers, using the concept of equivalent fractions.	Add and subtract simple fractions.

Preparation

Lesson 1: draw the 'pizza' diagrams on the board, and write up the fraction lists for paired work

Lesson 2: put the lists of fractions on the board; prepare number lines for support

Lesson 3: copy 'All change' for each pair

Lesson 4: write up the fractions for group work

Lesson 5: draw the divided square and circle on the board

You will need

Photocopiable sheets
'All change'; 'Fraction shapes'

General resources
'Fraction wall'

Equipment
Individual whiteboards; fraction sets; blank number lines; calculators

Further practice

Use the 'All change template' to further practice fractions and their decimal equivalents. Adapt to reflect children's level of confidence (see lesson 3 differentiation section).

Oral and mental starters suggested for week 2

See the bank of starters on pages 84 and 85. Oral and mental starters are also on the CD-ROM.

17 How many?

18 You owe

19 Which order?

20 Fractions and decimals

21 Cancel down

Overview of progression

Some revision will be necessary to revise fractions work from Year 5. This includes changing mixed numbers to improper fractions, and vice versa, and comparing and ordering fractions using the lowest common denominator. Work is also done on converting fractions into decimal numbers, and the concepts of terminating, infinite and recurring decimal numbers are introduced. The children learn how to use common factors to simplify fractions, known as cancelling down or putting fractions into their lowest terms. At the end of the week the children have the opportunity to add and subtract simple fractions in an investigation.

Watch out for

It is essential that children appreciate that fractions are parts of whole numbers. A full understanding of fractions is also dependent on knowledge of key words and phrases and children need to be acquainted with these as quickly as possible. Using fraction walls and number lines may help children when they are ordering and comparing the sizes of fractions. When cancelling down, encourage children to look for the highest common factor so that the process does not have to be repeated several times. When adding and subtracting fractions, whole numbers should be dealt with first and then fractions, once they have been put into the same family.

Creative context

Measurements can be expressed as fractional parts of main units. At the supermarket, for example, goods are often sold by half kilogram (sugar, butter) and half litre (milk, lemonade). Time is expressed as quarter past, half past and quarter to the hour. Help children appreciate that parts of wholes can be expressed as fractions, decimals and percentages: ½, 0.5 and 50% are exactly the same amount.

Vocabulary

cancelling down, denominator, division, eighth, equivalent fraction, factor, fraction, half, highest common factor, improper fraction, infinite decimal number, **lowest common denominator**, lowest terms, mixed number, numerator, quarter, recurring decimal number, reduced, terminating decimal number

Curriculum objectives
● To compare fractions, including fractions >1.
Success criteria
● I can convert mixed numbers into improper fractions, and vice versa.

You will need
General resources
'Fraction wall'
Equipment
Individual whiteboards; fraction sets

Differentiation
Less confident learners
There will be some support through working in mixed-ability pairs. Plastic fraction sets or a printed fraction wall might be useful for children who require apparatus to help their understanding.
More confident learners
Challenge children to include some simple mixed numbers with the fractions, and some whole numbers, such as $2\frac{1}{4} + 1\frac{3}{4}$.

Lesson 1
Oral and mental starter 17

Main teaching activities

Whole-class work: Explain to the children that they are going to begin this week by revising some fractions work from Year 5. Ask the children if they can explain *numerator* and *denominator*. Draw three large 'pizzas' on the board, each divided into six equal portions. Ask what fraction of pizza one slice is ($\frac{1}{6}$). Establish with the children that six pieces make a whole one, that is: $\frac{6}{6} = 1$. Now suggest to the children that they have eaten $1\frac{1}{6}$ of the pizzas. Ask: *How many sixths are left in the pizza that has been started?* (5.) *How many sixths have been eaten?* (7.) Can the children recall that $1\frac{1}{6} = \frac{7}{6}$ and that $1\frac{1}{6}$ is known as a *mixed number* because it is a mixture of a whole number and a fraction? Recap too that $\frac{7}{6}$ is known as an *improper fraction* because the numerator is greater than the denominator.

Now ask the children: *If I had $\frac{19}{6}$, what would this be as a mixed number?* ($3\frac{1}{6}$) *How many pizzas could I make from $\frac{23}{6}$?* ($3\frac{5}{6}$)

Continue this with the following questions, asking the children to show the answers on their whiteboards:

- *Change $3\frac{1}{4}$ into an improper fraction.*
- *Change $\frac{12}{5}$ into a mixed number.*
- *If each cake can be cut into eight pieces, how many cakes do I need to hand out 30 pieces? How many pieces will be left?*

Progress check: Check through the children's answers on their whiteboards. Encourage volunteers to explain the processes they have gone through in the lesson. Ask: *How do you convert a mixed number into an improper fraction? How do you convert an improper fraction into a mixed number?*

Paired work: Organise the children to work in mixed-ability pairs, and put the following challenges on the board:

- *Change to mixed numbers: $\frac{13}{4}$, $\frac{17}{2}$, $\frac{8}{3}$, $\frac{23}{7}$, $\frac{17}{9}$, $\frac{28}{3}$, $\frac{46}{5}$, $\frac{52}{10}$.*
- *Change to improper fractions: $2\frac{1}{3}$, $4\frac{1}{2}$, $5\frac{3}{5}$, $7\frac{3}{8}$, $4\frac{5}{6}$, $6\frac{4}{9}$, $8\frac{2}{3}$, $10\frac{7}{10}$.*

Review

Go over the questions when the children have completed them. Discuss the methods used, and work through any problems encountered. Finally, put the following four statements on the board: $4\frac{4}{5} = \frac{26}{5}$; $3\frac{9}{12} = \frac{45}{12}$; $5\frac{2}{6} = \frac{31}{6}$ and $7\frac{3}{4} = \frac{29}{4}$. Ask: *Which of these statements is correct?* ($3\frac{9}{12} = \frac{45}{12}$). *What should the other correct answers be?* ($4\frac{4}{5} = \frac{24}{5}$; $5\frac{2}{6} = \frac{32}{6}$; $7\frac{3}{4} = \frac{31}{4}$.)

Curriculum objectives
● To compare and order fractions, including fractions >1.
● To use common multiples to express fractions in the same denomination.

Success criteria
● I can compare and order fractions, including those greater than 1.
● I can use multiples to put fractions into the same denomination.

You will need
General resources
'Fraction wall'
Equipment
Individual whiteboards

Differentiation
Less confident learners
Provide a long strip of paper with a number line marked at regular intervals. Work with children to change fractions into the same fraction family, and ask children to write the positions of the fractions on the line.

More confident learners
Give a greater range of fractions for children to solve, including some mixed numbers such as 1½ and 2¼.

Lesson 2

Main teaching activities

Whole-class work: Write a group of unit fractions on the board and show the children that they are fractions that have 1 as the numerator. For example: ⅓, ½, ⅙ and ⅒. Ask the children to put them in order, smallest first, on their whiteboards. Check answers, and establish that, with unit fractions, the larger the denominator the smaller the fraction will be, so: ⅒ means only 1 part out of 10, while ½ means 1 part out of 2.

Then ask the children to order ¹²⁄₁₅, ¹³⁄₁₅, ⁹⁄₁₅ and ⁷⁄₁₅, smallest to largest. Ask: *Why is it so easy to do?* (They have the same denominator.) Now ask them to try ⅗, ⅚, ⅔ and ⁷⁄₁₀, and ask: *Why is this more difficult?* (The denominators are different.) Do the children know how to do it? Elicit or explain that the solution lies in finding a denominator that is common to 5, 6, 3 and 10. Ask: *What is the lowest number that is common to the 5×, 6×, 3× and 10× tables?* Establish that 30 is the common number here. Show the children how to convert each of the fractions into 30ths by multiplying the denominator and then the numerator by the same number:

● $3 \times 6 = 18$ $5 \times 5 = 25$ $2 \times 10 = 20$ $7 \times 3 = 21$
   $5 \times 6 = 30$ $6 \times 5 = 30$ $3 \times 10 = 30$ $10 \times 3 = 30$
       ⁸⁄₃₀   ²⁵⁄₃₀   ²⁰⁄₃₀   ²¹⁄₃₀

Now they are all in thirtieths, we can clearly see that ⅗ (¹⁸⁄₃₀) is smallest, then comes ⅔ (²⁰⁄₃₀), followed by ⁷⁄₁₀ (²¹⁄₃₀), with ⅚ (²⁵⁄₃₀) the largest fraction in the group. Ask the children to sort the following groups of fractions in the same way:

● Group A: ⅛, ⁴⁄₁₂, ⁹⁄₂₄ and ¾.
● Group B: ¾, ½, ⅘ and ³⁄₁₀.

Progress check: Check through the children's ordering of the two groups given above. Ask: *How did you sort the fractions in Group A? What is the lowest number on the 8×, 12×, 24× and 4× tables? In Group B, what is the lowest number that 4, 2, 5 and 10 will go into?*

Independent work: Put the following information on the board, and ask the children to put each group of fractions into order, running from smallest to largest.

● A: ⅔, ⅙, ¾, ⁷⁄₁₂.
● B: ⅙, ⁵⁄₉, ⅔, ¹¹⁄₁₈.
● C: ¾, ⅘, ⁷⁄₁₀, ¹¹⁄₂₀.
● D: ¼, ⁵⁄₁₂, ⅔, ⅚.
● E: ½, ⁷⁄₁₂, ⅚, ⅔.
● F: ¼, ⅘, ⅝, ⁷⁄₁₀.

Review

Ask the children: *Would you rather have ⅝ or ⅗ of a bar of chocolate? Which is the bigger of the two?* Prompt them to explain what they would need to do to find out which would be the larger piece. (Change both into 40ths, so: ⅝ = ²⁵⁄₄₀ and ⅗ = ²⁴⁄₄₀.)

Curriculum objectives
- To associate a fraction with division and calculate decimal fraction equivalents.

Success criteria
- I can change fractions into decimal numbers using division.

You will need

Photocopiable sheets
'All change'

Equipment
Calculators

Differentiation

Less confident learners
Work with children initially, and give them less demanding conversions from fractions to decimals, such as $\frac{1}{2}$, $\frac{1}{4}$, $\frac{1}{5}$ and $\frac{1}{10}$.

More confident learners
Children should tackle more demanding conversions. Encourage them to make logical steps from some of the answers they find. For example, if $\frac{1}{3}$ = 0.3333 recurring, then $\frac{2}{3}$ = 0.6666 recurring; and if $\frac{1}{8}$ = 0.125, then $\frac{2}{8}$ = 0.125 × 2.

Lesson 3

Oral and mental starter 19

Main teaching activities

Whole-class work: Ask the children if they know how to convert a fraction into a decimal number. Elicit the response that suggests fractions can be turned into decimal numbers by dividing the denominator into the numerator, with a zero being placed alongside each remainder. Write some examples up on the board. Try: $\frac{1}{4}$, $\frac{3}{10}$ and $\frac{1}{8}$:

0.25	0.3 r 1	0.125
4 ⟌ 1.00	10 ⟌ 3.0	8 ⟌ 1.000
− 8	30	− 8
20	00	20
− 20		− 16
00		40
		− 40
		00

Display on the board and work out together some more difficult answers. For example: $\frac{1}{3}$ is 0.3333 recurring, $\frac{5}{6}$ is 0.8333 continuing. Use these examples to explain the difference between *terminating decimal numbers* (0.125), *infinite decimal numbers* (0.8333 continuing) and *recurring decimal numbers* (0.3333 recurring) where the same digit comes in every place. Explain that in the last two cases, the display on a calculator shows only part of the decimal representation.

Paired work: Organise the children to work in mixed-ability pairs. Provide each pair with photocopiable page 'All change' from the CD-ROM where they are required to sort fractions by changing them first into decimal numbers. Let them use a calculator only to check their answers.

Progress check: Pause the children when most of them have completed up to $\frac{1}{10}$ on the photocopiable sheet. Go through the answers produced so far. Ask the children to explain the method they are using and encourage them to make comments on anything interesting they have found so far.

Review

Check all the decimal numbers that have been completed and the order produced. Discuss any significant relationships that have been noticed, for example $\frac{1}{5}$ and $\frac{3}{5}$ and $\frac{1}{3}$ and $\frac{2}{3}$. Challenge more confident children to report any interesting discoveries they have made. For example: $\frac{1}{9}$ has 1 in every place, $\frac{2}{9}$ has 2 in every place. Can the children predict the rest of the 'ninths' family from this?

Curriculum objectives
● To use common factors to simplify fractions.
Success criteria
● I can cancel down fractions into their lowest terms.

You will need
General resources
'Fraction wall'
Equipment
Individual whiteboards

Differentiation
Less confident learners
Ask children to focus on the support section of the cancelling down task.

More confident learners
Expect children to work more on the extension section of the cancelling down task.

Lesson 4 — Oral and mental starter [20]

Main teaching activities

Whole-class work: Discuss how it is easier to work with fractions if they are in their simplest form. Refer to photocopiable page 'Fraction wall' from the CD-ROM and show that $\frac{1}{3}$ can be written as $\frac{2}{6}$ or $\frac{3}{9}$. Ask: *What is $\frac{1}{8}$ in its simplest form?* Also investigate $\frac{5}{9}$, $\frac{4}{12}$ and $\frac{12}{15}$. Explain that we can use factors and division in a similar way that multiplication is used for finding equivalence. Demonstrate, using $\frac{6}{18}$ as an example. Ask: *What number is a factor of 6 and 18?* Children could offer a range. Accept one (such as 2) and divide the numerator and the denominator by it: $\frac{6}{18} \div 2 = \frac{3}{9}$. Ask: *Does this fraction have factors too?* (Yes, divide by 3: $\frac{3}{9} \div 3 = \frac{1}{3}$.) Ask: *Was there a factor that would have got to $\frac{1}{3}$ at the first attempt?* (Yes, 6.) Try other examples: $\frac{4}{16}$, $\frac{7}{21}$...

Group work: Write up lists of fractions for the children to cancel down into their lowest terms:
● Support: $\frac{2}{8}$, $\frac{8}{10}$, $\frac{4}{6}$, $\frac{9}{12}$, $\frac{3}{30}$.
● Core: $\frac{10}{16}$, $\frac{10}{25}$, $\frac{15}{20}$, $\frac{6}{15}$, $\frac{20}{80}$.
● Extension: $\frac{24}{60}$, $\frac{12}{72}$, $\frac{16}{48}$, $\frac{24}{36}$, $\frac{50}{75}$.

Progress check: Remind the children they should be looking: a) for common factors for both the numerator and the denominator first, and then: b) finding the highest common factor to cut down on the stages of cancelling involved.

Review

Use the greater than and less than signs ($<$ and $>$) to check children's understanding of cancelling down and simplest form. For example, ask: *Which is the largest of these pairs of fractions, $\frac{3}{24}$ or $\frac{6}{36}$?* ($\frac{1}{8} < \frac{1}{6}$), ...$\frac{21}{28}$ or $\frac{15}{30}$? ($\frac{3}{4} > \frac{1}{2}$), ... $\frac{10}{50}$ or $\frac{20}{60}$? ($\frac{1}{5} < \frac{1}{3}$).

Curriculum objectives
● To add and subtract fractions with the same denominator.
Success criteria
● I can add and subtract simple fractions.

You will need
Photocopiable sheets
'Fraction shapes'
General resources
'Fraction wall'
Equipment
Individual whiteboards

Differentiation
Less confident learners
Children might benefit from using the fraction wall to see halves, quarters and eighths clearly.

More confident learners
Challenge children to devise their own shapes. How many addition and subtraction statements can they make about a shape divided into tenths or twelfths?

Lesson 5 — Oral and mental starter [21]

Main teaching activities

Whole-class work: Tell the children that they are going to investigate how many addition and subtraction statements they can make about shapes that have been divided into equal parts. Show a square on the board, divided into quarters. Ask the children to write as many addition and subtraction statements about this shape as possible. Stress the whole number 1 can also be used. For example: $\frac{1}{2} + \frac{1}{2} = 1$; $\frac{1}{4} + \frac{1}{2} = \frac{3}{4}$; $1 - \frac{1}{2} = \frac{1}{2}$; $\frac{1}{2} - \frac{1}{4} = \frac{1}{4}$.

Repeat the process, this time for a circle divided into eighths. Again, offer some suggestions: $\frac{1}{8} + \frac{1}{8} = \frac{1}{4}$; $\frac{1}{4} + \frac{1}{8} = \frac{3}{8}$; $1 - \frac{1}{8} = \frac{7}{8}$; $\frac{1}{2} - \frac{1}{8} = \frac{3}{8}$.

Paired work: Give out copies of photocopiable page 'Fraction shapes' from the CD-ROM. Tell the children that they will have 15 minutes to write down as many different addition and subtraction statements as they can about the shapes.

Progress check: At the end of the 15 minutes, stop the children and check the statements completed so far. Check the answers with some leading questions: *How many quarters make a half? How many eighths make one whole one? How many eighths make three quarters?*

Review

Further investigate the possibilities within the shapes by revising equivalent fractions: *Find a fraction that is equivalent to: $\frac{1}{2}$, ...$\frac{3}{4}$, ...$\frac{3}{8}$, ...$\frac{5}{8}$. What is $\frac{5}{8} - \frac{1}{2}$? Give the answer in its lowest terms.*

Multiplying and dividing decimal numbers

Expected prior learning

Children should be able to:

- round decimal numbers to one decimal place
- multiply and divide decimal numbers by 10 and 100.

Topic	Curriculum objectives	Expected outcomes
Fractions (including decimals and percentages)	**Lesson 1**	
	To identify the value of each digit in numbers given to three decimal places and multiply and divide numbers by 10, 100 and 1000 giving answers up to three decimal places.	Identify the value of each digit in decimal numbers up to three decimal places.
	Lesson 2	
	To solve problems which require answers to be rounded to specified degrees of accuracy.	Round and order decimal numbers to two decimal places.
	Lesson 3	
	To identify the value of each digit in numbers given to three decimal places and multiply and divide numbers by 10, 100 and 1000 giving answers up to three decimal places.	Multiply decimal numbers by 10, 100 and 1000.
	Lesson 4	
	To identify the value of each digit in numbers given to three decimal places and multiply and divide numbers by 10, 100 and 1000 giving answers up to three decimal places.	Divide decimal numbers by 10, 100 and 1000.
	Lesson 5	
	To solve problems which require answers to be rounded to specified degrees of accuracy.	Solve problems involving decimal numbers.

Preparation

Lesson 1: copy 'Decimal circles' for each pair of children

Lesson 2: write up the core, support and extension exercises on the board

Lesson 5: enlarge 'Fishing contest (1)'; copy a copy for each child

You will need

Photocopiable sheets
'Decimal circles'; 'Fishing contest (1)'

General resources
'Number cards 0–9'

Equipment
Individual whiteboards

Further practice

'Fishing contest (2)' presents further practice using decimal numbers in a problem-solving situation.

Oral and mental starters suggested for week 3

See the bank of starters on pages 84 and 85. Oral and mental starters are also on the CD-ROM.

13 Decimal digits

14 Decimals at the double

16 Ten times more

22 On the line

23 Decimal roundup

Overview of progression

During the opening lesson the children identify digits in decimal numbers to be familiar with tenths, hundredths and thousandths in place value. Work then follows on rounding decimal numbers to one and two decimal places. The children then spend time on multiplying and dividing decimal numbers by 10, 100 and 1000. In a problem-solving activity at the end of the week the children work with decimal numbers in context.

Watch out for

Ensure from the outset that children understand the difference between whole numbers and decimal fractions. The decimal point acts as a kind of wall or fence between the two. Digits on the left-hand side of the decimal point are whole numbers and those on the right-hand side are fractions or parts of whole numbers. When multiplying and dividing decimal numbers by 10, 100 and 1000 it is important to stress that it is *not* the decimal point that moves. The digits move around it. Emphasise too that multiplying decimal numbers will make them larger while dividing decimal numbers will make them smaller.

Creative context

On a historical note, the Scottish mathematician John Napier (1550–1617) is one of those credited with bringing the use of the decimal point to Britain. He may have come across the idea during his travels in Europe as a way of separating whole numbers from fractions. Napier made other important contributions to the mathematics we use today. The study of decimal numbers links well with the gathering of sports statistics. Results of running events and jumping and throwing competitions are often recorded up to two or three decimal places.

Vocabulary

decimal fraction, decimal number, decimal place, decimal point, digit, divide, hundredth, multiply, place value, tenth, thousandth

■SCHOLASTIC

Curriculum objectives
- To identify the value of each digit in numbers given to three decimal places.

Success criteria
- I can identify the value of digits in decimal numbers up to three decimal places.

You will need
Photocopiable sheets
'Decimal circles'
Equipment
Individual whiteboards

Differentiation
Less confident learners
Children will benefit from spending more time on expressing decimal numbers in expanded notation.

More confident learners
Ensure children can express decimal numbers as fractions in different ways.

Lesson 1 — Oral and mental starter 22

Main teaching activities

Whole-class work: Explain to the children that they will be identifying the digits in decimal numbers. Put some examples on the board to work through. Remember to include some whole numbers to set the task in context. For example, for: 175.239. *What is the value of the 5? ...the 3? ...the 9? ...the 7?* Ask the children to show answers on their whiteboards. Encourage children to use precise terminology when using decimal numbers. Suggest that it is better to say, for instance, that 3.6 is *3 and ⁶⁄₁₀* rather than *3 point 6*. Also explain that writing numbers in full, using expanded notation, can also show the value of single digits. For example: 125.348 in full notation would be 100 + 20+ 5 + ³⁄₁₀ + ⁴⁄₁₀₀ + ⁸⁄₁₀₀₀. Children should see the advantages of using the place value system in preference to this. Work through several more examples on the board.

Paired work: Provide each pair with photocopiable page 86 'Decimal circles' to identify the values in decimal numbers. Revise the *less than* and *more than* signs. The sheet also gives the opportunity to write numbers in expanded notation as a way of reinforcing digit recognition.

Progress check: Stop children at intervals to see how they are getting on. Ask: *What column is to the right of the decimal point? What comes between the tenths and the thousandths? How would 65.749 be written in expanded notation?*

Review

Discuss some real-life situations in which decimal numbers are used. For example, in sport, winning times are usually given to at least two decimal places, such as 10.73 seconds; a person's height can be shown as 1m 35cm or 1.35m tall.

Curriculum objectives
- To solve problems which require answers to be rounded to specified degrees of accuracy.

Success criteria
- I can round and order decimal numbers to one or two decimal places.

You will need
Equipment
Individual whiteboards

Differentiation
Less confident learners
Expect children to round decimal numbers to the nearest whole number or the nearest tenth.

More confident learners
Expect children to round decimal numbers to the nearest hundredth.

Lesson 2 — Oral and mental starter 13

Main teaching activities

Whole-class work: Revise rounding decimal numbers to the nearest whole. Elicit that digits in the tenths column up to and including 4 will not change the whole number, but if the digit is 5 or more the whole number will increase by 1. So: 6.3 rounds down to 6, 7.9 rounds up to 8 and 4.5 rounds up to 5. Extend this to include rounding to one decimal place. For example: 8.72 rounds down to 8.7, 12.47 rounds up to 12.5 and 23.75 rounds up to 23.8. Continue the process to incorporate rounding to two decimals places: 9.735 rounds up to 9.74, 15.641 rounds down to 15.64 and 35.939 rounds up to 35.94.

Independent work: Ask the children to round the following decimal numbers, then put them in order, smallest to largest.
- Support: Round these to the nearest whole: 3.4, 5.7, 4.5, 7.2, 9.8, 10.7, 9.4, 12.6.
- Core: Round these to the nearest tenth (one decimal place): 7.29, 6.45, 8.23, 7.31, 8.46, 10.29, 6.91.
- Extension: Round these to the nearest hundredth (two decimal places): 24.237, 23.869, 24.002, 25.123, 24.735, 23.417, 22.904, 24.116.

Progress check: Check that children have remembered the rules that govern rounding decimal numbers. Ask: *Which digits affect whether other digits are changed or not? When ordering decimal numbers, what do you do when the whole numbers are the same as each other? What about when the tenths are the same?*

Review

Tell the children that these are the times of six runners in a 100m race. Ask them to round the times first to the nearest second, then the nearest tenth of a second. *David 15.09 seconds, Nina 16.56 seconds, Alan 15.47 seconds, Natalie 12.53 seconds, Robin 15.09 seconds, Mary 13.74 seconds. Who came first, second and third?*

Curriculum objectives

● To identify the value of each digit in numbers given to three decimal places and multiply and divide numbers by 10, 100 and 1000 giving answers up to three decimal places.

Success criteria

● I can multiply decimal numbers by 10, 100 and 1000.

You will need

General resources

'Number cards 0–9'

Equipment

Individual whiteboards

Differentiation

Less confident learners

Ask children to focus first on multiplying small decimal numbers by 10 before moving on to multiply by 100, for example: 3.5×10, 4.63×100.

More confident learners

Encourage children to work with larger decimal numbers and to focus on multiplication by 100 and 1000, for example: 27.45×100 and 3.796×1000.

Lesson 3   Oral and mental starter 23

Main teaching activities

Whole-class work: Tell the children that they are going to find out what happens when decimal numbers are multiplied by 10, 100 and 1000. Encourage the children to speculate if they do not already know. Work through some examples together on the board to show the movement of the digits to the left relative to the decimal point. For example: $0.5 \times 10 = 5$, $0.5 \times 100 = 50$ and $0.5 \times 1000 = 500$. Reinforce understanding that in some cases, like the previous two answers, zeros have to be included as place-holders to give the correct place value to the other digits. Try other examples, such as: 0.8, 2.3, 6.8.

Then introduce numbers written to two decimal places. For example: $0.42 \times 10 = 4.2$, $0.42 \times 100 = 42$ and $0.42 \times 1000 = 420$. Continue with other examples. Try: 0.73, 1.27 and 13.59.

Finally, repeat the process using numbers to three decimal places. For example: $0.764 \times 10 = 7.64$, $0.764 \times 100 = 76.4$ and $0.764 \times 1000 = 764$. Ensure the children understand that, when multiplying by 10, 100 and 1000, digits move one, two and three places to the left respectively. The decimal point does *not* move; it is only the digits.

Group work: Organise the children into small groups. Provide each group with a set of number cards that also includes a decimal point card (included in 'Number cards 0–9'). Ask them to choose four number cards to go with the decimal point card. They should work together to arrange the cards to make: a decimal number to three decimal places, a decimal number to two decimal places and a decimal number to one decimal place. Explain that each of these numbers should then be multiplied by 10, 100 and 1000, and the number sentences written on their whiteboards. For example:

$1.345 \times 10 = 13.45$, $1.345 \times 100 = 134.5$, $1.345 \times 1000 = 1345$

$34.51 \times 10 = 345.1$, $34.51 \times 100 = 3451$, $34.51 \times 1000 = 34,510$

$543.1 \times 10 = 5431$, $543.1 \times 100 = 54,310$, $543.1 \times 1000 = 543,100$

Progress check: See how the groups are doing by looking at their cards, then asking important questions, such as: *Will multiplying make decimal numbers bigger or smaller? Which way will the digits move when decimal numbers are multiplied? How many places will the digits move when multiplied by 10, 100 and by 1000?*

Review

Check through the sentences and answers the children have produced. Can they explain clearly the methods they used?

Now challenge them to make some money amounts 10×, 100× and 1000× bigger. For example: £1.50 × 10 = £15, £1.50 × 100 = £150, and £1.50 × 1000 = £1500.

Curriculum objectives

● To identify the value of each digit in numbers given to three decimal places and multiply and divide numbers by 10, 100 and 1000 giving answers up to three decimal places.

Success criteria

● I can divide decimal numbers bu 10. 100 and 1000.

You will need

General resources

'Number cards 0–9'

Equipment

Individual whiteboards

Differentiation

Less confident learners

Ask children to focus first on dividing small decimal numbers by 10 before moving on to divide by 100.

More confident learners

Encourage children to work with larger decimal numbers and to move on quickly to dividing by 100 and 1000: 148. 72 ÷ 100 and 3205.9 ÷ 1000.

Lesson 4   Oral and mental starter 14

Main teaching activities

Whole-class work: Following the work on multiplying, tell the children they will now look at dividing decimal numbers by 10, 100 and 1000. Work through some examples on the board to show the movement of the digits to the right relative to the decimal point. For example: 3.8 ÷ 10 = 0.38, 3.8 ÷ 100 = 0.038, 3.8 ÷ 1000 = 0.0038. Stress the importance of using zero as a place-holder. Then try: 6.2, 9.7 and 13.5. Then introduce numbers to two decimal places: 16.57, 12.72, 37.54 and 205.93. Ensure the children appreciate that dividing decimal numbers by 10, 100 and 1000 will make them smaller, and that, when dividing by 10, 100 and 1000, digits move one, two and three places to the right respectively. The decimal point does not move.

Group work: Provide each group with a set of number cards and a decimal point card. They should arrange the cards to make decimal numbers in the same way as in lesson 3, to be divided by 10, 100 and 1000.

Progress check: Pause the groups to ask: *Will dividing numbers by 10, 100 and 1000 make them bigger or smaller? Which way will the digits move? How many places will the digits move when the number is divided by 1000?*

Review

Check the sentences and answers. Ask volunteers to explain the methods they used. Then ask the children to help you share some money! For example: £3520 shared by 10 people is £352 each, £3520 shared by 100 is £35.20 each, £3520 shared by 1000 is £3.52 each.

Curriculum objectives

● To solve problems which require answers to be rounded to specified degrees of accuracy.

Success criteria

● I can solve problems involving the use of decimal numbers.

You will need

Photocopiable sheets

'Fishing contest (1)'

Differentiation

Less confident learners

Provide support when decimal numbers are being rounded to one and two decimal places and with adding and subtracting decimals.

More confident learners

Challenge children to make up further questions once they have completed the original eight questions.

Lesson 5   Oral and mental starter 16

Main teaching activities

Whole-class work: Tell the children that they are going to be rounding some decimal numbers and solving some decimal number problems by looking at the results of a fishing competition. Go through the information shown on photocopiable page 87 'Fishing contest (1)'. Establish that the weight of fish caught by each of the anglers on each day is in kilograms and is given to three decimal places.

Paired work: Divide the class into pairs and provide each pair with a copy of photocopiable page 87 'Fishing contest (1)'. Tell children to record the answers in their maths books.

Progress check: Stop the children at intervals. Ask them to explain the rules about rounding decimal numbers to the nearest whole one, to one decimal place and to two decimal places. Ask: *What are the important rules to remember when adding and subtracting decimal numbers?*

Review

Check answers to the photocopiable sheet. Then tell the children that in a diving competition, three divers scored the following marks: Frank Swift: 43.715, Angela Rush 54.186, Carl Dash 54.852. Challenge the children to round each set of marks to the nearest hundredth and then to the nearest tenth. Who came first, second and third in the competition?

Order of operations

Expected prior learning

Children should be able to:

- carry out mental calculations with mixed operations
- solve word problems involving the four operations.

Topic	Curriculum objectives	Expected outcomes
Addition, subtraction, multiplication and division	**Lesson 1**	
	To perform mental calculations, including with mixed operations and large numbers.	Carry out mental calculations involving mixed operations.
	Lesson 2	
	To solve addition and subtraction multi-step problems in contexts, deciding which operations and methods to use and why.	Solve addition and subtraction problems choosing the correct operations and methods.
	Lesson 3	
	To use their knowledge of the order of operations to carry out calculations involving the four operations.	Know that in a calculation, items inside brackets need to be dealt with first.
	Lesson 4	
	To use their knowledge of the order of operations to carry out calculations involving the four operations.	Use knowledge about the correct order of operations.
	Lesson 5	
	To solve problems involving addition, subtraction, multiplication and division.	Solve practical problems involving all four main rules of calculation.

Preparation

Lesson 1: copy 'All three sides' for each pair of children

Lesson 2: copy 'Tram travel' for each pair

Lesson 3: write the group-work calculations on the board

Lesson 5: copy 'In a word' for each pair

You will need

Photocopiable sheets

'All three sides'; 'Tram travel'; 'In a word'

Equipment

Individual whiteboards; tables squares

Further practice

Give children the BIDMAS practice sheet to consolidate understanding of the order of operations. If necessary, work through examples with less confident learners.

Oral and mental starters suggested for week 4

See the bank of starters on pages 84 and 85. Oral and mental starters are also on the CD-ROM.

13 Decimal digits

14 Decimals at the double

15 Decimal times

16 Ten times more

20 Fractions and decimals

Overview of progression

This week opens with strategies that can be used mentally for adding and subtracting numbers more quickly. This is followed by problem-solving addition and subtraction which requires the children to decide which operations are needed and what methods should be used. Then the children look at the use of brackets in calculations, and the acronym BIDMAS which determines the order in which to work through calculations requiring several operations. The final lesson involves the use of all four operations, and the children have to decide which operation to use based on the wording in a problem.

Watch out for

Stress that children should not only decide the right operations to use but also the right methods. Some tasks may be completed mentally, others mentally with the aid of jottings, while others will require full formal written methods. Also point out that when carrying out a calculation such as $3 + 4 \times 5$, the answer could be either 35 or 23 ($7 \times 5 = 35$ or $3 + 20 = 23$). Which is correct? This is why brackets are included in some number statements so that priority can be given to certain parts. Tell children that even when brackets are not included they should remember division before multiplication and addition before subtraction.

Creative context

We read English from left to right, while Arabic is read from right to left. Some Chinese writing is read from top to bottom. In mathematics, too, we have rules to tell us which way to read and solve calculations. This is why rules about the order of operations, usually referred to as BIDMAS, are important. Let the children investigate how the order of operations is a key part of daily life. Can you, for example, make a hot cup of coffee without boiling the kettle first? Which operation should come first – *leave the house* or *get dressed*? Also consider sequences of events in other school areas like the order of activities in a science experiment, the sequence of movements in a gymnastics routine and the placing of historical events on a timeline.

Vocabulary

altogether, BIDMAS (brackets, indices, divide, multiply, add, subtract), counting on, decrease, difference, indices, increase, method, number sentence, operation, order, partition, share, sign, strategy, sum

Curriculum objectives
- To perform mental calculations, including with mixed operations.

Success criteria
- I can carry out mental calculations with mixed operations.

You will need
Photocopiable sheets
'All three sides'

Differentiation
Less confident learners

Children should use smaller numbers initially when adding and subtracting numbers mentally. Encourage children to use jottings if numbers aren't recalled easily.

More confident learners

Gradually increase the size of numbers. Even though working mentally, challenge children to explain their methods in writing or with a diagram.

Lesson 1 — Oral and mental starter 20

Main teaching activities

Whole-class work: Tell the children they are going to work on improving their mental skills when adding and subtracting. Start with partitioning, for example: $57 + 65 = 50 + 60 + 7 + 5 = 110 + 12 = 122$, and $84 - 15 = 84 - 10 - 5 = 74 - 5 = 69$. Work through other examples on the board. Then find a difference by counting on: $95 - 36 = 4 + 50 + 5 = 59$, and $152 - 78 = 2 + 20 + 50 + 2 = 74$. Also try changing the order in which numbers are added by looking for pairs that make multiples of 10 or 100: $14 + 29 + 16 = (14 + 16) + 29 = 30 + 29 = 59$, or $9 + 36 + 41 = (9 + 41) + 36 = 50 + 36 = 86$, or $121 + 12 + 79 + 6 = (121 + 79) + 12 + 6 = 200 + 12 + 6 = 218$.

Paired work: Distribute photocopiable page 'All three sides' from the CD-ROM. Tell the children that to complete the triangles they need to add and subtract numbers mentally.

Progress check: Make sure children are using the strategies discussed. Ask: *What does partition mean? How can subtractions be solved by counting on? Multiples of which numbers should you look out for? Must numbers always be added in the order given?*

Review

Check the work on the photocopiable sheet. Then draw a 3 × 3 magic square on the board with 4, 6 and 8 in the diagonal from top left to bottom right. Explain that in a magic square each vertical line, horizontal line and the two diagonals add up to the same total. Say that the magic square total is 18. Ask the children to fill in the empty boxes.

Curriculum objectives
- To solve addition and subtraction multi-step problems in context, deciding which operations and methods to use and why.

Success criteria
- I can solve addition and subtraction problems choosing which operations and methods to use.

You will need
Photocopiable sheets
'Tram travel'

Differentiation
Less confident learners

Ask children to write down their working out to analyse the strategies they are using.

More confident learners

Extend the activity by asking children for questions of their own, particularly to include fractions and decimal numbers in amounts of money.

Lesson 2 — Oral and mental starter 14

Main teaching activities

Whole-class work: Tell the children that in this lesson they are going to choose and use suitable operations to solve word problems involving numbers and amounts of money. Explain that they will need to decide which operations need to be carried out and which strategies they will need to use. For example, when looking at a problem, they should consider: *Can I calculate answers mentally? Do I need the help of jottings? Are formal written calculations like adding and subtracting in columns necessary? Is long multiplication involved?* Stress that, where possible, answers should be estimated/approximated first and checked at the end.

Paired work: Organise the children to work in mixed-ability pairs on photocopiable page 'Tram travel' from the CD-ROM so that they can fully discuss operations and strategies.

Progress check: Go through some of the early questions once they have been completed. Prompt the children to explain how, once a question has been read, they knew which operation to carry out. How did they decide on the best strategy or method to use for solving the problem? What affected their decisions most?

Review

Check through the solutions from the photocopiable sheet with the children. Discuss the strategies they have used. What alternative approaches were there? Did the working out of estimated answers first prove helpful?

 SCHOLASTIC

Curriculum objectives

● To use knowledge of the order of operations to carry out calculations involving the four operations.

Success criteria

● I can deal with items inside brackets first when working on a calculation.

You will need

Equipment

Individual whiteboards; tables squares

Differentiation

Less confident learners

Children should work first on the simpler of the 'bracket' questions. Provide tables squares, if necessary, so that multiplication and division problems can be solved quickly.

More confident learners

Provide children with more demanding 'bracket' questions. They should also be able to devise their own problems involving the use of one or two sets of brackets.

Lesson 3

Oral and mental starter 13

Main teaching activities

Whole-class work: Explain to the children that they are going to investigate how brackets are used in calculations. Put an example on the board to illustrate how calculations can provide different answers depending on the order in which operations are carried out. Invite volunteers to help you demonstrate that $10 \times 3 + 6$, for instance, can produce either 36 or 90. Establish with the children how the use of brackets in a calculation like this can tell us which operation to carry out first, so: $(10 \times 3) + 6 = 36$, or $10 \times (3 + 6) = 90$. Show other examples incorporating each of the four main operation signs. Ask the children to work out on their whiteboards which answers are possible and then indicate where brackets have to be positioned to produce these answers. Share the children's answers and then show that another example could be $90 \div 10 + 5$, which can produce $(90 \div 10) + 5 = 14$ or $90 \div (10 + 5) = 6$.

Move on to consider number statements that have more than one set of brackets. Explain that in such cases it does not matter which of the set of brackets is done first as long as both brackets are dealt with before any other operation is carried out.

Group work: Organise the children into similar-ability groups to work through a selection of 'Bracket' questions shown on the board. Try:

- Support: $(4 \times 2) + 3$; $7 + (10 - 5)$; $(16 \div 2) + 9$; $(6 \times 3) + 7$; $9 + (5 \times 4)$; $(7 \times 5) - 6$; $(17 + 8) \div 5$; $12 + (9 - 7)$.
- Core: $34 - (18 \div 2)$; $(4 \times 5) + 3$; $(20 - 3) \times 5$; $10 \times (7 - 4)$; $4 \times (6 - 3)$; $(15 + 3) \div 6$; $(5 \times 3) + 6$; $40 - (0 \times 4)$.
- Extension: $(16 + 2) \div (19 - 12)$; $(5 \times 4) \times (28 - 25)$; $(8 + 6) \times (3 - 2)$; $(6 \times 3) - (7 \times 2)$; $(13 - 9) \times (4 - 2)$; $(2 + 3) - (10 - 5)$; $(27 \div 3) \div (5 - 2)$; $(8 \times 10) \div (3 + 2)$.

Progress check: Pause the children as they are working to check they are reading the signs correctly and that they are always calculating the solution to the statement inside the brackets first. What strategy are they using when there are two sets of brackets in a statement?

Review

Quickly go through a selection of the answers to the calculations.

Write the following statements, or similar, on the board: $2 + 4 \times 3 = 14$; $10 - 3 \times 3 = 21$; $12 \div 3 + 1 = 3$; $5 + 4 \times 3 = 27$ and $14 + 4 \div 2 = 9$. Challenge the children to put brackets in these calculations to make them correct. Then ask the class to choose two calculations and work together to put the brackets in different places to make new calculations with a different answer.

Curriculum objectives
• To use knowledge of the order of operations to carry out calculations involving the four operations.

Success criteria
• I can carry out operations in the correct order.

You will need

Equipment
Individual whiteboards

Differentiation

Less confident learners
Ensure children investigate smaller target numbers when they are making statements using brackets and the four operations.

More confident learners
Children should graduate quickly to use larger target numbers when they are making their statements.

Lesson 4

Main teaching activities

Whole-class work: Quickly revise the work carried out in the last lesson on the order of operations in calculations, and elicit that any numbers inside brackets must always be dealt with first.

Move on to explain that to make it simpler to work out the answers to calculations that have more than one type of operation in them, it has been agreed that, as well as brackets first, there is a particular order in which the operations should be done, regardless of their position in the calculation. Introduce the children to the acronym BIDMAS, writing it vertically on the board. Explain, encouraging the children to make suggestions, that it stands for *Brackets, Indices, Division, Multiplication, Addition* and *Subtraction*. Then say that if there are several multiplication and division or addition and subtraction calculations, these should be done one at a time from left to right. If appropriate, explain *indices*, which are used as a shorthand way of identifying how many times a number is multiplied by itself. For example, 1000 can be written as 10^3 instead of $10 \times 10 \times 10$. Give children some examples of how and when indices are used, for example: $3^2 = 3 \times 3$ and not 3×2.

Work through some simple examples without brackets where the children need to use BIDMAS and work out which operation to do when. For example: $11 - 2 + 6$ (subtraction and addition, so work from left to right $9 + 6 = 15$), $4 \times 3 - 7$ (multiplication first, so $12 - 7 = 5$), $6 + 15 \div 5$ (division first, so $6 + 3 = 9$).

Also work through several 'target number' questions where children have to make the target number given certain numbers, any of the four operations and brackets. For example: use 14, 6 and 5 to reach the target number 4 $(14 + 6 \div 5)$; 30, 6 and 2 for the target number 7 $(30 \div 6) + 2$; 3, 2, 4 for the target number 2 $(3 \times 2) - 4$.

Paired work: Organise the children into similar-ability pairs to play a target game. Explain that one person writes down four numbers under 10 and then chooses a target number between 10 and 40. Say that the first person to write a mathematical statement that gives the target answer using some or all of the four numbers plus any of the four operations signs and brackets wins a point. Ensure that the children take it in turns to choose the target number. Tell the children that the first person to three points wins that round of the game.

Progress check: Check some of the target numbers and sentences the children are producing. Do they need to use all four of the numbers? *Can they use all four numbers?* Ask: *What do the letters that make up BIDMAS mean? What happens if there are several parts of a calculation with the same operation?*

Review

Invite some of the pairs to share some of the sentences they produced. Try to reach the target numbers as a class.

Then challenge the children to add brackets to some number statements that include indices. Remind them that the index number 2 indicates squaring a number not multiplying it by 2. For example, $3^2 = 3 \times 3 = 9$. Try these examples: $4 + 2^2 \times 1 = 8$; $4 \times 3^2 + 6 = 60$; $6^2 + 2^2 \times 4 = 160$; $10^2 - 7 - 2 = 95$.

Curriculum objectives
- To solve problems involving addition, subtraction, multiplication and division.

Success criteria
- I can solve practical problems involving the four operations.

You will need

Photocopiable sheets
'In a word'

Equipment
Individual whiteboards

Differentiation

Less confident learners

Understanding the meaning of key words and phrases will be important, such as *share* and *altogether*. Support children with definitions.

More confident learners

Based on the questions that they have done, children should be able to devise their own one-step and two-step problems.

Lesson 5

Oral and mental starter 15

Main teaching activities

Whole-class work: Explain to the children that this last lesson of the week will focus on solving word problems using the operations and strategies they have been exploring in the previous lessons.

Discuss with the children the sorts of key words and phrases that might come up in the questions, such as *how many, share, in total, altogether, much more* and *how much*. Explain to the children that they will have to make decisions about which operations to use, as they have been practising. Advise them that some of the problems may be two-step or three-step questions. In other words, they will have to carry out several operations in order to get to the solution.

Also remind children of the following points:

- They should think carefully about which strategies/methods to use.
- They should try to work out approximate answers first.
- They should aim to check solutions at the end.

Paired work: Since discussion is a vital part of the activity, children should work in pairs or groups of three. Distribute photocopiable page 'In a word' from the CD-ROM to each of the pairs or groups and check that the children understand what they need to do.

Progress check: Pause the children to ask: *What are the key words in the question? What information is* not *needed to answer the question? Which key numbers have to be used? What operations are involved? What is the best method to use?*

Review

Go through the questions on the photocopiable sheet as a class. Clarify any difficulties.

Then provide a set of number statements and ask the children to make up their own 'real life' problem from them for the rest of the class to solve. For example: 108, 15 and 32: 108 runners enter a long-distance race. If 15 fail to start and 32 drop out during the race, how many complete the course? (61.) For £50, ½, and 10%: Paul is given £50 for his birthday. If he puts ½ into a building society account and spends 10%, how much money will he have left? (£20.)

2D and 3D shapes

Expected prior learning

Children should be able to:

- draw and measure angles using a protractor
- recognise and know the properties of 2D shapes
- recognise 3D shapes.

Topic	Curriculum objectives	Expected outcomes
Geometry: properties of shapes	**Lesson 1**	
	To compare and classify geometric shapes based on their properties and sizes and find unknown angles in any triangles, quadrilaterals, and regular polygons.	Find missing angles within triangles, quadrilaterals and regular polygons.
	Lesson 2	
	To draw shapes and nets accurately.	Draw 2D shapes from dimensions.
	To compare and classify geometric shapes based on their properties and sizes and find unknown angles in any triangles, quadrilaterals, and regular polygons.	Identify, compare, classify and know the properties of a range of common 2D shapes.
	Lesson 3	
	To recognise, describe and build simple 3D shapes, including making nets.	Identify, compare, classify and know the properties of a range of common 3D shapes.
	Lesson 4	
	To recognise, describe and build simple 3D shapes, including making nets.	Construct simple 3D shapes from nets.
	Lesson 5	
	To recognise, describe and build simple 3D shapes, including making nets.	Find out about the properties of 3D shapes through investigation.
	To compare and classify geometric shapes based on their properties and sizes and find unknown angles in any triangles, quadrilaterals, and regular polygons.	

M SCHOLASTIC

Preparation

Lesson 2: draw on the board or have available for display a selection of quadrilaterals

Lesson 3: collect a range of 3D shapes in the form of models and 'real-life' examples

Lesson 4: copy 'Net gain' for each small group

Lesson 5: draw the recording table on the board

You will need

Photocopiable sheets

'Net gain'

Equipment

Protractors; a pair of compasses; collections of large plastic, wooden or card 2D shapes (including hexagons, octagons and trapezia) and 3D shapes; illustrations of different kinds of angle; plain paper; dotty paper; 2cm-squared paper; thin card; 3D objects, such as ball (sphere), tin (cylinder), box (cuboid); art straws; sticky tap; sticky tack; glue; scissors; construction equipment (such as Polydron and Clixi); poster of 2D drawings of 3D shapes; cardboard boxes; nail boards and elastic bands

Further practice

Use the interactive activity 'Shapes' to review children's understanding of shape properties.

Oral and mental starters suggested for week 5

See the bank of starters on page 85. Oral and mental starters are also on the CD-ROM.

20 Fractions and decimals

21 Cancel down

24 Name it (1)

25 Name it (2)

26 In the net

Overview of progression

At the beginning of the week the children revise some of the work on angles from the previous half term. After looking at angles in triangles and quadrilaterals, they examine the internal angles of hexagons and octagons. Much of the week is then devoted to identifying, comparing, classifying and examining 2D and 3D shapes, including drawing 2D shapes and constructing 3D shapes from a net. During the final session the children carry out an investigation in which they try to prove Euler's Rule about the properties of straight-sided 3D shapes.

Watch out for

Make sure children are able to use a protractor correctly when drawing and measuring angles. A common difficulty is reading off or marking information from the wrong scale. Also check that children do not think the size of an angle is dependent on the length of the lines used to draw it. When using a ruler for accurate drawings, ensure children start lines from zero, not from the end of the ruler or the 1cm mark. Angle sums are often confused: 180 degrees for the angles of a triangle and 360 degrees for those in a quadrilateral. To help children remember, use an equilateral triangle for the former (3 × 60 degrees = 180 degrees) and a square for the latter (4 × 90 degrees = 360 degrees).

Creative context

Much of the work being done this week is an area where mathematics and art and craft are closely linked. Investigate tessellation, for example, working with shapes that fit naturally together (squares), shapes that need help to tessellate (regular pentagons) and shapes that are difficult or impossible to tessellate (circles). Examine the use of 2D shapes in Hindu rangoli patterns and how geometric shapes feature strongly in Islamic art. Triangular designs have long been used to give structures strength and rigidity as seen in bridges and pylons, for example. Look at the way 3D shapes are used in product packaging, and study origami, the ancient art of folding paper to make 3D shapes.

Vocabulary

acute angle, adjacent, angle, cone, cube, cuboid, cylinder, diagonal, edge, equilateral, face, hemisphere, hexagon, isosceles, **kite**, net, obtuse angle, octagon, opposite, parallel, **parallelogram**, perpendicular, quadrilateral, rectangle, reflex angle, regular, rhombus, right angle, scalene, side, sphere, square, square-based pyramid, symmetry, tetrahedron, **trapezium**, triangle, triangular prism, vertex, vertices

Curriculum objectives
• To find unknown angles in triangles, quadrilaterals and regular polygons.

Success criteria
• I can find angles in triangles, quadrilaterals and regular polygons.

You will need
Equipment

Protractors; rulers; wooden, plastic or card 2D shapes; illustrations of different kinds of angle; plain paper

Differentiation
Less confident learners

Provide plenty of practice and support when children are using protractors. Assist with calculations when finding missing angles.

More confident learners

Help children to draw the shapes without the templates. Then, using protractors, ask this group to draw examples of angles on a straight line and angles around a point.

Lesson 1 — Oral and mental starter 20

Main teaching activities

Whole-class work: Revise quickly some of the main topic learning covered previously in Autumn 1, Week 5, Lessons 2, 3 and 4. Check that the children know how to measure angles using a protractor, establishing that it must be positioned correctly with the cross placed accurately on the intersection of the line making the angle. Ensure the measurement is done using the correct scale on the protractor. Provide paper, and ask the children to practise drawing a few angles with their protractors.

Then show the children a collection of different-sized angles so they can also revise their names. Focus particularly on *acute, right angle, obtuse, straight angle* and *reflex*. Also revise the names given to triangles depending on their angles: *equilateral* (all three angles the same), *isosceles* (two angles equal) and *scalene* (all three angles different).

Give the children some calculations to find angles in a triangle. Say, for example: *If two angles in a triangle are known to be 120 degrees and 40 degrees, what will the third angle be?* (20°.)

Repeat the process with quadrilaterals. For example: *If three angles in a quadrilateral are 90 degrees, 125 degrees and 76 degrees, what is the fourth angle?* (69°.)

Tell the children that now they are going to draw and measure angles found internally in two polygons – a regular hexagon and a regular octagon. Elicit from the children that *regular* means that all the sides will be the same length.

Independent work: Provide the children with plain paper and large plastic, wooden or card hexagons and octagons to draw around. Tell them that they should draw around each of the two shapes carefully and then, using a ruler, draw in the diagonal lines, corner to corner. Once this is done, explain that they should accurately measure the angles made at the centre of the shape using a protractor. Ask them to think about what they discover about the angles at the centre of the hexagon. What do they find out about the angles at the centre of the octagon?

Progress check: Check the children have drawn straight lines and that their diagonal lines are positioned accurately between the corners of the shapes. Ensure angles at the centre of the shapes are being measured accurately with the protractors.

Review

Encourage the children to share their shapes and angles. Assess their results by asking the following questions:

- *What shapes are formed by the diagonals of the hexagon?* (Equilateral triangles.)
- *How many angles are there?* (6.)
- *What shapes are formed by the diagonals in the octagon?* (Isosceles triangles.)
- *How many angles are formed at the centre of octagon?* (8.)
- *What is the value of each angle at the centre of the hexagon?* (60 degrees.)
- *What is the value of each angle at the centre of the octagon?* (45 degrees.)
- *Could these angles have been calculated?* (Hexagon: 360 degrees ÷ 6 = 60 degrees. Octagon: 360 degrees ÷ 8 = 45 degrees.)

Curriculum objectives
● To draw shapes accurately.
● To compare and classify geometric shapes based on their properties and sizes.

Success criteria
● I can draw shapes from given dimensions.
● I can compare, classify and name 2D shapes based on their properties and sizes.

You will need

Equipment

Plastic, wooden or card 2D shapes; dotty paper; protractors; rulers

Differentiation

Less confident learners

When constructing quadrilaterals, children may find it easier to use nail boards and elastic bands.

More confident learners

Encourage children to focus on drawing the parallelogram, kite, trapezia.

Lesson 2
Oral and mental starter 21

Main teaching activities

Whole-class work: Display a collection of quadrilaterals including square, rectangle, rhombus, parallelogram, kite and trapezia. Ask the children to name each shape. Elicit that they are all quadrilaterals and recap on vocabulary such as *perpendicular, parallel, acute, obtuse, right angle, symmetrical*. Check with the children that they understand that a trapezium must have one set of parallel sides that must be unequal in length, but that the other sides can be equal or unequal in length. Invite volunteers to draw some examples to illustrate the point. Explain that an arrow symbol is often used to show parallel lines.

Group work: Ask the children to list the properties of the 2D shapes discussed, using the criteria of sides, angles and lines of symmetry. When this is complete, they should move on to draw examples of quadrilaterals of their own using dotty paper, rulers and protractors.

Progress check: Visit the groups, and ask them about some of the shapes they are describing and drawing. *Which shapes have right angles? Which shapes have parallel sides? Which shapes have only one line of symmetry? Which shapes have more than one line of symmetry?*

Review

Ask for volunteers (who can work in pairs). Ask one to describe on the board one of the quadrilaterals that has been discussed, and ask the other to draw it from the description. For example: *All my sides are equal in length. Opposite sides are parallel. I have two acute angles and two obtuse angles. What am I?* (Parallelogram.)

Curriculum objectives
● To recognise, describe and build 3D shapes.

Success criteria
● I can identify and know the properties of a range of 3D shapes.
● I can build 3D shapes.

You will need

Equipment

3D shapes and objects of the same shapes; art straws; sticky tape; sticky tack; scissors; construction equipment; poster of 2D drawings of 3D shapes

Differentiation

Less confident learners

Focus on the skeletal models and discuss their properties. Stress the edges need to be measured and cut before assembly.

More confident learners

Children can investigate the set of 3D shapes known as the Five Platonic Polyhedra.

Lesson 3
Oral and mental starter 24

Main teaching activities

Whole-class work: Display some 3D shapes including cube, cuboid, prisms, pyramids, cylinder, cone and sphere. Include models of the shapes, but also examples as they occur in everyday life, such as cylinder (drink or food can), sphere (ball), cuboid (cereal packet), triangular prism (chocolate bar). Discuss key words like *edge, face* and *vertex* and examine the properties of each shape. Ask: *How many faces does it have? What shapes are the faces? How many edges are there? How many vertices are there? Which shapes are regular polyhedra (with faces of the same shape and size)?* Also revise *parallel* and *perpendicular* when applied to faces and/or edges.

Group work: Organise small groups and provide art straws, sticky tape, sticky tack, rulers and scissors. Ask the children to make skeletal models of some of the straight-sided shapes on display. This will require careful measuring, cutting and fixing. Then ask children to write as detailed a description of each shape as they can. Also make available construction kits which can also be assembled into 3D shapes.

Progress check: Make sure children are measuring and cutting the art straws correctly in order to make the straight edges of the 3D shapes. Prompt with questions: *How many edges does the cube need? Will all the edges be the same length? What about the cuboid? Will all its edges be the same size? How many edges are needed for the tetrahedron?*

Review

Share some of the children's descriptions, then play a game of 'Back to back' where a child sits back-to-back with a partner, chooses a shape and describes it to the other for guessing. Display the poster and check the children can recognise 3D shapes from 2D drawings.

Curriculum objectives

- To recognise, describe and build 3D shapes, including making nets.

Success criteria

- I can construct straight-sided 3D shapes from their nets.

You will need

Photocopiable sheets

'Net gain'

Equipment

Cardboard boxes; 2cm-squared paper; thin card; scissors; glue, a pair of compasses

Differentiation

Less confident learners

Provide children with the nets of some of the 3D shapes already drawn.

More confident learners

Challenge children to find other versions of the nets of 3D shapes.

Lesson 4 — Oral and mental starter 25

Main teaching activities

Whole-class work: Ensure first that the children appreciate the meaning of the word *net* when applied to 3D shapes. Revise it using several types of cardboard box. Demonstrate by flattening them out to show how they were made. Invite a child to help you reassemble the shape to see how it fits together. Point out that, to hold boxes together, special gluing flaps are needed and that the children will need to include them when making their own nets. These flaps mean the shapes can be fixed together without visible joins.

Group work: Provide children with thin card, craft materials and a pair of compasses and ask them to draw and make up into 3D shapes the nets given on photocopiable page 88 'Net gain'. The groups starting with the cube might prefer to use 2cm-squared paper.

Progress check: Work with the children when they are drawing the nets. Ask: *How can right angles be checked? Are lines being measured accurately? How can a pair of compasses help with drawing triangles? Where should glueing flaps be positioned?*

Review

Invite volunteers to display some of the shapes they have made. Set up a display of all of the 3D shapes in the classroom. How many different nets of the cube did the more confident group find?

Curriculum objectives

- To recognise and describe 3D shapes.
- To compare and classify geometric shapes based on their properties.

Success criteria

- I can find out about the properties of 3D shapes by carrying out an investigation.

You will need

Equipment

Straight-sided 3D shapes

Differentiation

Less confident learners

Calculating the correct number of faces, edges and vertices is very important, and support may be needed.

More confident learners

Children find out more about Leonhard Euler.

Lesson 5 — Oral and mental starter 26

Main teaching activities

Whole-class work: Tell the children the they are going to carry out an investigation using a group of straight-sided 3D shapes. Say that, about 300 years ago a famous Swiss mathematician called Leonhard Euler (pronounced 'oiler') studied 3D shapes and discovered an important relationship. Euler's Rule states: *In a straight-sided 3D shape, the number of edges equals the number of faces + the number of vertices − 2.* Tell the children they should test out the rule with at least five straight-sided 3D shapes. Point out that the rule does not apply to 3D shapes with curved edges like cones, cylinders and spheres.

Group work: Provide groups of children with straight-sided 3D shapes and ask them to test Euler's Rule. Display this table on the board for children to copy.

Shape	Number of faces	Number of vertices	Faces + Vertices − 2	Edges

Progress check: Encourage the children to discuss the properties of the shapes first before counting edges, vertices and faces carefully. Make sure results are recorded in the correct column of the table.

Review

Discuss the results to see if Euler's Rule has been confirmed. What significance does the relationship have? Can it be used as a way of checking that properties have been calculated correctly? An alternative version of the rule says that Faces + Vertices = Edges + 2. Does this also work?

Pie charts

Expected prior learning

Children should be able to:

- complete tables and bar charts from given information
- solve problems using data presented in bar chart, tables and simple pie charts.

Topic	Curriculum objectives	Expected outcomes
Statistics	**Lesson 1**	
	To interpret and construct pie charts and line graphs and use these to solve problems.	Read and interpret information shown in a simple pie chart.
	Lesson 2	
	To interpret and construct pie charts and line graphs and use these to solve problems.	Read, interpret and compare information shown on two pie charts showing similar data.
	Lesson 3	
	To interpret and construct pie charts and line graphs and use these to solve problems.	Construct a pie chart from given information.
	Lesson 4	
	To interpret and construct pie charts and line graphs and use these to solve problems.	Accurately construct a pie chart from given information, using a protractor.
	Lesson 5	
	To interpret and construct pie charts and line graphs and use these to solve problems.	Read, interpret and contrast the same set of data given in a pie chart and a bar graph.

Preparation

Lesson 1: draw the 'School travel' pie chart on the board; copy 'My day' for each pair of children

Lesson 2: draw the 'Play hockey' pie chart on the board; copy 'Spending money' for each pair

Lesson 3: prepare large blank pie charts with eight sectors; write up the data table on the board

Lesson 4: write up the data table on the board

Lesson 5: copy 'Home heating' for each small group

You will need

Photocopiable sheets
'My day'; 'Spending money'; 'Home heating'

General resources
Interactive teaching resource 'Graphing tool'

Equipment
Plain paper; coloured pencils or crayons; large paper circles divided into eight sectors; a pair of compasses; protractors (360° if possible)

Further practice

The interactive teaching resource 'Graphing tool' could be used for all of the pie chart activities in this chapter. For further practice extend to other projects establishing whether pie charts are the most effective method of displaying data (for example, favourite sport teams, hair colour).

Oral and mental starters suggested for week 6

See the bank of starters on page 85. Oral and mental starters are also on the CD-ROM.

22 On the line

24 Name it (1)

25 Name it (2)

26 In the net

Overview of progression

Most of the activities during the week are based around reading, interpreting, contrasting and constructing pie charts. Children are given a simple pie chart to interpret during the first part of the week. They progress to interpret two pie charts showing similar, but not identical, information before learning the skills that will enable them to construct pie charts of their own. The week is rounded off with an activity that allows children to consider identical data shown on both a pie chart and a bar graph and to assess which of the methods used is the best way to illustrate and display data.

Watch out for

The use of pie charts is a bright, colourful way of showing information but important points need to be remembered when they are being constructed. Make children aware that the 'pieces' of the pie are actually sectors of a circle and careful angle measurements are required to divide the circle up. It may help to provide some children with circles that have already been marked in sectors. Point out that in order to fit some information into a pie chart some rounding or 'tidying up' of the data may need to be done. Make sure that pie chart information occupies the whole of the circle with no blank spaces remaining. Pie charts can become difficult to read if too much information and cramped wording is used and, as in all graphs, colour-coding and careful labelling of what is being shown is essential.

Creative context

Pie charts are believed to have been first used by Florence Nightingale during the Crimean War. She used them to support her argument that more soldiers were dying from disease than from wounds sustained during battle. Children could find out more about the things Florence Nightingale did for the soldiers. Pie charts are a colourful and accessible way of showing information and they have become particularly popular in newspapers and magazines. Maths apart, they are equally good at showing data in other curriculum areas like science, geography and history. Discuss the advantages and disadvantages of using a pie chart to show data, contrasting it with other ways of recording statistics like pictograms, bar charts and line graphs.

Vocabulary

angle, bar graph, classify, data, diagram, contrast, construct, fraction, frequency, interpret, key, label, pie chart, proportion, sector, table, represent, statistics, title

Curriculum objectives
● To interpret pie charts and use these to solve problems.

Success criteria
● I can read and interpret information in a pie chart.

You will need
Photocopiable sheets
'My day'

Differentiation

Less confident learners
Some help with vocabulary may be needed when interpreting the 'My day' chart, such as *complete*, *fraction*, *together* and *exactly*.

More confident learners
Encourage children to think about how time passes during their own day so that they can compare it with Bryony's day.

Lesson 1 — Oral and mental starter 22

Whole-class work: Establish that a pie chart is a type of graph. It displays data by showing each data item as a fraction or proportion of a complete circle. The 'pieces of the pie' are sectors of a circle. Point out that sectors can be considered as angles and as such drawn and measured using a protractor. Display the 'School travel' pie chart. Explain that it shows how the children in one class travel to school. Ask general questions about the information shown, pointing out that, in this case, the sectors cannot be converted into numbers because we do not know how many children were surveyed. Ask: *How do most children travel? What about the fewest? About what fraction of the class travel by car?* Ask whether these statements are true or false: More children walk than cycle. More children walk than travel by car. More than half the class travel either by bus or by car.

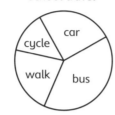

School travel

Paired work: Give out photocopiable page 'My day' from the CD-ROM. Explain that it shows how one child spends one day. Point out that 24 hours are shown on the pie chart so they will be able to work out actual hours.

Progress check: Make sure children are interpreting the time scale around the edge of the chart correctly. Check they are calculating the number of hours accurately. Explain that any 'fraction' answers they give will be approximate.

Review
Check the answers from the 'My day' pie chart. Ask: *Did the way in which the information was shown make it easy to read? Which questions did you find difficult? Did colour-coding help? Was the labelling suitable?*

Curriculum objectives
● To interpret pie charts and use them to solve problems.

Success criteria
● I can read, interpret and compare information shown on two pie charts.

You will need
Photocopiable sheets
'Spending money'

Differentiation

Less confident learners
Stress the importance of considering the two pie charts in relation to one another rather than looking at them in isolation.

More confident learners
Challenge children to come up with other situations when using a pair of pie charts alongside each other would be useful for making comparisons.

Lesson 2 — Oral and mental starter 24

Main teaching activities

Whole-class work: Display large versions of the pie charts 'Play hockey' on the board. Explain that this is an example where two pie charts about the same topic can be used together to make comparisons. Say that this time the frequency is known – 24 matches – so actual figures can be used about the results. Prompt the children to interpret the chart by asking: *Who won more matches? Who drew more matches? Who lost more matches? How many games did Southwick School win? How many games did Northport School lose? Which team had the best results overall?* Encourage children to explain their answers.

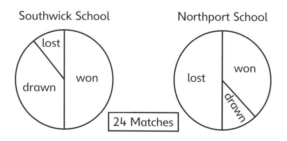

Southwick School   Northport School

24 Matches

Paired work: Provide pairs with photocopiable page 'Spending money' from the CD-ROM. Note that it shows how two children spend their money during a typical week. Point out that actual amounts can be worked out, approximately.

Progress check: Remind children that in most cases they are looking at the fraction or the proportion of the full circle when they give their answers. Point out too that, when working out money amounts, they will only be able to give approximate answers.

Review
Go through the children's answers, especially those where opinions may vary. Discuss: *What were the main advantages of considering the two pie charts together?* Ask confident children to suggest other everyday situations where pairs of pie charts like this could be used.

Curriculum objectives
- To interpret and construct pie charts and use them to solve problems.

Success criteria
- I can construct pie charts from given information.

You will need

General resources
Interactive teaching resource 'Graphing tool'

Equipment
Paper; coloured pencils or pens; large circles divided into eighths

Differentiation

Less confident learners
Work with children to give particular support when odd numbers are being converted into sectors on the pie chart.

More confident learners
Extend children by asking them to carry out their own favourite music survey with 16 children in the class, and convert the information into a pie chart using an eight-sector circle.

Lesson 3

Oral and mental starter 25

Main teaching activities

Whole-class work: Tell the children that in this lesson they are going to make their own pie charts based on the favourite music of a group of children. First, revise quickly the work already done on pie charts. Establish that pie charts show how data is shared or divided up. Explain that pie charts are divided into sectors and that the size of the angle in each sector represents the frequency of certain data.

Show a pie chart on the board, and elicit from the children that the largest sector shows the category of data that occurs with the highest frequency and the smallest sector shows the category with the smallest frequency.

Tell the children that they will be provided with a circle marked into eight equal parts to help them make the pie chart. Explain that 16 children were questioned in this particular survey, so each sector marked on the circle will represent two children ($16 \div 8 = 2$). Present the results of the survey in table form on the board.

Type of music	Frequency
Reggae	4
Garage	2
Hip hop	2
Rap	1
Heavy metal	7
Total	**16**

Independent work: Provide the children with large circles divided into eighths on which to make the pie chart. Stress the importance of using colour coding and/or a key to display the results, and remind the children to make sure the pie chart has a title. Tell them they should write as much information about the pie chart as possible once it has been made. If time available, the children could input the data using the interactive teaching resource 'Graphing tool' on the CD-ROM. Compare with the paper version in the Review section of the lesson.

Progress check: Observe children as they are coming to the end of constructing and colouring their charts. Make sure they are successfully converting the information shown on the table onto the eight-sector circle. To check understanding, ask: *How many children does each sector represent? How will four children be shown on the pie chart? How will the odd numbers, 1 and 7, be shown on the pie chart?*

Review

Display some of the pie charts the children have produced. Enlarge some of them, if possible for the whole class to see. Discuss: *Has a colour-coding system been used? What labelling was necessary? Has a key been included?* Ask the children to give statements about the information shown in answer to the following questions: *Which type of music was most popular? Which type of music was least popular? Which types of music had the same number of votes? How many children were surveyed altogether?*

Oral and mental starter 26

Lesson 4

Curriculum objectives
- To interpret and construct pie charts and use these to solve problems.

Success criteria
- I can construct pie charts from given information by drawing angles.

You will need

General resources

Interactive teaching resource 'Graphing tool'

Equipment

Individual whiteboards; plain paper; a pair of compasses; protractors (preferably 360°); coloured pens or pencils

Differentiation

Less confident learners

Provide support when children are working out and drawing angles for each sector.

More confident learners

Set the children up to use the interactive teaching resource 'Graphing tool' to make the same pie chart digitally.

Main teaching activities

Whole-class work: Tell the children they are going to make another pie chart, this time using measured angles. (360° protractors can be used to draw the circle to start with.) The pie chart will show the types of cars spotted in a car park one afternoon. Explain that dividing the whole circle (360°) by the total of the frequencies will give the angle for one data item. There is a total of 60 cars, so 360 ÷ 60 = 6: each car will have an angle of 6°. Elicit that to work out the appropriate angle each time, the number of cars must be multiplied by 6. Display this table and ask the children to work out the angle needed for each group of cars.

Car manufacturer	Number	Angle
Ford	18	18 × 6 =108°
Vauxhall	12	12 × 6 = 72°
Nissan	10	10 × 6 =
Toyota	5	5 × 6 =
BMW	3	3 × 6 =
Others	12	12 × 6 =

Group work: Ask the children to make the pie chart. Reinforce that they must use the whole circle and that each angle must be measured from the previous line drawn. Remind them to include a title, colour coding and a key.

Progress check: Ensure the children have converted car numbers into angles correctly. Check the angles add up to 360.

Review

Ask volunteers to share their pie charts. Ask: *Which make of car was most/least common? Which two sectors of the pie chart were the same?*

Lesson 5

Oral and mental starter 25

Curriculum objectives
- As lesson 4.

Success criteria
- I can read, interpret and contrast the same set of data on a pie chart and a bar chart.

You will need

Photocopiable sheets

'Home heating'

Equipment

Paper; coloured pens/pencils; protractors (preferably 360°)

Differentiation

Less confident learners

Some children will require help converting into angles.

More confident learners

Ask children to see if other forms of graph, such as line graphs and pictograms, could be converted into pie charts.

Main teaching activities

Whole-class work: This lesson compares the way the same information can be shown in two different kinds of chart – a bar graph and a pie chart. The children should focus on which type of graph does the job most effectively. Explain that the graphs will show the main fuel used for heating in a survey of 90 houses. Quickly revise the methods from the previous lesson: converting data into angles and drawing the angles on the pie chart with a protractor. Stress that, this time, the information will be read from the bar chart to calculate the angles.

Group work: Provide photocopiable page 89 'Home heating', with a bar chart of how 90 different houses are heated, for converting to a pie chart.

Progress check: Observe the groups early on. Have children read the bar chart correctly? Have they converted the number of houses into angles successfully? Have the angles been drawn accurately? Is the circle complete?

Review

Look carefully at the pie charts and check answers. Compare pie charts with bar graphs. Discuss: *What advantages do pie charts have over other forms of chart or graph? What disadvantages do they have?* Agree that bar charts are best used to show specific values and pie charts are best used to show proportions.

You will need
1. Check
Oral and mental starter
[21] Cancel down

2. Assess
Individual whiteboards

3. Further practice
Oral and mental starter
[19] Which order?

Photocopiable sheets
'Fraction shapes'

Comparing, ordering and simplifying fractions

Most children should be able to cancel fractions down into their lowest terms by finding the highest common factor, and order fractions by size.

Some children will need support in finding relevant factors and multiples and will need tables squares. They may also find fraction walls helpful in finding equivalent fractions.

1. Check

[21] Cancel down

Encourage children to always look for the highest common factor first. Stress the factor must be common to both the numerator and the denominator. If the highest common factor is not used first time, the fraction will need to be cancelled down several times.

2. Assess

Tell the children that they will be presented with three fractions to put in order from smallest to largest. Stress that they should put all three fractions into the same fraction family by finding the lowest common denominator. Try: ⅗, ½, ⁷⁄₁₀; ⅚, ¹¹⁄₁₂, ¾; ⅔, ½, ⁷⁄₁₂; ⅗, ⅔, ¹¹⁄₁₅; ⅓, ⅜, ¼; ⅔, ⅚, ¼; ⁹⁄₂₀, ⅖, ¼; ⅔, ¾, ⅘. Extend by including some mixed numbers: 1 ⅔, 1 ¾. Set a word problem that involves sorting fractions: *Last weekend, Damien read 3/8 of his book. The weekend before he read ¼ of it. What fraction of the book is left to read?*

3. Further practice

Oral and mental starter 'Which order' will provide further practice in sorting fractions. Ask the children to name the lowest common denominator they have used each time. Photocopiable page 'Fraction shapes' asks the children to compare fractions, find equivalent fractions and add and subtract simple fractions.

You will need
1. Check
Oral and mental starter
[13] Decimal digits

2. Assess
Individual whiteboards

3. Further practice
Oral and mental starters
[15] Decimal times
[16] Ten times more

Photocopiable sheets
'Fishing contest (2)'

Multiplying and dividing decimal numbers

Most children should be able to multiply and divide small decimal numbers by 10 and 100 and work to at least two decimal places.

Some children will need to be reminded that it will be the digits that move to the right or left and not the decimal point itself.

1. Check

[13] Decimal digits

Make sure the children are aware that some of the circled numbers will be whole numbers and some will be decimal fractions.

2. Assess

The children should work in pairs to discuss the number statements they make. Write the following statements on the board for completion (one set for multiplying by 10, 100 and 1000, and one for dividing):

$? \times 0.4 = 4$; $3.25 \times ? = 325$; $2.79 \times ? = 27.9$; $? \times 2.71 = 2710$; $? \times 43.7 = 437$; $9.01 \times ? = 90.1$; $4.57 \times ? = 4570$; $0.8 \times ? = 8$; $28.7 \times ? = 287$; $? \times 10 = 90.1$.

$5.7 \div ? = 0.57$; $? \div 10 = 0.6$; $39.4 \div ? = 0.0394$; $? \div 1000 = 0.018$; $472 \div ? = 4.72$; $? \div 1000 = 0.00417$; $31.6 \div ? = 0.316$; $7.65 \div ? = 0.765$; $? \div 10 = 2.76$; $8.72 \div ? = 0.0872$.

3. Further practice

The suggested starters will reinforce multiplying decimal numbers and making decimal numbers ten times bigger. Photocopiable page 'Fishing contest (2)' from the CD-ROM presents tasks using decimal numbers in a problem-solving situation.

Curriculum objectives
- To draw 2D shapes given dimensions and angles.

You will need
1. Check
Oral and mental starter
 Name it (1)

2. Assess
Plain paper, rulers, a pair of compasses, protractors; nail boards and elastic bands, dotty or squared paper

3. Further practice
Oral and mental starters
 Name it (2)
 In the net

2D and 3D shapes

Most children should be able to draw 2D shapes accurately given lengths and certain other dimensions including angles.

Some children may still need to practise making 2D shapes using nail boards and elastic bands or by drawing them with the aid of dotty paper or squared paper.

1. Check
 Name it (1)

In this starter, the children need to identify 2D shapes and describe their properties.

2. Assess

Ask the children to construct four different 2D shapes after being given some of their dimensions:

1. An isosceles triangle with two angles of 40 degrees and two sides 4cm long. Ask: *What is the size of the third angle?*

2. A rectangle with opposite sides 10cm and 4.5cm long. *How long are the two diagonals?*

3. A circle with a radius of 4.8cm. *What is the diameter?*

4. A trapezium with a base of 4cm, two sides 5cm long and two angles measuring 115 degrees. *What is the length of the fourth side?*

3. Further practice

The starters will allow children to practise identifying and describing 3D shapes and how to construct them from nets.

Curriculum objectives
- To interpret and construct pie charts and use them to solve problems.

You will need
1. Check
General resources
Interactive teaching resource 'Graphing tool'

2. Assess
Plain paper; dice; protractors

3. Further practice
Photocopiable sheets
'Home heating'

Pie charts

Most children will be able to read and interpret the information shown on a pie chart and will be able to make a simple pie chart.

Some children will be able to read and interpret information shown on a pie chart but will need prepared circles or help when working out and drawing the angles to construct them.

1. Check

Use the interactive teaching resource 'Graphing and charting tool' to check children's knowledge of some of the important rules involved in making a pie chart, including: The whole circle has to be used. Lines are drawn from the centre of the circle. Colour coding or symbols should be used to denote the different parts of the pie chart. Each part of the pie chart must be clearly labelled.

2. Assess

Ask the children, in pairs, to roll a dice 18 times and to record the results in a tally chart. They should then draw a pie chart to show how many times each number was thrown. Protractors should be used to measure the angles for the sectors. Once complete, ask the children to write about the information shown on the pie chart. Record the outcomes.

3. Further practice

Photocopiable page 89 'Home heating' requires the children to use the information in a bar graph to make a pie chart and then to compare the two.

Oral and mental starters

Decimals and fractions

13 Decimal digits

Write the following numbers on the board, circling certain digits: 2.37, 12.25, 5.349, 10.87, 27.35, 8.205, 11.274, 14.573, 27.306, 42.159. Ask the children to identify the digit and say its place value in words (three tenths, five hundredths...) Ensure children know that digits left of the decimal point are whole numbers and that digits to the right are parts of whole numbers (fractions).

14 Decimals at the double

Ask the children to double numbers that contain a decimal point. Some children may find it easier to remove the decimal point, double the whole number and then reinstate the decimal point. Try: 2.5, 3.1, 4.2, 2.6, 5.9, 1.2, 0.8; and 2.03 and 1.92.

15 Decimal times

Set some quick-fire multiplication questions involving decimals. Remind them that they can work out the whole number multiplication first and then place the decimal point in the correct place in the answer. For example: $6 \times 3 = 18$, so $0.6 \times 3 = 1.8$. Try these: 0.4×5, 0.2×8, 0.9×2, 0.5×7, and 1.1×3, 1.2×4, 1.5×2, 2.2×3.

16 Ten times more

Call out a series of decimal numbers for children to multiply by 10. Remind them that when multiplying a decimal number by 10, the digits move one place to the left. Try: 1.7, 3.5, 5.2, 7.6, 9.3, 10.5, 12.9, 8.84, 12.65, 97.358.

17 How many?

Make sure that children appreciate one whole one is the same as two halves, four quarters, six sixths and so on. Ask: *How many fifths... eighths... tenths in one whole one?* Then ask: *How many... halves in* $1\frac{1}{2}$, *halves in* $3\frac{1}{2}$, *quarters in 2, quarters in* $3\frac{3}{4}$, *fifths in 3, fifths in* $4\frac{2}{5}$, *tenths in 4, tenths in* $5\frac{3}{10}$, *eighths in* $1\frac{3}{8}$, *thirds in* $5\frac{1}{3}$ *?*

Extension

Challenge children to convert their answer into a different fraction family: *How many... eighths in* $1\frac{3}{4}$, *quarters in* $10\frac{1}{2}$, *fifths in* $3\frac{3}{10}$, *sixths in* $2\frac{1}{2}$*?*

18 You owe

Say that some children need to find fractions of their money to pay for some items. Ask the class to calculate how much each child has to pay. Remind them that when finding a fraction of an amount they should divide by the denominator and multiply by the numerator. Try: $\frac{1}{2}$ of £1, $\frac{1}{4}$ of £2, $\frac{3}{4}$ of £8, $\frac{4}{5}$ of £5, $\frac{3}{10}$ of £5, $\frac{9}{10}$ of £8, $\frac{2}{5}$ of £5, $\frac{3}{4}$ of £20.

Extension

Extend the questions to include pounds and pence. Try: $\frac{3}{8}$ of £3.20, $\frac{2}{7}$ of £2.80, $\frac{5}{12}$ of £2.40, $\frac{7}{9}$ of £4.50.

19 Which order?

Ask the children to sort the following pairs of fractions into order of size so they can be labelled 'greater than' (<) and 'smaller than' (>). Ask volunteers to add the correct symbol and name the highest common factor they have used. Recall that, when converting fractions, the denominator and numerator must be multiplied by the same number. For example: $\frac{3}{5}$ and $\frac{2}{3}$, $\frac{2}{3}$ and $\frac{3}{4}$, $\frac{3}{4}$ and $\frac{4}{5}$, $\frac{5}{6}$ and $\frac{7}{9}$, $\frac{3}{4}$ and $\frac{5}{7}$, $\frac{5}{12}$ and $\frac{3}{7}$, $\frac{4}{5}$ and $\frac{7}{9}$, $\frac{9}{10}$ and $\frac{4}{5}$.

Extension

Challenge children to order a group of three fractions, smallest first. Try: $\frac{1}{2}$, $\frac{2}{3}$ and $\frac{2}{5}$; $\frac{2}{3}$, $\frac{3}{4}$ and $\frac{1}{2}$; $\frac{6}{7}$, $\frac{7}{21}$ and $\frac{2}{3}$.

20 Fractions and decimals

Ask the children to give you the decimal equivalent of each fraction you give them. For example: you say ½, and they reply 0.5. Then reverse the process: provide the decimal for the children to say the fraction.

Extension
Include whole numbers to give children more digits to consider: 2 ³/₁₀, 5 ⁷/₁₀₀, 11 ¼; 5.7, 9.02.

21 Cancel down

Ask children to cancel down these fractions into their lowest terms using the highest common factor possible each time. Stress the factor must be common to both the numerator and the denominator. Try: ⁵/₁₀, ⁶/₉, ⁴/₈, ¹⁰/₁₅, ²/₁₀, ¹⁶/₂₀, ⁷/₂₁, ⁹/₃₆.

22 On the line

Draw a line on the board from 1.5 to 4.5 marked off in tenths, with every 0.5 labelled. Ask the children to come out and draw a line showing the position of each given number. They should also state where the number is being placed. For example: 3.8 lies between 3.7 and 3.9; 4.12 lies between 4.1 and 4.2.

23 Decimal roundup

Ask the children to round these heights to the nearest metre: 2.34m, 1.78m, 2.16m, 3.21m, 4.02m, 5.71m, 2.75m, 3.69m, 7.31m. Then round these distances to the nearest tenth of a metre: 2.34m, 1.78m, 2.16m, 3.21m, 4.02m, 5.71m, 2.75m, 4.48m.

Geometry: properties of shapes

24 Name it (1)

Point to some 2D shapes at random for the children to name. Also ask them to describe the shape according to its sides and angles. Look for words like *parallel* and *perpendicular*. For example: *It has four equal sides. It has four right angles. Opposite sides are parallel.* (Square.)

Extension
Describe a 2D shape for the children to name and/or draw: *A three-sided shape with two equal angles.* (Isosceles triangle.)

25 Name it (2)

Collect common 3D shapes. As you point to each one, ask the children to name the solid and discuss its properties. Ensure children are clear about words like *face*, *edge* and *vertex/vertices*. Ask: *How many faces does it have? What shape(s) are the faces? How many edges does it have? How many vertices does it have?*

Extension
Discuss which shapes might qualify as regular polyhedra (all faces are the same shape and size).

26 In the net

Display nets of some 3D solid shapes (cuboid, triangular prism, tetrahedron, square-based pyramid, cone, cylinder, for example). Ask the children to name the shapes and list as many properties as possible.

Name: _____   Date: _____

Decimal circles

■ What is the value of each digit circled? Some are whole numbers and some are decimal numbers.

1. 1⑦.45 _____   6. 408.55⑦ _____

2. 115.②7 _____   7. 48.25① _____

3. 33.6②9 _____   8. 5⑨4.287 _____

4. 248.6③1 _____   9. ⑤0.007 _____

5. ③5.07 _____   10. ①354.098 _____

■ Fill in the missing numbers.

11. 4.38 = 4 + ☐/10 + ☐/100 = 4 ☐/100

12. 9.376 = 9 + ☐/10 + ☐/100 + ☐/1000 = 9 ☐/1000

13. 12.745 = 10 + 2 + ☐/10 + ☐/100 + ☐/1000 = 12 ☐/1000

14. 247.83 = 200 + 40 + 7 + ☐/10 + ☐/100 = 247 ☐/100.

■ Write these numbers in decimal form.

15. $4 \frac{3}{10}$ _____   19. $\frac{3}{1000}$ _____

16. $5 \frac{7}{100}$ _____   20. $4 \frac{2}{1000}$ _____

17. $8 \frac{9}{1000}$ _____   21. $17 \frac{23}{100}$ _____

18. $\frac{37}{100}$ _____   22. $\frac{237}{100}$ _____

■ Put the correct sign (< , > or =) between the numbers.

23. 2.200 _____ 2.2   27. 0.701 _____ 1.0

24. 2.02 _____ 2.2   28. 0.304 _____ 1.104

25. 0.17 _____ 0.5   29. 0.17 _____ 0.5

26. 3.004 _____ 3.012   30. 0.4 _____ 0.36

I can identify the values of digits in decimal numbers.

How did you do?

Fishing contest (1)

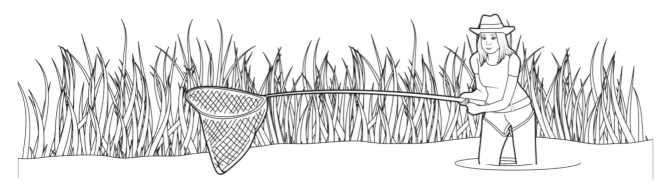

This table shows the weight of fish caught by four anglers in a two-day fishing contest.

Angler	Weight of catch in kilograms		Total weight
	Day 1	Day 2	
Angus	6.259	4.435	
Pearl	5.862	7.046	
Brian	3.577	8.248	
Maeve	5.874	6.365	

1. Round Angus' results to the nearest whole number. _____

2. Round Pearl's results to one decimal place. _____

3. Round Brian's results to two decimal places. _____

4. Who had the heaviest catch on Day 1? _____

5. Who had the heaviest catch on Day 2? _____

6. Find the total weight of fish caught by each angler. Add the figures to the table.

7. Name the winners of the 1st, 2nd and 3rd prizes in the competition based on the heaviest weight caught.

1. _____   2. _____   3. _____

8. What was the difference in weight between the 1st and 2nd prizes?

_____

I can solve problems involving the use of decimal numbers.

How did you do?

Net gain

- Here are the nets of five 3D shapes.
- Draw your own versions of these shapes.
- Don't forget to include gluing flaps.
- Now construct the shapes.
- Which shapes have you made?

1.

2.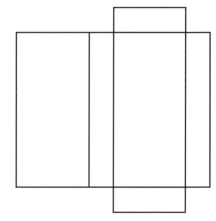

4.

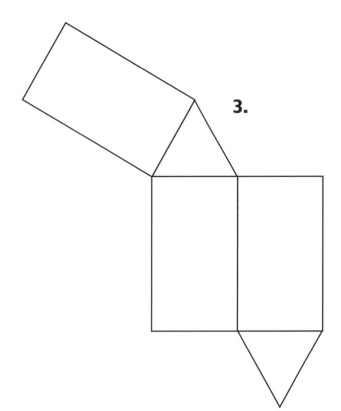

3.

5.

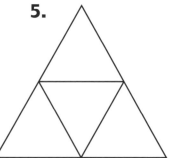

I can construct straight-sided 3D shapes from their nets.

How did you do?

Home heating

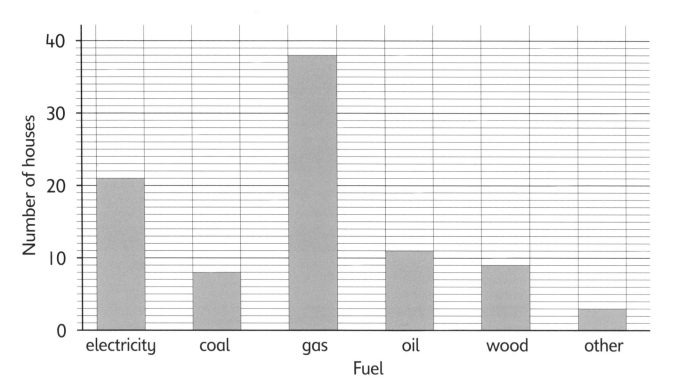

- This bar graph shows the main fuel used for heating 90 houses.
- Make a pie chart that shows the same information. Then answer the questions.

1. Which is the most popular fuel? _____

2. How many homes use mainly electricity? _____

3. How many homes use either oil or coal? _____

4. What fraction of the houses use wood? _____

5. Which chart shows more clearly:

a) the number of houses which use each fuel? _____

b) that about a quarter of the houses use electricity for heating? _____

c) that more of the houses use oil than use coal? _____

d) that two-thirds of the houses use either electricity or gas? _____

I can contrast the same set of data on a pie chart and a bar graph.

How did you do?

Negative numbers and problem-solving

Expected prior learning

Children should be able to:

- read write, order and compare numbers up to 1,000,000 and determine the value of each digit
- round numbers up to 1,000,000.

Topic	Curriculum objectives	Expected outcomes
Number and place value	**Lesson 1**	
	To read, write, order and compare numbers up to 10,000,000 and determine the value of each digit.	Read and write numbers in figures and words up to 10,000,000 and find the value of each digit.
	Lesson 2	
	To read, write, order and compare numbers up to 10,000,000 and determine the value of each digit.	Order and compare numbers to at least 10,000,000.
	Lesson 3	
	To round any whole number to a required degree of accuracy.	Round whole numbers accurately.
	Lesson 4	
	To use negative numbers in context, and calculate intervals across zero.	Use negative numbers in context. Calculate with negative and positive numbers.
	Lesson 5	
	To use negative numbers in context, and calculate intervals across zero.	Solve problems that involve negative numbers.

■SCHOLASTIC

Preparation

Lesson 1: prepare a set of number cards for each child

Lesson 3: write up the population figures given in the lesson; arrange internet access or atlases for more confident learners to find population figures

Lesson 5: copy 'Maximum and minimum temperatures' for each child; arrange internet access for more confident learners to find weather information

You will need

Photocopiable sheets
'Maximum and minimum temperatures'

General resources
'Number cards 0–9'; interactive teaching resource 'Number line'

Equipment
Individual whiteboards; sets of number cards (0–20) and negative number cards (−20 to 0); number lines; notation cards showing columns up to ten million; internet access; atlases

Further practice

Use real time temperature data from websites such as www.timeanddate.com to further practice calculating intervals across zero.

Oral and mental starters suggested for week 1

See the bank of starters on pages 44 and 125. Oral and mental starters are also on the CD-ROM.

3 Roundup

27 Jumping forwards and backwards

28 Number order

29 Temperature change

Overview of progression

This week children will be using and exploring large numbers. As well as saying and writing them in numbers and in words, the children will be able to identify the value of each digit. They will also be able to order the numbers, round them and calculate with them. Later in the week they will be looking at negative numbers and using them in context, including finding differences.

Watch out for

Children need to be very clear about place value and about the value of each digit. They will often be confused if there is a zero in the number, especially when writing the number in figures. Make sure that children can group the digits correctly so that they talk in millions, thousands and then hundreds, tens and units.

Creative context

There are cross-curricular links with geography and citizenship when using large numbers, especially when talking about populations. Large numbers are also encountered in science, for example when looking at distances in the solar system. Encourage children to notice negative numbers with food technology, particularly when looking at safe storage of chilled and frozen food.

Vocabulary

approximately, compare, difference, digit, hundred, hundred thousand, million, minus, nearly, nearest, numeral, negative, order, place value, £ (pound), roughly, rounding, ten million, ten thousand, thousand

Curriculum objectives
● To read and write numbers up to 10,000,000, and determine the value of each digit.

Success criteria
● I can read and write large numbers in figures and in words.
● I know the value of each digit.

You will need

General resources
'Number cards 0–9'

Equipment
Individual whiteboards

Differentiation

Less confident learners

Make sure children work methodically, starting with the lower values and working up. When they choose their own numbers, encourage them to record their work so that you are able to check their understanding.

More confident learners

Children may like to try even bigger numbers, up to a billion or more, but check they are sure about the number of digits in these numbers.

Lesson 1 Oral and mental starter 27

Main teaching activities

Whole-class work: Tell the children that this week they will be using large numbers. Remind them that a hundred is ten tens, with three digits; a thousand is ten hundreds, with four digits; and a million is a thousand thousands, with seven digits.

Ask the children if they can think of any examples of when they have seen really large numbers. For example, sports stars' earnings, people in the world, possible grains of sand on a beach.

Start by looking at the following number on the board: 34,612,789. Ask the children to talk in pairs about how to read out the number. Elicit that they read it as *34 million, 612 thousand, 789*. Show the children that it can help to use the commas in the number when reading. Point out that, if the number is not shown with commas, they can insert them by counting back in sets of three digits. For example, ask the children where they should put the commas in 193762458. (After the 2, then after the 3.) Then ask the children to read out the number.

Now ask the children to tell you the value of different digits in the number. Say, for example: *What is the value of the 7?* (Seven hundred thousand.) Or: *What is the value of the 2?* (Two thousand.)

Paired work: Organise the children into pairs and ask them to look at each digit in the number above and decide upon the value of the digit.

Then hand out a set of number cards to each child. Tell the children that they should each select between six and nine number cards to generate a number, write down the number, and then challenge their partner to read out the number and give the value of each digit.

Progress check: After the first part of the activity, visit the children, particularly those you wish to assess. Ask the children to tell you the value of various digits in the number on the board. Provide help with any difficulties they have encountered.

Then check with the children again at intervals, taking numbers from different pairs to challenge other class members.

Review

Work through any difficulties the children encountered. Then write the following on the board: 300,104,096. Ask the children to say the number. Check that they can tell you the value of some of the digits.

Now ask the children to write the number *twenty million, two hundred and six thousand, nine hundred and five* on their whiteboards. Check that they have written this correctly (20,206,905), then ask them to write the following number: *eight million, three hundred and five* (8,000,305).

Curriculum objectives
● To read, write, order and compare numbers up to 10,000,000 and determine the value of each digit.

Success criteria
● I can order and compare numbers up to 10,000,000.

You will need

General resources
'Number cards 0–9'

Equipment
Individual whiteboards; notation cards

Differentiation

Less confident learners

Children may find it helpful to have notation cards showing the values for each column when writing numbers.

More confident learners

Encourage children to work with even larger numbers, and to order them.

Lesson 2 — Oral and mental starter 27

Main teaching activities

Whole-class work: Tell the children that you would like them to write some numbers on their whiteboards, but first, remind them to think carefully about the position of each digit and its value. Ask them to write *three hundred and twelve thousand and ninety six* (312,096) and then *thirteen million ninety-three thousand and five* (13,093,005).

Ask a volunteer to show and explain how they have written the numbers. Point out where the zeros need to be written and why. Explain to the children that, if they are having difficulty, they might find it helpful to label the columns for the number, from the left: *ten millions, millions, hundreds of thousands, tens of thousands, thousands, hundreds, tens* and *units*; then, as they write the number, to be sure to put the zeros in the appropriate columns.

Paired work: Hand out a set of number cards to each pair of children. Explain that each of the children should select eight or more cards to generate a number, without revealing the cards to their partner. Ask them to write down their number, again hiding it, and then say the number in words for their partner to write down in figures. The children should then compare their numbers. When they have done this at least three times each to generate six numbers, they should then write the numbers in order. Suggest to the children that if they disagree on any of the answers, they should check them with another pair.

Progress check: Monitor the children as they work, and ask those pairs you particularly wish to assess to tell you the order they have put their numbers in. If necessary, remind the children how to order numbers, comparing the digits with the highest value first.

Review

Invite a volunteer to write one of their numbers on the board, then ask another child to write one of their numbers below the first one, keeping the digits in line. Continue until there are six numbers listed on the board. Ask the class about how to order the numbers. Check that they are comparing the correct digits, starting with the digits with the highest value.

Curriculum objectives
● To round any whole number to a required degree of accuracy.

Success criteria
● I can round numbers to the nearest ten, hundred, thousand, ten thousand, hundred thousand and million.

You will need

Equipment
Individual whiteboards; atlases or access to the internet

Differentiation

Less confident learners
Suggest to children that they round all the numbers to the nearest ten and then the nearest hundred. Check that these are correct before rounding higher numbers. Let them work in pairs or a small group to discuss their thinking.

More confident learners
After the main activity, let children research the populations of other large cities in the world and to add these to their charts, rounding them in the same way.

Main teaching activities

Whole-class work: Explain to the children that you will be looking at rounding numbers. Establish that often, when we are dealing with very large numbers, it can be useful to round them. For example, we may say for convenience that the population of a city is 6 million, although the actual figure will be specific down to the unit (one person), and, of course, the population is changing by small amounts all the time.

Show the children the following information about the populations of different Chinese cities. Ask different children to read out the population of each city.

Shanghai	22,315,426
Beijing	18,827,000
Tianjin	11,090,314
Guangzhou	11,070,654
Shenzhen	10,357,938

Revise with the children that, when you are rounding, if the digit is 5 or more you round *up*, and if it is less than 5 you round *down*. Ask the children: *What would the population of Shanghai be rounded to the nearest hundred (22,315,400)?* Then ask what it would be rounded to the nearest million (22 million, or 22,000,000).

Independent work: Ask the children to look at the population of each of the cities and round them to the nearest hundred, thousand, ten thousand, hundred thousand and million. Tell the children to design a table to show each of the cities rounded to the required numbers, or provide them with one like this to copy:

City	Population	Rounded to the nearest...				
		hundred	**thousand**	**ten thousand**	**hundred thousand**	**million**
Shanghai	22,315,426					
Beijing	18,827,000					
Tianjin	11,090,314					
Guangzhou	11,070,654					
Shenzhen	10,357,938					

Progress check: Check that the children can round 22,315,426 to the nearest ten thousand. Point out that they must be careful when rounding a number with several zeros, such as 22,315,000. Make sure the children realise that 315,000 rounded to the nearest ten thousand is 320,000.

Review

Ask the children to read out some of their answers and explain how they decided to round the numbers. Work through any difficulties, and check that the children have been clear about when to round up and when to round down.

Curriculum objectives
- To use negative numbers in context, and calculate intervals across zero.

Success criteria
- I can use negative numbers in context.
- I can calculate using negative and positive numbers.

You will need

General resources
'Number cards 0–9'; interactive teaching resource 'Number line'

Equipment
Individual whiteboards; negative number cards; printed number lines

Differentiation

Less confident learners
Encourage children to use number lines and physically count the steps.

More confident learners
Ask children to use a wider range of numbers and go on to using decimal numbers.

Lesson 4 — Oral and mental starter 28

Main teaching activities

Whole-class work: Tell the children that they will be looking at negative numbers and how we use them. Ask the children where they have come across negative numbers; for example with temperatures which they would have covered in year 5.

Display the interactive teaching resource 'Number line' on the CD-ROM. Ask volunteers to come up and use the tools to write numbers on the line, such as −7, 15, −1 and 16. Then tell the children that you want them to find the difference between −7 and 15. Elicit that it is necessary to count the steps between the numbers, so, from −7 to 0 is 7 and from 0 to 15 is 15, hence the overall difference is 22. This could be written as $15 - (-7) = 22$.

Paired work: Provide pairs of children with two sets of cards; one showing numbers from −20 to 0 and the other 0 to 20. Explain that each child should choose a card from each set for both children to record and then position on a number line. Then ask them to find the difference between the two numbers.

Ask the pairs to repeat this with two more cards.

Progress check: Pause the children after the first set. Ask them to select two cards from the negative set and calculate the difference between the two. Check that the children realise the difference will be positive.

Review
Establish with the children that day-time temperatures are often much higher than night-time temperatures. Challenge them to work out the temperature difference between a night-time temperature of −5°C and a day-time temperature of 12°C. (17°C.)

Curriculum objectives
- To use negative numbers in context, and calculate intervals across zero.

Success criteria
- I can solve problems that involve negative numbers.

You will need

Photocopiable sheets
'Maximum and minimum temperatures'

Equipment
Individual whiteboards; internet access

Differentiation

Less confident learners
Children should work as a group with adult support.

More confident learners
Children should investigate other places with extreme temperatures, and devise their own questions.

Lesson 5 — Oral and mental starter 29

Main teaching activities

Whole-class work: Tell the children that as they have been learning about negative numbers, you want them to see more about how they are used. Ask the children to recall where they have seen negative numbers, for example, to do with temperature, including in weather reports and on the packaging of chilled and frozen foods.

Explain that they are going to complete an investigation looking at day-time and night-time temperatures in different parts of the world.

Independent/group work: Hand out photocopiable page 'Maximum and minimum temperatures' from the CD-ROM for the children to complete, working individually if appropriate. Read through and discuss the information with them.

Progress check: Pause the children after a short while and check that they have completed the first one or two questions successfully.

Review
Go through the questions from the photocopiable sheet and clarify any misconceptions. Invite more confident children to share some of the questions that they have devised themselves. Work as a class to answer them.

Addition and subtraction of decimals and money

Expected prior learning

Children should be able to:

- explain their reasoning using text, diagrams and symbols
- use mental methods to find sums, differences, doubles and halves of decimals
- use rounding and inverse operations to estimate and check calculations.

Topic	Curriculum objectives	Expected outcomes
Addition, subtraction, multiplication and division	**Lesson 1**	
	To perform mental calculations, including with mixed operations and large numbers.	Use mental methods to add and subtract large numbers.
	Lesson 2	
	To solve addition and subtraction multi-step problems in contexts, deciding which operations and methods to use and why.	Decide which methods to use to solve addition and subtraction problems involving large numbers.
	Lesson 3	
	To solve addition and subtraction multi-step problems in contexts, deciding which operations and methods to use and why.	Solve problems in context, deciding which operations and methods to use. Use estimation to check answers.
	Lesson 4	
	To solve addition and subtraction multi-step problems in contexts, deciding which operations and methods to use and why. To use estimation to check answers to calculations and determine, in the context of a problem, an appropriate degree of accuracy.	Solve problems in context, deciding which operations and methods to use. Use estimation to check answers.
	Lesson 5	
	To solve addition and subtraction multi-step problems in contexts, deciding which operations and methods to use and why.	Solve problems in context, deciding which operations and methods to use.

■ SCHOLASTIC

Preparation

Lesson I: prepare the board with the calculations

Lesson 2: display a large version of 'Five steps to successful problem solving'; copy 'Step by step' for each child

Lesson 3: write up the problem given at the start of the lesson; copy 'Solve these (1)' for each child

Lesson 4: write up the problems; copy 'Solve these (2)' for each child, adapting as appropriate

Lesson 5: copy 'Goals galore' for each child

You will need

Photocopiable sheets
'Solve these (1)'; 'Solve these (2)'; 'Goals galore'; 'Step by step'

General resources
'Five steps to successful problem solving'

Equipment
Individual whiteboards

Further practice

Photocopiable sheets
'Jumbled calculations (2)'

Oral and mental starters suggested for week 2

See the bank of starters on pages 125 and 126. Oral and mental starters are also on the CD-ROM.

30 Quick additions

33 Decimal additions

34 Decimal differences

Overview of progression

At the start of the week the children revisit mental calculation strategies involving addition and subtraction of large numbers and decimal numbers, and then progress to solving problems and using approximation and other strategies for checking their answers.

Watch out for

A stumbling block can be in extracting the calculation from a word problem. Make sure that children read questions carefully, and help them to identify the important points in the questions. Encourage children to approximate before they do a calculation and then check that their answer makes sense. Remind them to check the place value of digits and ensure that they are adding or subtracting like with like.

Creative context

There are many real-life contexts for the work covered this week. Ask the children to think of situations where they can use the strategies that they are practising, for example when shopping. They could also look at house prices and compare them.

Vocabulary

approximate, calculation, estimate, number bonds, problem, strategy

Curriculum objectives
● To perform mental calculations, including with large numbers.
Success criteria
● I can add and subtract large numbers mentally using a range of strategies.

You will need
Equipment
Individual whiteboards

Differentiation
Less confident learners
Encourage children to make jottings so they can check their strategies.
More confident learners
Encourage children to use much larger numbers.

Lesson 1
Oral and mental starter 30

Main teaching activities

Whole-class work: Remind the children that they have a number of mental calculation strategies available when working with large numbers. First, ask the children to add 4250 and 3536 on their whiteboards. Compare answers and invite volunteers to explain how they worked it out. Next, write the following calculations on the board for the children to work out mentally. Remind them that number bonds or doubles are a good place to start.

3965 + 1024	2135 + 4335 (double 35 = 70)
6362 + 205	3712 + 1248 (12 + 48 = 60)
4123 + 3263	4465 + 2435 (65 + 35 = 100)

Progress check: Check answers. See if the children noticed that they could use doubling or number bonds, for example, for the last three calculations.

Whole-class work: Now work on some mental subtraction calculations. Write 40,000 − 3275 on the board. One way to calculate this is by counting up from the smaller number to the larger number. For example: 40,000 − 3275 is 5 + 20 + 700 + 6000 + 30,000 = 36,725.

Ask the children how they would subtract 399 from 550. They should realise that they could subtract 400 and add 1 to get 151. Next, ask them to subtract 785 from 1320. Point out that they can use rounding to start, to subtract 800 from 1320 to get 520, then add 15 to get 535.

Review
Give the children the following quick-fire calculations. Then check answers and compare strategies. 394 + 595 (Possible strategy 400 + 600 − 6 − 5.); 898 − 350 (900 − 350 − 2.); 6456 − 3098 (6456 − 3000 − 100 + 2.)

Curriculum objectives
● As lesson 1.
● To solve addition and subtraction problems in contexts, deciding which operations and methods to use and why.
Success criteria
● I can decide how to solve addition and subtraction problems.

You will need
Photocopiable sheets
'Step by step'
General resources
'Five steps to successful problem solving'

Differentiation
Less confident learners
Children should work as a group.
More confident learners
Children should devise simple word problems to challenge others in their group.

Lesson 2
Oral and mental starter 30

Main teaching activities

Whole-class work: Write two simple addition problems on the board – the first involving a one-step process, and the second incorporating at least two steps, for example: *There are 752 pages in one book of a trilogy, 596 in the second and 721 in the third. How many pages are there altogether?* (2069.) Go on to say: *I have read the first three chapters of Book 1, with 149, 78 and 126 pages. How many more pages do I have left to read?* Encourage the children to use mental strategies to solve the problem. (Step 1: 149 + 78 + 126 = 353. Step 2: 2069 − 353 = 1716.) Display photocopiable page 'Five steps to successful problem solving' from the CD-ROM, and discuss the different approaches that the children suggest to solve the problem.

Independent/group work: Ask the children to work on photocopiable page 'Step by step' from the CD-ROM, working individually if appropriate. Stress that you will want them to explain their reasoning.

Progress check: Pause the children after a short while and check their progress. Are they using the five-step strategy? Ask how it is helping them. Have they approximated an answer?

Review
Take feedback from the children about the activity on the photocopiable sheet. Ask them how they decided which were the key words and numbers they needed, and which operations to use.

ⓜSCHOLASTIC

Curriculum objectives
● To solve addition and subtraction problems in contexts, deciding which operations and methods to use and why.

Success criteria
● I can decide which operations to use to solve addition and subtraction problems.

You will need
Photocopiable sheets
'Solve these (1)'
Equipment
Individual whiteboards

Differentiation
Less confident learners
Provide support to help children with deciding the operations and strategies to use.
More confident learners
Encourage children to devise some questions of their own to challenge each other.

Lesson 3   Oral and mental starter 33

Main teaching activities

Whole-class work: Write this problem on the board:

A garden centre is situated on a busy main road. It is open every day until 7pm. It sells a variety of rose bushes that are kept in five plots of land measuring 7 metres by 12 metres each. The owner wants to enclose the plots with new fencing. How much fencing must he buy?

Tell the children to look carefully at the question, then ask what information is needed to solve the problem. Establish that they need first to find the perimeter of each plot of land and then multiply the answer by 5. Read through the information again. Are there any details that do not help to solve the problem? (Yes. The location of the garden centre and its opening times are irrelevant.)

Establish with the children that, therefore, when solving problems they need to:
- Read the question carefully to identify key words and numbers (underlining or highlighting can help).
- Decide what operation(s) will need to be done.
- Estimate the answer.
- Decide which method of accurate calculation is required.
- Check to see that the answer makes sense and is correct.

Ask the children to complete the calculation from the question above. Check the answer and discuss the strategies used.

Then write up this next part of the problem:

The roses at the garden centre cost £5.95 each. Jayne buys five of them – three pink and two yellow. How much change does she get from £30?

Ask the children to solve the problem, reminding them to follow the steps above.

Progress check: Notice children's different calculation strategies. Some may need to use written methods; others may do the calculations mentally.

Check their answers and make sure that they have answered the question, which was *How much change does she get from £30?* Discuss the importance of re-reading the question to confirm what answer is required.

Group work: Provide the children with photocopiable page 'Solve these (1)' from the CD-ROM which gives practice in solving real-life problems.

Progress check: Stop the children after the first three questions to ensure they are identifying the necessary calculations.

Group work: As they complete the sheet, encourage the children to notice and talk about any patterns and relationships.

Review

Choose one or two questions from the photocopiable sheet to solve together. Go over the strategies that the children used.

Curriculum objectives
● To solve addition and subtraction problems in context, deciding which operations and methods to use and why.

Success criteria
● I can solve problems involving money and decide which operations and methods to use.

You will need
Photocopiable sheets
'Solve these (2)'
Equipment
Individual whiteboards

Differentiation
Less confident learners
Provide support to help children convert the word problems into numerical calculations.
More confident learners
Adapt 'Solve these (2)' to offer more complex problems.

Lesson 4 — Oral and mental starter 33

Main teaching activities

Whole-class work: Give the children this problem: *Grant is planning his eleventh birthday party. He has this menu to choose from. What is the difference in price between the cheapest and most expensive item?*

- Pizzas £54.40
- Burgers £40.88
- Sandwiches £43.92
- Chicken pieces £58.56
- Spaghetti £47.76

Grant decides to buy chicken and spaghetti. How much does it cost? What change does he get from £110? Ask the children, working in pairs, to calculate the answers on their whiteboards. Share answers. Could any part be done mentally? For instance, the last question required subtracting £106.32 from £110. This can be done mentally by counting up. Choose one part of the question for a volunteer to work out on the board. Ask the rest of the class to check the answer by using the inverse operation.

Then ask the next question: *Grant's mum decides to add one more item to his choice. The food now costs £147.20. Which extra item did she buy?* Ask the children, again in pairs, to complete the calculation and feed back.

Group work: Provide the children with photocopiable page 'Solve these (2)' from the CD-ROM. Advise the children that they need to choose the most efficient method to use (mental or written).

Progress check: Remind the children to estimate an answer first and then check their answer afterwards for reasonableness.

Review
Choose one or two of the problems from the photocopiable sheet to discuss and solve.

Curriculum objectives
● To solve addition and subtraction problems in contexts, deciding which operations and methods to use and why.

Success criteria
● I know how to solve real-life addition and subtraction problems.

You will need
Photocopiable sheets
'Goals galore'
Equipment
Individual whiteboards

Differentiation
Less confident learners
Children may need support to help them choose the best strategies to use.
More confident learners
Suggest that children research and compare local team results.

Lesson 5 — Oral and mental starter 34

Main teaching activities

Whole-class work: Remind the children of the strategies they have for adding and subtracting mentally.

Tell the children that they are going to complete an activity about football. Ask if they know the term 'goal difference' and elicit that it is the difference between the goals scored 'for' a team and the goals scored 'against' it. For example: Anytown United scored 93 goals and had 76 scored against it, so, what is the goal difference? (17.) Luckytown Rovers scored 57 goals, but had 73 scored against it. What is their goal difference? (−16.) Note that in this instance the answer is negative because Luckytown conceded more goals than it scored.

Independent work: Give each child photocopiable page 'Goals galore' from the CD-ROM and ask them to complete the goal difference table.

Progress check: Monitor the children as they work and ask which teams have negative goal differences. Check that the children are clear about why they are negative.

Review
Go through the photocopiable sheet together. Encourage the children to discuss any difficulties they encountered. Then ask the children to work out as quickly as they can the total number of goals scored by all of the teams (the sum of the 'goals for' column). (410.)

Briefly recap on the week. They should be able to use and choose mental and written methods of calculation; know how to use the inverse operation, especially for checking; and understand the importance of setting out calculations accurately, especially with decimal points.

SCHOLASTIC

Multiplication and division

Expected prior learning

Children should be able to:

- identify multiples, including common multiples, and factors, including common factors
- multiply and divide numbers mentally
- multiply and divide numbers by 10, 100 and 1000
- recognise and use square numbers and square roots.

Topic	Curriculum objectives	Expected outcomes
Multiplication and division	**Lesson 1**	
	To perform mental calculations, including with mixed operations and large numbers. To identify common factors, common multiples and prime numbers.	Use prime factors to aid multiplication.
	Lesson 2	
	To perform mental calculations, including with mixed operations and large numbers. To identify common factors, common multiples and prime numbers.	Use prime factors to aid division.
	Lesson 3	
	To identify common factors, common multiples and prime numbers. To use estimation to check answers to calculations and determine, in the context of a problem, an appropriate degree of accuracy.	Use tests of divisibility and approximations to check answers to calculations.
	Lesson 4	
	To use their knowledge of the order of operations to carry out calculations involving the four operations. To use estimation to check answers to calculations and determine, in the context of a problem, an appropriate degree of accuracy.	Calculate using all four operations. Estimate to predict or check answers.
	Lesson 5	
	To use their knowledge of the order of operations to carry out calculations involving the four operations.	Solve word problems that involve all four operations.

Preparation

Lessons 1 and 2: write appropriate calculations on the board

Lesson 3: copy 'Check it!' for each child

Lesson 4: enlarge 'How many rolls?' or have it available on the whiteboard; prepare a copy for each child

Lesson 5: copy 'Shelf fit' for each child

You will need

Photocopiable sheets
'Check it!'; 'How many rolls?'; 'Shelf fit'

General resources
Interactive activity 'Prime time'

Equipment
Individual whiteboards

Further practice

Photocopiable sheets
'Sponsored walk'

Oral and mental starters suggested for week 3

See the bank of starters on pages 125, 126 and 164. Oral and mental starters are also on the CD-ROM.

31 Multiplication rounds

32 Venn division

35 Factors

43 Target 100

Overview of progression

At the start of the week children revisit prime factors and look at how they can use prime factors to help them solve multiplication and division problems. The children then look at approximation and tests of divisibility. The final two lessons include practical problems involving all four operations and encouraging the children to use different methods to check their answers.

> ### Watch out for
>
> Check that children are sure about the difference between a factor and a multiple, and when they are finding factors check that they have the correct power, for example 16 is 2^4. Make sure that the children read problem texts carefully to find out what is being asked.

Creative context

The final lessons of the week involve redecorating a room and building furniture, so this can be linked with computer design programs and be developed in art and design and design and technology lessons.

Vocabulary

approximate, division, estimate, factor, inverse, method, multiple, operation, power, prime number, problem, solution, square number, strategy

Curriculum objectives
● To perform mental calculations, including with large numbers.
● To identify factors.

Success criteria
● I can use prime factors to help with multiplication calculations.

You will need

General resources
Interactive activity 'Prime time'

Equipment
Individual whiteboards

Differentiation

Less confident learners
Provide adult support to help children find the prime factors of the multiplier.

More confident learners
Encourage children to extend the activity to multiplying three-digit numbers by two-digit numbers.

Lesson 1 — Oral and mental starter 35

Main teaching activities

Whole-class work: First, have a quick recap of the children's knowledge and understanding of factors. Ask the children: *Who can tell me what factors are? What are the factors of 6?*

Then write the calculation 16 × 12 on the board. Ask: *How can factors be used to help make this multiplication easier?* Look at factors of 12 first. Ask the children to give you the pairs of factors of 12, and establish with them that the problem could be broken down into: 16 × 2 × 6, or 16 × 3 × 4. Ask the children to work out the answer and then identify which way they found most straightforward. Then look at ways of factorising the 16 as well. Try: 8 × 2 × 3 × 4, or 4 × 4 × 2 × 6. Again, discuss the most efficient method.

Explain to the children that prime factors are prime numbers that divide exactly into the number. Show the interactive activity 'Prime time' on the CD-ROM and work through it as a class.

Move on to show how you could use prime factors to help you multiply, for example, 36 × 18. Find the prime factors of 18 (2 and 3^2). So: 36 × 3 = 108, then 108 × 3 = 324, then 324 × 2 = 628.

Repeat for 25 × 28. The prime factors of 28 are 2^2 and 7. So: 25 × 7 = 175, then 175 × 2 = 350, then 350 × 2 = 700.

Paired work: Organise the children to work on their whiteboards in pairs to use prime factors to find 42 × 32 and then 21 × 56.

Progress check: Go though the two examples with the children and discuss how they reached their answers.

Independent work: Write on the board more examples involving the use of factors in multiplication calculations. Ask the children to work these out individually. Tell them that they should use the factors they feel are most suitable. Examples to try might include: 16 × 8 (128), 19 × 12 (228), 20 × 24 (480), 28 × 14 (392), 45 × 30 (1350).

Review

Ask the children:

- *Which prime numbers are greater than 30 but less than 50?* (31, 37, 41, 43, 47.)
- *Can you tell me why 81 is not prime number?* (81 is divisible by 3 and 9, so is not a prime number.)
- *What are the prime factors of 64? How can we use this information to multiply 35 by 64?* (The prime factors of 64 are 2^6 (2 × 2 × 2 × 2 × 2 × 2). So, 35 × 2 = 70; 70 × 2 = 140; 140 × 2 = 280; 280 × 2 = 560; 560 × 2 = 1120; 1120 × 2 = 2240.)

Curriculum objectives
- To perform mental calculations, including with large numbers.
- To identify factors.

Success criteria
- I can use prime factors to help me with division calculations.

You will need

Equipment

Individual whiteboards

Differentiation

Less confident learners

Again, provide adult support to help children find the prime factors.

More confident learners

Ask children to challenge each other with more complex division problems using bigger numbers.

Lesson 2

Main teaching activities

Whole-class work: Refer to the previous lesson and remind the children that they were using prime factors to help them solve multiplication calculations. Explain to the children that they will now be using prime factors to help them solve *division* problems.

First, ask them to find the prime factors of 18 (2 and 3^2). Then show them how they could use this information to divide 288 by 18: $288 \div 2 = 144$; $144 \div 3 = 48$; $48 \div 3 = 16$. (Some children may be able to miss a step and divide 144 by 9 to get 16.)

Independent work: As with the multiplication questions, write up on the board some examples showing the use of factors in division calculations. Ask the children to work these out individually, writing the answers on their whiteboards. Advise them again that they should use the factors they feel are most suitable. Examples to try could include: $112 \div 14$ (8), $324 \div 36$ (9), $432 \div 18$ (24), $456 \div 24$ (19), $570 \div 15$ (38).

Progress check: Stop the children after a short while and ask them to go through the first one or two problems with you. Encourage the children to explain how they worked out their answers.

Then give the children some further examples with a four-digit number divided by a two-digit number. Use examples such as $1449 \div 21$ (69), $1608 \div 24$ (67), $2106 \div 39$ (54).

Review

Play a game in which the children have to spot the odd one out in a list of factors. For example, if the factors of 21 were given as 1, 3, 4, 7 and 21, then 4 would be the odd one out because 21 does not come in the 4-times table. Or, leave out a factor and ask the children to tell you which one is missing. For example, if the factors of 24 are given as 1, 2, 3, 4, 6, 12 and 24, then the missing factor would be 8. Ensure that the children understand the difference between the terms *multiple* and *factor*. Elicit that the multiples of 9, for example, are 9, 18, 27, 36... while the factors of 9 are 1, 3 and 9.

Curriculum objectives

- To perform mental calculations, including with large numbers.
- To use estimation to check answers to calculations and determine levels of accuracy.

Success criteria

- I can use tests of divisibility and approximation to check answers.

You will need

Photocopiable sheets

'Check it!'

Equipment

Individual whiteboards

Differentiation

Less confident learners

Let children work in a group with some support to decide which strategies to use.

More confident learners

When children have completed 'Check it!', suggest they devise their own questions for each other using real-life situations.

Lesson 3
Oral and mental starter

Main teaching activities

Whole-class work: Tell the children that you will be looking at ways to check calculations. Ask them for suggestions. Note their ideas and establish that one helpful way is to approximate the numbers as they would do when estimating. Encourage the children to tell you how they would estimate 3926 × 7 (27482). For example: 4000 × 7 = 28000. Then try: 6291 × 49 (308,259). The most likely way is 6000 × 50 = 300,000). Point out that, although this is 8,259 less than the correct answer, it could still be considered a reasonable approximation. Do the children agree?

Paired work: Organise the children into pairs and ask them to write on their whiteboards the tests for divisibility that they can remember for 2, 3, 4 and 5:

- A number is divisible by 2 if it is even.
- A number is divisible by 3 if the sum of its digits is a multiple of 3.
- A number is divisible by 4 if its last two digits are divisible by 4.
- A number is divisible by 5 if it ends in a 5 or 0.

Progress check: Ask the children for the tests they have remembered and check that they are correct. Now ask them to use these to find tests for divisibility for 6, 8, 9 and 10. You are looking for:

- A number is divisible by 6 if it is even and divisible by 3.
- A number is divisible by 8 if half of it is divisible by 4, or, with larger numbers, if the number made by the last three digits is divisible by 4.
- A number is divisible by 9 if the sum of its digits is divisible by 9.
- A number is divisible by 10 if it ends in 0.

Explain to the children that these tests of divisibility can be used to check calculations and also to help in identifying prime factors.

Independent work: Give out photocopiable page 'Check it!' from the CD-ROM. Advise the children that they need to use the tests of divisibility, and approximations, to find the answers to the questions.

Progress check: After the children have had time to complete the first one or two questions on the photocopiable sheet, visit them, particularly those you wish to assess, and ask what approximations they have used. Discuss which they think are the most suitable.

Review

Ask the children the following:

- Is 362 divisible by 4? (No.) What about 932? (Yes, 233.)
- Is 271 divisible by 3? (No.) What about 507? (Yes, 169.)
- Was 2008 a leap year? How do you know? (2008 can be divided exactly by 4 – to give 502 – so it is a leap year, as a leap year happens every 4 years.)
- Is 8244 divisible by 9? (Yes, 916.)

Curriculum objectives
● To use knowledge of the order of operations to carry out calculations involving the four operations.
● To use estimation to check answers and determine levels of accuracy.

Success criteria
● I can carry out calculations using all four operations.
● I can estimate to predict or check my answers.

You will need
Photocopiable sheets
'How many rolls?'
Equipment
Individual whiteboards

Differentiation
Less confident learners
Adapt 'How many rolls?' with simpler numbers.
More confident learners
Children can plan for rooms with different dimensions or more expensive wallpaper.

Lesson 4
Oral and mental starter 31

Main teaching activities

Whole-class work: Ask the children to recall some of the strategies they have been using so far this week: finding prime factors, doubling, halving, approximating and testing for divisibility.

Tell them that the next two lessons are about redecorating a room. Discuss what might need to be done, such as wallpapering, changing the carpets, fitting cupboards. Consider the measurements they would need to take and how they would calculate the quantities. Point out that when costing this type of project people often approximate before making their final purchases.

Display the table from the photocopiable page 'How many rolls' from the CD-ROM. Explain that it will help them to calculate how many rolls of wallpaper would be needed. Simplifying the numbers to estimate, ask the children to recall how to calculate the perimeter of a rectangular room which is 2.5m wide by 3m long: $(2.5 \times 2) + (3 \times 2) = 11$m. Say that the height of the walls is 2.5m, and ask the children to look along the table to see how many rolls of paper will be needed (6).

Independent work: Ask the children to work on the photocopiable sheet to calculate and cost the amount of wallpaper needed for that room. Remind them to approximate first.

Progress check: Stop the children to check that they have been approximating before calculating the final cost.

Review

Check the children's estimates and actual calculations. Were the approximations accurate enough to buy the correct amount of wallpaper?

Curriculum objectives
● To use their knowledge of the order of operations to carry out calculations involving the four operations.

Success criteria
● I can solve problems using all four operations.

You will need
Photocopiable sheets
'Shelf fit'
Equipment
Individual whiteboards

Differentiation
Less confident learners
Suggest the children work with just the one-metre lengths of timber.
More confident learners
Encourage children to cost their own designs.

Lesson 5
Oral and mental starter 31

Main teaching activities

Whole-class work: Tell the children that this lesson continues from the previous one. Discuss with the children what furniture they may want in the newly wallpapered bedroom; perhaps fitted wardrobes, built-in cupboards or fixed wall-shelves. Explain that for this lesson they will be thinking first about putting wooden shelves into the room. Explain that timber suitable for shelving comes in various lengths and qualities. Sometimes it is easier to use several shorter lengths and cut off any surplus, or it may be possible, and probably cheaper, to buy fewer longer lengths and cut them to size.

Independent work: Explain to the children that you want them to calculate the cost of shelves using photocopiable page 'Shelf fit' from the CD-ROM.

Progress check: Stop the children after the first part of the sheet and ask how well they are doing. Check their understanding that the timber comes in different lengths but is priced by the metre. Ask them what the cost of a 3m length of timber would be. ($£4.95 \times 3 = £14.85$.)

Independent work: If there is time once the children have completed the photocopiable sheet, let them design their own shelf unit for the bedroom, listing and pricing the wood they need.

Review

Check answers to the photocopiable sheet. Invite volunteers to explain what strategies they used. Ask the children to show their designs for the shelf unit. Discuss what timber might be needed as well as shelves. (Side panels and a back panel, for example.)

■SCHOLASTIC

Calculating with fractions

Expected prior learning

Children should be able to:

- recognise and find equivalent fractions
- add and subtract fractions with the same denominator
- multiply simple fractions by whole numbers.

Topic	Curriculum objectives	Expected outcomes
Fractions (including decimals and percentages)	**Lesson 1**	
	To add and subtract fractions with different denominators and mixed numbers, using the concept of equivalent fractions.	Use the concept of equivalent fractions to add fractions with different denominators.
	Lesson 2	
	To add and subtract fractions with different denominators and mixed numbers, using the concept of equivalent fractions.	Use the concept of equivalent fractions to add and subtract fractions with different denominators. Find lowest common denominators.
	Lesson 3	
	To multiply simple pairs of proper fractions, writing the answer in its simplest form.	Multiply pairs of proper fractions.
	Lesson 4	
	To associate a fraction with division and calculate decimal fraction equivalents for a simple fraction.	Calculate the decimal equivalent of a fraction.
	Lesson 5	
	To divide proper fractions by whole numbers.	Divide proper fractions by whole numbers and relate this to equivalent fractions.

Preparation

Lessons 1 and 2: make a set of fraction cards for each pair using 'Fraction cards' o; enlarge one set of fraction cards; copy 'Fraction wall' for support

Lessons 3 and 5: copy an enlarged copy of 'Fraction wall' or have it available from the CD-ROM; make a set of fraction cards for each pair

Lesson 5: put up displays showing pictures of pizza, cakes, or similar, in parts

You will need

General resources
'Fraction cards'; 'Fraction wall'

Equipment
Individual whiteboards; dice; fraction boards, fractions blocks or similar; calculators

Further practice

Photocopiable sheets
'Fraction calculations'

Oral and mental starters suggested for week 4

See the bank of starters on pages 125 and 126. Oral and mental starters are also on the CD-ROM.

31 Multiplication rounds

32 Venn division

35 Factors

Overview of progression

At the start of the week children will revise adding fractions with the same denominator. They will then start to add fractions with different denominators by finding equivalent fractions leading to finding the lowest common denominator. They move on to learning to multiply simple pairs of fractions. They will investigate the decimal equivalents of fractions and will go on to divide fractions by whole numbers.

Watch out for

Children may confuse the numerator with the denominator. Make sure they are clear: the denominator is the number of parts to make the whole, and the numerator is the number of those parts. Some children are often confused that multiplying pairs of fractions gives a smaller fraction, as they expect multiplication to make things larger. Point out that, if we are multiplying by a number less than 1, then the result will be smaller. Similarly, when dividing fractions by a whole number, children are sometimes confused by the fact that they have to multiply the denominator.

Creative context

Encourage the children to talk about real-life contexts when we may be calculating with fractions. Think about examples using cake-cutting, for instance, for equal sharing.

Vocabulary

decimal fraction, denominator, equivalent fraction, fraction, **lowest common denominator**, numerator, **product**

Curriculum objectives

● To add fractions with different denominators, using the concept of equivalent fractions.

Success criteria

● I can add fractions with different denominators.

You will need

General resources

'Fraction cards'; 'Fraction wall'

Equipment

Individual whiteboards; fraction blocks or similar

Differentiation

Less confident learners

Limit the fraction cards given to this group and support them with concrete materials such as fraction blocks and 'Fraction wall', and also help them to use diagrams.

More confident learners

Encourage children to add more than two fractions with different denominators.

Lesson 1   Oral and mental starter 35

Main teaching activities

Whole-class work: Remind the children that they have already started to learn to add fractions, and now they will learn how to add and subtract fractions with different denominators. Recall that the denominator is the number of parts that make the whole.

Ask the children to find the sum of $\frac{1}{8} + \frac{3}{8} + \frac{1}{8}$. Elicit that, as the denominator is the same for all three fractions, they just need to add together the numerators, hence the total is $\frac{5}{8}$ ($1 + 3 + 1$).

Now ask the children to add $\frac{1}{4}$ and $\frac{1}{2}$. They will undoubtedly tell you $\frac{3}{4}$! Point out that this means they have changed the half to its equivalent fraction $\frac{2}{4}$ and added it to one quarter, and hence the total is three-quarters.

Establish that, therefore, in order to add or subtract fractions, the fractions need to have the same denominator. Ask the children to total $\frac{1}{3}$ and $\frac{1}{6}$. Elicit that an equivalent fraction for $\frac{1}{3}$ is $\frac{2}{6}$, hence you can add together $\frac{2}{6}$ and $\frac{1}{6}$ to get $\frac{3}{6}$, which can then be simplified to $\frac{1}{2}$.

Paired work: Give each pair of children a set of fraction cards (you can use 'Fraction cards' from the CD-ROM). Explain that each child should select a fraction card and then they should independently calculate the sum of the two fractions before comparing answers. Ask them to repeat the exercise with another two cards, and so on.

Progress check: Pause the children after a few minutes and check their answers. Ask them to look at $\frac{1}{2} + \frac{1}{3}$. Ask what equivalent fractions they used to calculate this: $\frac{3}{6} + \frac{2}{6}$ (= $\frac{5}{6}$). Check if they understand that to find a common denominator for these two fractions they must find the lowest number with factors 2 and 3 (6).

Review

Ask the children if there were any fractions they found difficult to add. If so, encourage a class discussion on how to find a common denominator.

Ask two volunteers to come out to the front and select a fraction card each from your enlarged set. Write them on the board and ask the children to find a common denominator. Point out that one way of finding the common denominator is to find the product of the numbers and them simplify it if necessary. For example: if the fractions chosen were $\frac{1}{6}$ and $\frac{3}{8}$, they could multiply 6 and 8 to get 48; they could then halve this to 24 as 6 and 8 are both factors of 24. Hence 24 is the lowest common denominator.

Curriculum objectives
● To add and subtract fractions with different denominators, using the concept of equivalent fractions.

Success criteria
● I can add and subtract fractions with different denominators.
● I can find the lowest common denominator of fractions.

You will need

General resources
'Fraction cards'; 'Fraction wall'

Equipment
Individual whiteboards; fraction blocks or similar

Differentiation

Less confident learners
Limit the fraction cards children work with, and encourage them to use fraction blocks to convert the fractions to equivalent fractions and refer to 'Fraction wall'.

More confident learners
Challenge children with a wider range of fractions.

Lesson 2

Oral and mental starter 32

Main teaching activities

Whole-class work: Remind the children that in the previous lesson they were adding fractions with the same denominator and also fractions where they could find equivalent fractions with the same denominator. Tell them that they will now be adding and subtracting fractions with different denominators.

Ask the children how they could subtract $\frac{1}{4}$ from $\frac{1}{3}$. Elicit that to find equivalent fractions with the same denominator they need to find a common denominator. Prompt them to explain that to do this they need to find a number divisible by both 3 and 4. Identify that the lowest number divisible by both 3 and 4 is 12, so this is the lowest common denominator. The fraction with the denominator 12 that is equivalent to $\frac{1}{4}$ is $\frac{3}{12}$ and that equivalent to $\frac{1}{3}$ is $\frac{4}{12}$. (Explain that, as we have multiplied the denominator by 3, we must also multiply the numerator by 3. So, we can subtract $\frac{3}{12}$ from $\frac{4}{12}$ to get $\frac{1}{12}$.)

Paired work: As in lesson 1, give each pair of children a set of fraction cards. Again, they should take one each and independently calculate the difference between the two fractions, before comparing answers. Ask them to continue with another two cards, and so on.

Progress check: Pause the children after a few calculations, and ask if they are encountering any particular difficulties. Ask them how they could use the same method to find the difference between, for example, $\frac{1}{4}$ and $\frac{1}{5}$. Explain that this would be $\frac{5}{20} - \frac{4}{20}$ which is equal to $\frac{1}{20}$.

Review

Ask two children to come out to the front and select a fraction card each from your enlarged set. Write them on the board and ask the children to find the lowest common denominator. Remind the children that one way of finding the lowest common denominator is to find the product of the numbers and then simplify it if necessary.

Now write $\frac{3}{8} - \frac{1}{6}$ on the board and ask the children to work out the difference. Check that they have found the lowest common denominator as 24 by finding the product of 8 and 6 as 48 and then reducing it to 24 and hence $\frac{9}{24} - \frac{4}{24} = \frac{5}{24}$. Point out that this can be written as: $\frac{3}{8} - \frac{1}{6} = \frac{9}{24} - \frac{4}{24} = \frac{5}{24}$.

Curriculum objectives

● To multiply simple pairs of proper fractions, writing the answer in its simplest form.

Success criteria

● I can multiply simple pairs of fractions.

You will need

General resources

'Fraction cards'; 'Fraction wall'

Equipment

Individual whiteboards; fraction blocks or similar

Differentiation

Less confident learners

Children may need the support of a teaching assistant to ensure that they are applying the strategy correctly.

More confident learners

Encourage children to progress to multiplying three fractions together.

Lesson 3
Oral and mental starter 31

Main teaching activities

Whole-class work: Tell the children that in this lesson they will move on to multiplying fractions. Display photocopiable page 'Fraction wall' from the CD-ROM. Ask: *What is ½ of ¼?* They will probably respond with ⅛. Show this on the fraction wall and use fraction blocks or similar to confirm it visually. Invite a volunteer to write the calculation on the board, as ½ × ¼ = ⅛.

Explain that when we multiply fractions we multiply both the numerators and the denominators. Demonstrate how to multiply ¾ by ¼: 3 × 1 = 3 and 4 × 4 = 16, giving ³⁄₁₆.

Paired work: Give each pair a set of fraction cards to select pairs of fractions as before. Remind them to work independently, this time to calculate the product of the two fractions, before comparing answers.

Progress check: Remind the children that they should be multiplying the numerators together and then the denominators. Prompt them to check for answer fractions that can be reduced to a simpler form, such as ³⁄₁₂ to ¼.

Review

Ask the children to find the product of ¼ × ¼. (¹⁄₁₆.) Work through any difficulties or misconceptions that the children encountered in the paired work. Then ask the children to find the product of ³⁄₁₆ and ⅔. Invite a volunteer to demonstrate: 3 × 2 = 6 and 16 × 3 = 48, giving ⁶⁄₄₈. Prompt the children to notice that this can be simplified to ⅛.

Curriculum objectives

● To associate a fraction with division to calculate decimal fraction equivalents for a simple fraction.

Success criteria

● I can calculate the decimal equivalent of a fraction.

You will need

General resources

'Fraction cards'

Equipment

Individual whiteboards; calculators

Differentiation

Less confident learners

Limit the range of fraction cards for this group, and avoid them having fractions which will give an infinite decimal equivalent unless they have some support.

More confident learners

Ask children to challenge their partners with more complex fractions, including mixed fractions.

Lesson 4
Oral and mental starter 31

Main teaching activities

Whole-class work: Tell the children that now they are looking at division. Explain that, if you want to convert a fraction to a decimal, you need to divide the numerator by the denominator. So, if we want to convert ½ to a decimal, we divide 1 by 2 (= 0.5). Ask the children to convert ⅕ to a decimal fraction. Elicit: dividing 1 by 5 (= 0.2).

Ask the children what the decimal equivalent of ⅜ is. Recall that they must divide 3 by 8 hence ⅜ = 0.375. You could use a calculator to check the answer.

Now find the decimal equivalent of ⅔. Explain that, if necessary, they should round to three decimal places. Look for the answer 0.667, noting that this is an infinite decimal equivalent: 0.666 recurring.

Paired work: Ask the pairs to select fraction cards as before, but this time, one child should calculate the decimal equivalent as near as they can, and their partner should check the answer on a calculator. Then they should reverse roles.

Progress check: Stop the children after a few turns each, and ask them to tell you some of their answers. See if any of them needed to round any answers, and check that they have understood when it is necessary to round the answer.

Review

Invite the children to share some of their answers with the class and explain how they calculated the decimal equivalents. Ask: *What is the decimal equivalent of ⅝?* Elicit that this would be 5 divided by 8 (0.625). Ask children to challenge the class with similar questions.

Curriculum objectives
- To divide proper fractions by whole numbers.

Success criteria
- I can divide proper fractions by whole numbers.

You will need

General resources
'Fraction cards'; 'Fraction wall'

Equipment
Individual whiteboards; dice; pictures of divided pizzas or similar; fraction blocks and fraction boards or similar

Differentiation

Less confident learners
Limit children to using simple fractions and a limited number of whole number divisors, such as 2, 3 and 4. Provide access to fraction boards, fraction blocks and similar materials.

More confident learners
Give children more complex fractions and ask them to draw diagrams to represent their calculations.

Lesson 5
Oral and mental starter **31**

Main teaching activities

Whole-class work: Tell the children that in this final lesson they will be dividing fractions by whole numbers.

Show a picture of half a pizza, and demonstrate that when this half is divided by 2, you are left with $\frac{1}{4}$. Tell the children that you want to divide this $\frac{1}{4}$ into 4. How would they do it? Explain that $\frac{1}{4} \div 4$ can be calculated by *multiplying* just the denominator of the fraction by the whole number. Hence: $\frac{1}{4} \div 4$ is: $\frac{1}{4 \times 4} = \frac{1}{16}$.

Use photocopiable page 'Fraction wall' or a similar resource to check the answer, looking at equivalent fractions. Demonstrate that $\frac{4}{16}$ is equivalent to $\frac{1}{4}$. Look at $\frac{1}{4}$ on the fraction wall and look down to the sixteenths to show that one-quarter is four-sixteenths.

Demonstrate with another example: $\frac{3}{4} \div 3$ (which the children should be able to tell you is $\frac{1}{4}$) can be written as $\frac{3}{4 \times 4} = \frac{3}{12}$. Again, refer to fraction display materials to show this. Ask the children to tell you whether or not the calculation is quite complete. Elicit that the answer $\frac{3}{12}$ can be reduced to its simplest form, $\frac{1}{4}$.

Paired work: For this game, the children will need a set of fraction cards and a dice per pair. Explain that one child in the pair should select a fraction card and the other child should roll the dice. They should then agree on how to divide the fraction shown on the card by the whole number shown on the dice. Tell them then to swap roles in terms of taking a card or throwing the dice. Ask them to record their calculations each time.

Progress check: Pause the children after they have had the opportunity to do two or three calculations. Check that the children are clear about multiplying the denominator by the whole number.

Review

Ask some pairs to share their calculations with the class.

Challenge the children to work out $\frac{1}{5} \div 5$ ($\frac{1}{25}$). Point out that the equivalent fraction for $\frac{1}{5}$ is $\frac{5}{25}$, hence $\frac{5}{25}$ divided by 5 is $\frac{1}{25}$. Give them another example, such as $\frac{3}{8} \div 2$ ($\frac{3}{16}$).

Reflections and translations on coordinate axes

Expected prior learning

Children should be able to:

- use reflection and translation in a variety of diagrams
- use a 2D grid and coordinates in the first quadrant
- be able to use reflection in a line parallel to the axes.

Topic	Curriculum objectives	Expected outcomes
Geometry: position and direction	**Lesson 1**	
	To describe positions on the full coordinate grid (all four quadrants).	Draw and label axes. Place points in all four quadrants.
	Lesson 2	
	To describe positions on the full coordinate grid (all four quadrants).	Describe positions on the full coordinate grid. Calculate measurements between different points.
	Lesson 3	
	To draw and translate simple shapes on the coordinate plane, and reflect them in the axes.	Draw and reflect shapes on the coordinate plane and reflect them in the axes.
	Lesson 4	
	To draw and translate simple shapes on the coordinate plane, and reflect them in the axes.	Draw and translate shapes on the coordinate plane.
	Lesson 5	
	To draw and translate simple shapes on the coordinate plane, and reflect them in the axes.	Draw and translate shapes on the coordinate plane, using all four quadrants.

Preparation

Lesson 1: draw a blank grid showing the first quadrant for display; prepare a second version with the examples drawn on

Lessons 1–5: draw a second grid showing all four quadrants, with x-axes labelled from −10 to 10 and y-axes from 10 to −10; draw another version with the shapes drawn at the coordinates given

You will need

General resources

'Grids'

Equipment

Individual whiteboards; grid paper

Further practice

Photocopiable sheets

'Mirror image'

Oral and mental starters suggested for week 5

See the bank of starters on pages 126 and 165. Oral and mental starters are also on the CD-ROM.

37 Coordinate square practice

39 Pentominoes

53 Get the point

Overview of progression

At the start of the week the children will use their knowledge of coordinates in one quadrant to extend to all four quadrants, which will include the use of negative numbers. The children will then be drawing simple shapes on the coordinate plane and reflect them in the axes.

Watch out for

Make sure that the children are clear about which axis is which and that they write the coordinates (x,y). Check too that they write the x coordinate first, even for negative coordinates.

Creative context

To link with art and design work, give children the opportunity to investigate textile designs, particularly in eastern-influenced fabrics and ceramics, which use translated and reflected patterns and shapes. Encourage the children to create their own similar designs.

Vocabulary

axes, coordinate, origin, **quadrant**, **reflection**, **rotation**, translation, x axis, y axis

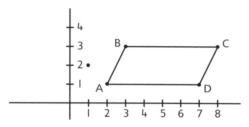

Curriculum objectives

● To describe positions on the full coordinate grid (all four quadrants).

Success criteria

● I can draw and label axes.
● I can plot the positions of points in all four quadrants.

You will need

General resources

'Grids'

Equipment

Individual whiteboards

Differentiation

Less confident learners

Ask children to work within one quadrant at a time, and give them suggestions about what shape to draw (square, rectangle, parallelogram and so on).

More confident learners

Encourage children to draw more complex shapes, including those which cross the axes.

Lesson 1 — Oral and mental starter 37

Main teaching activities

Whole-class work: Display grid A from photocopiable page 'Grids' from the CD-ROM. Ask the children which is the x-axis and which is the y-axis. Recap important vocabulary, ensuring that the children are fully conversant with x-axis, y-axis, quadrant and origin.

Tell the children that you are going to label the axes on the grid. Ask them to tell you where you should start. Elicit: at the origin, which is where the two axes meet. Establish that this is the point (0,0). Use this to recall that a point on the grid can be identified by its coordinates, the two numbers used to pinpoint the position. Discuss that coordinates tell us how many steps across and how many steps up or down from the origin a point is. Show the children that coordinates are written in brackets and that the x-coordinate (referring to the x-axis) is always written first. Point to different points on the grid and ask the children what the coordinates are. Now show the grid with this parallelogram drawn on labelled A, B, C, D:

Point to position A on the grid and ask the children for the coordinates (2,1). Check that they recall how to write down pairs of coordinates, including that the numbers are enclosed in brackets. Ask for the coordinates of each other points.

Paired work: Organise the children to work in pairs on grid paper. Explain that one child should draw a simple shape, without showing their partner, and then tell their partner the coordinates for them to draw the shape. Ask them to compare their shapes before they swap roles.

Whole-class work: Now display the second grid, which illustrates all four quadrants. Explain the numbering of each quadrant (first is top-right, second is top-left, third is bottom-left and fourth is bottom-right.) Ask the children to help you label the x- and y-axes, establishing that the x-axis in the second and third quadrant and the y-axis in the third and fourth quadrants will have negative numbers. Fill in the axes labels. Draw a parallelogram in the second quadrant and ask the children for the coordinates:

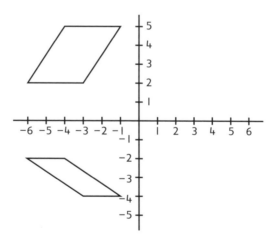

Check that the children understand that the x-coordinate will be negative. Repeat for the third and fourth quadrants.

Paired work: Let the children carry on with the activity begun above, but this time drawing shapes with coordinates using all four quadrants.

Progress check: Visit the pairs as they work, particularly those you wish to assess. Check that the children are labelling the coordinates correctly.

Review

Ask one pair to challenge the class with one of their shapes, then ask another pair to challenge the class with their most interesting shape. Discuss any difficulties, making sure that the children are clear about using coordinates with negative numbers.

Curriculum objectives
● To describe positions on the full coordinate grid (all four quadrants).

Success criteria
● I can describe positions on the full coordinate grid.
● I can understand measurements between different points on the grid.

You will need

Equipment
Individual whiteboards; grid paper

Differentiation

Less confident learners
Ask children to concentrate on drawing the shape in only one position.

More confident learners
Expect children to draw all four possible positions for the shape.

Lesson 2   Oral and mental starter 39

Main teaching activities

Whole-class work: Briefly recap the previous lesson. Then display the four-quadrant grid, with a rectangle drawn with the points A (−5,3), B (8,3), C (−5,−4) and D (8,−4), *without* labelling the coordinates. Ask the children to write the coordinates of each point on their whiteboards. Check these, then ask: *What is the length of side AB?* (13 units.) Confirm with the children that you don't know what the units are. Ask: *What is the length of CD?* (13 units.) Check that the children realise that this is the same as AB. Ask the children for the length of AC (7 units), and BD (also 7).

Independent work: Provide grid paper and tell the children that you want them to draw the following shapes:

- a square with sides of 6 units, with one coordinate (1,−5)
- a rectangle with sides of 3 and 8 units, with one coordinate (−3,6).

Progress check: Ask the children to show their work. Have they all drawn the square in the same position? Check that they understand that the coordinates given could be any one of the four corners of the shape.

Paired work: Ask the children to put similar shape-drawing challenges to their partners. Stress that each child should draw the shape independently and then compare them. Encourage them to discuss any differences.

Review

Invite children to give the coordinates of the rectangle they drew in the independent work. Ask a confident child to draw it on the grid on the board. If the children do not suggest all four positions for the rectangle, elicit the information from them to demonstrate all four possibilities.

Curriculum objectives
● To draw and translate simple shapes on the coordinate plane, and reflect them in the axes.

Success criteria
● I can draw shapes on the coordinate plane and reflect them in the axes.

You will need

Equipment
Individual whiteboards; grid paper

Differentiation

Less confident learners
Children may need the support of a teaching assistant. Make sure that they are clear about what a reflection is.

More confident learners
Ask children to continue the activity by suggesting another shape and reflecting that in the same way.

Lesson 3   Oral and mental starter 37

Main teaching activities

Whole-class work: Display the four-quadrant grid with an isosceles triangle drawn at A (2,2), B (5,7) and C (8,2). Tell the children that it is an isosceles triangle. Give them the coordinates of A and B, and ask them for the coordinates of C. Ask a volunteer to demonstrate how to calculate this. Elicit that, as we know the coordinates of A and B we can find the coordinates of the midpoint of AC (5,2) and hence the coordinates of C (8,2).

Remind the children about reflecting shapes, and explain that they are now going to reflect the triangle in the y axis. Establish that this will put the triangle in the second quadrant. Make sure the children understand that with a reflection: the shape will *always* change in orientation (this is not always clear when using regular shapes); distance between the shape and the mirror line is the same for the shape and the reflected image; size does not change.

Work together to fix the reflection at the coordinates A(2) (−2,2), B(2) (−5,7) and C(2) (−8,2).

Group work: Provide each group with grid paper and explain that you want them to find the reflection of the original triangle in the x axis (call this triangle 3) and label the points with the coordinates.

Progress check: Pause the children and check that their reflections and coordinates are correct: A3 (2,−2), B3 (5,−7) and C3 (8,−2). Then ask the groups to reflect triangle 2 in the x axis: A4 (−2,−2), B4 (−5,−7) and C4 (−8,−2).

Review

Check that the children have reflected the triangle correctly. What can they tell you about the coordinates in the different quadrants, including negative ones?

Curriculum objectives
● To draw and translate simple shapes on the coordinate plane, and reflect them in the axes.

Success criteria
● I can draw and translate shapes on the coordinate plane.

You will need
Equipment
Grid paper

Differentiation
Less confident learners
Limit children to simple shapes and keep the translation to just one direction to start with, such as *Move 2 squares up.*

More confident learners
Children could extend their work to include translating shapes over the axes.

Curriculum objectives
● To draw and translate simple shapes on the coordinate plane, and reflect them in the axes.

Success criteria
● I can draw and translate shapes on the coordinate plane, using all four quadrants.

You will need
General resources
'Grids'

Differentiation
Less confident learners
Provide support and direct children towards simple shapes. Ask them to translate the shape in one direction only.

More confident learners
Encourage children to investigate translating more complex shapes in a variety of directions.

Lesson 4 — Oral and mental starter 53

Main teaching activities

Whole-class work: Tell the children that in this lesson they will be translating shapes on the grid. Elicit that this means 'sliding' the shape, from one position to another without rotating or flipping it.

On your single-quadrant grid, ask the children to mark these points: A (1,1), B (2,3), C (4,3) and D (4,1). Join them to make a quadrilateral and colour it red. Tell the children that you are going to translate the red shape 2 squares up and 1 square to the left. Demonstrate how to find the new coordinates of A (0,3). Ask the children to draw the red shape on grid paper, then draw the new shape labelling the coordinates: B (1,5), C (3,5) and D (3,3).

Now display the four-quadrant grid with a shape at the coordinates A (1,2), B (3,4), C (4,3), D (7,5), E (6,1) and back to A. Tell the children that you want to translate the shape 2 squares up and 3 right. This means that each of the coordinates is moved 2 up and 3 to the right. Ask the children to draw the shape and then draw the translated shape. Check these as a class.

Paired work: Ask the children to draw a simple shape on grid paper and label its coordinates, then write instructions for a translation. They should then pass the sheet to their partner who should draw the translation.

Review
Ask a child to explain the term *translation*. Ask a pair of children to share their work with the class. Discuss any difficulties.

Lesson 5 — Oral and mental starter 53

Main teaching activities

Whole-class work: Recap work on translating shapes from the previous lesson and let the children know that this time they may be using all four quadrants.

Display the four-quadrant grid. In the first quadrant show a rhombus with coordinates P (1,2), Q (3,3), R (5,2) and S (3,1):

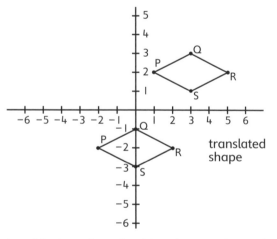

Tell the children that you are going to translate this shape 3 to the left and 4 down. Invite children to come to the board to show where each point will be translated to: P (−2,−2), Q (0,−1), R (2,−2) and S (0,−3).

Paired work: Distribute photocopiable page 'Grids'. Ask each child to draw a simple shape in grid A and label its coordinates. Then, as before, they should write instructions for a translation, but this time, they should make sure that at least part of the shape will move into a different quadrant. Their partner should then draw the translation.

Progress check: Pause pairs you wish to assess. Ask one child to give one of the coordinates from their original shape along with the translation instructions. Check that their partner can identify the new position for the point.

Review
Show them Grid B. Ask a child to design a simple shape and give the coordinates for the class to draw on their own grids. Then invite another child to suggest the criteria for the translation for the class to translate accordingly.

Perimeter, area and volume

Expected prior learning

Children should be able to:

- calculate the perimeter of a rectangle and related shapes
- use perimeter or area to find unknown lengths
- calculate the area of scale drawings using given measurements
- recognise and estimate volume.

Topic	Curriculum objectives	Expected outcomes
Measurement	**Lesson 1**	
	To recognise that shapes with the same areas can have different perimeters and vice versa.	Understand that rectangles with the same area might have different perimeters, and vice versa.
	Lesson 2	
	To calculate the areas of parallelograms and triangles.	Calculate the areas of parallelograms and triangles.
	Lesson 3	
	To recognise when it is possible to use formulae for area and volume of shapes.	Use formulae to find the volumes of shapes.
	Lesson 4	
	To calculate, estimate and compare volume of cubes and cuboids using standard units, including cubic centimetres (cm³) and cubic metres (m³), and extending to other units [for example, mm³ and km³].	Calculate and compare volumes of cubes and cuboids using standard units.
	Lesson 5	
	To calculate, estimate and compare volume of cubes and cuboids using standard units, including cubic centimetres (cm³) and cubic metres (m³), and extending to other units [for example, mm³ and km³].	Calculate and compare volumes of cubes and cuboids and use this to solve practical problems.

Preparation

Lesson 2: draw the triangles shown in the lesson; copy 'Triangle areas' for each child

You will need

Photocopiable sheets

'Triangle areas'

General resources

Interactive teaching resource 'Squared paper'

Equipment

Individual whiteboards; centimetre cubes; selection of cuboids; 6-sided dice; 12-sided dice; unit cards: cm, m and km; centimetre-squared paper

Further practice

General resources

Interactive activity 'Perimeter and area'

Oral and mental starters suggested for week 6

See the bank of starters on pages 126 and 165. Oral and mental starters are also on the CD-ROM.

36 Conversions

37 Coordinate square practice

38 4 squares

51 Converting up and down

Overview of progression

At the start of the week the children will be finding areas and perimeters and investigating shapes with the same area but different perimeters, and vice versa. They will progress to finding areas of triangles and parallelograms using formulae. Finally, they will calculate and compare volumes in a problem-solving context.

Watch out for

When finding the area of a triangle, children will sometimes confuse the height of the triangle with the length of one side. Make sure that the children understand the difference between area and perimeter and which units to use, in particular cm and cm^2. Also note that the cubic centimetres is a commonly used unit of volume, $1 cm^3$.

Creative context

Children could apply this work to designing and planning a garden and investigating sizes of flower plots and plant containers, and the capacities of items such as watering cans, water butts and compost bins.

Vocabulary

area, centimetre, cm^2, cm^3, cubic centimetre, cubic metre, dimension, metre, perimeter, volume

Curriculum objectives
● To recognise that shapes with the same area can have different perimeters and vice versa.

Success criteria
● I can show that rectangles with the same area may have different perimeters and vice versa.

You will need

General resources
Interactive teaching resource 'Squared paper'

Equipment
Individual whiteboards; centimetre-squared paper

Differentiation

Less confident learners
Encourage children to check the areas of the rectangles by counting squares.

More confident learners
Ask children to challenge their partners to draw rectangles with a certain area or perimeter.

Lesson 1
Oral and mental starter 38

Main teaching activities

Whole-class work: Tell the children that they will be looking at different shapes and their areas and perimeters. Ask the children to tell you the difference between an area of a shape and its perimeter. Then invite a volunteer to draw on the board a rectangle that is 2cm × 6cm on interactive teaching resource 'Squared paper' on the CD-ROM. Count the squares together to confirm that the area is 12cm². Ask the children to recall how to calculate the area of a rectangle: by finding the product of one short and one long side (width *multiplied* by length, or length × width).

Similarly, ask them to explain how to find the perimeter of the same rectangle: by *adding* the lengths of all the sides. Ask the children to work out the perimeter of the rectangle drawn on the board: 2 + 6 + 2 + 6 = 16cm.

Now ask one of the children to draw a rectangle that is 3cm × 4cm (taking each square on the board to be 1cm). Ask the children to quickly tell you what the area of this rectangle is (12cm²), and what the perimeter is (3 + 4 + 3 + 4 = 14cm).

Ask the children to look at both rectangles drawn on the board. Prompt the children to notice that although the *areas* of the two rectangles are the same, the perimeters are different.

Independent work: Provide the children with centimetre-squared paper and challenge them to draw another rectangle with the area 12cm². (It would be 1cm × 12cm.) Then, can they draw another rectangle with a perimeter of 14cm? (Possible rectangles would be 1cm × 6cm and 2cm × 5cm.)

Ask them to investigate other rectangles with, first, the same area, and then the same perimeter.

Progress check: Pause the children to ask them what they have found out about the areas of rectangles that have the same perimeter. (They will usually be different.)

Review

Challenge the children to draw or calculate the greatest area of a rectangle with a perimeter of 20cm. Tell them that you want them to work in whole centimetres. (The biggest is 4cm × 6cm = 24cm².) The children should suggest 1 × 9, 2 × 8, 3 × 7 and 4 × 6, as possible rectangles, as the sum of the shorter and the longer side must be half of 20 (the perimeter). When they then calculate the area they will find that 4 × 6 gives the biggest area. Share ideas and ask the children who found it: *How did you decide on 4 × 6cm?* Discuss with the children what they have found out about areas and perimeters of rectangles.

Curriculum objectives
● To calculate the areas of parallelograms and triangles.
Success criteria
● I can calculate the areas of parallelograms and triangles.

You will need
Photocopiable sheets
'Triangle areas'
Equipment
Individual whiteboards

Differentiation
Less confident learners
Encourage children to check approximate areas by counting squares and parts of squares.
More confident learners
Ask children to calculate areas of shapes combining triangles with parallelograms or rectangles.

Lesson 2 — Oral and mental starter 37

Main teaching activities

Whole-class work: Draw a rectangle on the board of 6cm × 8cm. Ask the children: *What is the area of the rectangle?* (48cm².) Now draw a diagonal to divide the rectangle into two triangles. Ask: *What is the area of each triangle?* (24cm².) This is ½ × base × height, and is the formula to find the area of a triangle. (The area of the rectangle is base × height.) Display these triangles:

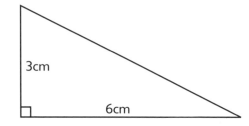
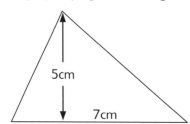

Notice that the first is right-angled, so we have the base length and the height, hence the area is ½ × 6cm × 3cm = 9cm². Then look at the second. The height is *not* the length of one of the sides, but the area is ½ × 7 × 5 = 17.5cm².

Independent work: Ask the children to start calculating the areas on photocopiable page 47 'Triangle areas'.

Progress check: Pause the children to check they have been using the correct dimensions. Look at question 3, and note that the parallelogram has been divided into two triangles and a rectangle.

Review
Check some of the areas on the sheet. Elicit that to find the area of a triangle or a parallelogram they need to know the base length and the height.

Curriculum objectives
● To recognise when to use the formulae for area and volume of shapes.
Success criteria
● I can use a formula to find the volume of a cube.

You will need
Equipment
Individual whiteboards; centimetre cubes; 6-sided dice; cm, m and km unit cards; 12-sided dice

Differentiation
Less confident learners
Give children 6-sided dice and the cm card to generate the dimensions of the cuboids.
More confident learners
Let children use 12-sided dice to generate their cuboids.

Lesson 3 — Oral and mental starter 36

Main teaching activities

Whole-class work: Remind the children of previous work estimating the volume of cuboids by using centimetre cubes. Now ask them to use the cubes to build a cuboid that is 3cm wide by 4cm by 5cm high. Invite individuals to build it a layer at a time. Then ask: *How many cubes are in the first layer? ... second layer?* to find the total number of cubes used. Establish that the number of cubes gives us the volume of the cuboid in cm³. In each layer there are 3 × 4 cubes (12), and there are five layers to give the height of 5cm, so the total number of cubes used is 12 × 5 = 60 (or 3 × 4 × 5), hence the volume of the cuboid is 60cm³. Extrapolate that the volume of a cuboid can be found by: width (w) × length (l) × height (h), and that for increasingly large cuboids, the formula is the only realistic way to work out the volume. Note that the volume will be written in cubed units (³).

Paired work: Explain that pairs should roll a dice three times between them to generate the dimensions for a cuboid and then select one of the unit cards. From this, they should calculate the volume of the cuboid.

Progress check: Pause the children and ask them to show you one of the cuboids they have generated. Check that they are showing the volume in units³.

Review
Ask the children to calculate the volume of a room that is 4m × 5m with a height of 2.5m. (50m³.) Discuss with the children when it is useful to find volumes, for example when we are trying to pack several items into a larger container.

Curriculum objectives
● To calculate and compare volumes of cubes and cuboids using standard units.

Success criteria
● I can calculate and compare the volumes of cubes and cuboids.

You will need

Equipment
Individual whiteboards; centimetre cubes or similar

Differentiation

Less confident learners
Let children use centimetre cubes to help them build their cuboids and to check the volumes.

More confident learners
Let children investigate the volumes of other cuboids and shapes built from joining cuboids.

Curriculum objectives
● To calculate, estimate and compare volumes of cubes and cuboids using standard units, including cubic centimetres (cm^3).

Success criteria
● I can calculate and compare the volumes of cuboids and use this to solve problems.

You will need

Equipment
Individual whiteboards; centimetre cubes or similar

Differentiation

Less confident learners
Children may need some support to think about the arrangements of the cartons in the boxes. Provide practical materials to help them.

More confident learners
Ask children to challenge each other with similar problems.

Lesson 4
Oral and mental starter 36

Main teaching activities

Whole-class work: Briefly recap the previous lesson and ask the children how they would find the volume of a cube with a side length of 4cm. Elicit that to calculate the volume of cuboid they multiply the length, by the width, by the height. So, for this cube, 4cm × 4cm × 4cm = $64cm^3$.

Next, ask the children to find the volume of a cuboid with dimensions 2cm, 8cm and 4cm. The children should confirm that this is again $64cm^3$.

Paired work: Organise the children to work in pairs to challenge each other to find the volumes of different cuboids. Explain that you want each of them to decide on the dimensions, put these to their partner to use to find the volume, while they work it out themselves too, before checking each other's calculations.

Progress check: Visit pairs you particularly wish to assess. Pause them to ask about some of their calculations. Have they found cuboids with the same volume but different dimensions? Remind them that in previous lessons they have found rectangles with the same area but different dimensions and this is similar with the volumes of cuboids.

Review

Ask the children about the cuboids they have investigated. Make a list of the dimensions and volumes, and compare the different cuboids. How many have they found with the same volume?

Lesson 5
Oral and mental starter 51

Main teaching activities

Whole-class work: Tell the children that in this lesson they will find volumes to help them solve practical problems. First, ask the children what the volume of a carton 30cm × 20cm × 10cm would be. ($6000cm^3$.) Then ask them to work out how many of these cartons can be packed into a box 60cm × 60cm × 30cm. Let the children discuss in pairs how they might work this out.

Progress check: Ask the children how they approached the problem. Some may have calculated the volume of the box and divided it by the volume of the carton; others may have tried to work it out practically. Elicit an answer of 18 cartons.

Point out that, in this example, the cartons will fit exactly into the box. Consider how many layers of cartons there will be and then how the cartons could be arranged in the box.

Paired work: Challenge the children to work out the best size of box to take 12 cartons. (Possible answers: 60cm × 60cm × 20cm; 60cm × 30cm × 40cm.)

The children should then challenge each other to work out the different-sized boxes that would hold certain numbers of cartons (of their choosing).

Review

Share answers for the 12-carton box. Then ask the children to think about how many cartons would fit into a box 65cm × 60cm × 30cm. Point out that, in this case, the cartons will *not* fit exactly into the box, so they have to think about how the cartons could be arranged. Establish that, if they just divide the volume of the box by the volume of the cartons, the answer would leave a space 5cm × 60cm × 30cm.

Curriculum objectives
• To perform mental calculations, including with mixed operations. and large numbers.

You will need
I. Check
Oral and mental starter
30 Quick additions

2. Assess
'Jumbled calculations (1)'

3. Further practice
Photocopiable sheets
'Jumbled calculations (2)'

Mental calculations

Most children should be able to add, subtract, multiply and divide large numbers mentally with the use of jottings.

Some children will not have made such progress and will need practical support to develop their mental strategies.

I. Check

30 Quick additions

Use this starter to check that the children have strategies which they apply, for example looking for pairs of digits that add up to 10. Progress the strings of numbers to three-digit numbers, then to simple decimal numbers. Can they add these numbers mentally: $24.5 + 16 + 31 + 105 + 9.4$? (185.9.)

2. Assess

On the photocopiable page 127 'Jumbled calculations (1)' make sure that the children are using mental calculations, with jottings where necessary. Encourage them to say how they are doing the calculations. To make sure the children can apply their mental strategies in different situations, ask a few extra related questions, such as: $42 \div 0.14$ (300); 55×6 (330); $2.8 \div 20$ (0.14). Record the outcomes.

3. Further practice

The photocopiable page 'Jumbled calculations (2)' from the CD-ROM will give children quick-fire practice with their mental calculation skills.

Curriculum objectives
• To add and subtract fractions with different denominators, using the concept of equivalent fractions.

You will need
I. Check
Oral and mental starter
50 Equivalent fractions

2. Assess
Individual whiteboards

3. Further practice
Photocopiable sheets
'Fraction calculations'
General resources
'Fraction wall'

Add and subtract fractions with different denominators

Most children should be able to convert fractions to equivalent fractions leading to finding the lowest common denominator to enable addition and subtraction.

Some children will require more help to identify equivalent fractions.

I. Check

50 Equivalent fractions

Begin with familiar unitary fractions such as ½, asking the children to write as many equivalent fractions as they can. Move on to other fractions to make sure that the children realise that, to find an equivalent fraction, they must either multiply or divide both the numerator and the denominator by the same number. Ask: *Why do we need to convert the fractions to those with the same denominator? If we are adding fractions, which part of the fraction tells us the number of parts?*

2. Assess

Remind the children that, if they are adding or subtracting fractions, the fractions must have the same denominator, so it is best to find the lowest common denominator. Give small groups two fractions for them to decide on the lowest common denominator, then find the sum and the difference between. Make sure that the children are clear about the difference between the numerator and denominator. Record the outcomes.

3. Further practice

The children should use photocopiable page 'Fraction wall' to help identify equivalent fractions. Photocopiable page 128 'Fraction calculations' will give further practice in adding and subtracting fractions.

Curriculum objectives
● To draw and translate simple shapes on the coordinate plane, and reflect them in the axes.

You will need
I. Check
Oral and mental starter
37 Coordinate square practice

2. Assess
'Mirror image'

3. Further practice
Photocopiable sheets
'On reflection'

General resources
Interactive teaching resource 'Reflection grid'

Reflecting shapes in the axes

Most children should be able to reflect regular and irregular shapes in the vertical and horizontal axes.

Some children will probably be able to reflect a shape when it touches the axis, but will be less confident with shapes not adjacent to the axes and those that are irregular.

I. Check

37 Coordinate square practice

Provide the children with a grid and ask them to label the axes −10 to 10. Check that they can identify positions from the coordinates and name the coordinates of different points on the grid. Check that they can identify the coordinates of different points reflected in the vertical and the horizontal axes. Look at the point −5,7, and ask: *What would the coordinates of the point be reflected in the vertical axis?* (5,7.) *What about in the horizontal axis?* (−5,−7.)

2. Assess

Give the children photocopiable page 129 'Mirror image' to complete. Point out that with the first example, one point (A) is touching the y axis. Make sure that the children can identify the coordinates of each point. *What will the coordinates of A1 be when the shape is reflected in the y-axis? What about in the x-axis?* Make sure the children take into account that the next shape is not adjacent to the axes. Record the outcomes.

3. Further practice

The interactive teaching resource 'Reflection grid' on the CD-ROM is useful to demonstrate how shapes are reflected, if children are having difficulty with this concept. And the photocopiable page 'On reflection' on the CD-ROM gives practice in drawing reflections without the coordinate grid.

Curriculum objectives
● To recognise that shapes with the same area can have different perimeters, and vice versa.

You will need
I. Check
Oral and mental starter
38 4 squares

Equipment
Squared paper

2. Assess
'Mr Fixit'; individual whiteboards

3. Further practice
General resources
Interactive activity 'Perimeter and area'

Calculating perimeter and area

Most children should be able to find the area and perimeter of rectangular shapes, parallelograms and triangles and will be able to find shapes with the same area but different perimeters, and vice versa.

Some children will require more practice at finding areas and perimeters and then relating the two.

I. Check

38 4 squares

Use this starter to check that the children can recognise that the area of each of the five shapes is 4cm². Next, ask them to calculate the perimeter of each shape. (Four have a perimeter of 10cm, and the square has a perimeter of 8cm.) Ask: *Why is the area of the five shapes the same? Why is the perimeter of the square less than the perimeter of the other shapes even though they have the same area?*

2. Assess

Photocopiable page 130 'Mr Fixit' involves a problem-solving activity that will assess how well the children understand the concepts. Make sure that the children find a number of solutions to the first part of the problem. Have they recognised a pattern, or are they working it out randomly? Possible answers: 1 × 60, 2 × 30, 3 × 20, 4 × 15, 5 × 12, 6 × 10. Record the outcomes.

3. Further practice

The interactive activity 'Perimeter and area' on the CD-ROM gives further practice in finding areas and perimeters and will also check the children's understanding.

Oral and mental starters

Number, place value and rounding

27 Jumping forwards and backwards

Revise counting up and back with positive and negative numbers. For example: count in threes in a negative direction from 10 (10, 7, 4, 1, −2, −5, −8...), or count in fives in a positive direction from −20 (−20, −15, −10, −5, 0, 5, 10, 15...).

Extension
Count backwards with different intervals such as 6 and 9, using different starting numbers and extending through zero.

28 Number order

Write five numbers on the board and ask the children to order them. Start with decimal numbers such as 9.01, 19.03, 10.90, 19.31, 9.19.

29 Temperature change

Revise finding the difference between positive and negative numbers. Ask the children questions such as: *By how many degrees does the temperature rise between −3°C and 5°C? By how many degrees does the temperature fall between 7°C and −4°C.*

Extension
Invite children to make up similar questions for the rest of the class.

Addition, subtraction, multiplication and division

30 Quick additions

Give the children a string of numbers to add together, such as 23 + 15 + 3 + 27 + 20.

Extension
Extend this to adding larger numbers, such as 123 + 54 + 76 + 261 (= 514). Include decimal numbers such as 2.5 + 8.6 + 7.7 + 9.3 (= 28.1).

31 Multiplication rounds

Practise the strategy of rounding numbers to find approximate answers to multiplication problems. For example: 19 × 9 (171, approximate answer 20 × 10); 48 × 11 (528, approximate answer 50 × 10); 289 × 58 (16,762, approximate answer 300 × 60).

32 Venn division

Draw a Venn diagram on the board, with one circle labelled *Can be divided by 3*, and the other labelled *Can be divided by 4*. Ask the children to copy this onto their whiteboards. Then call out the following numbers for the children to place in the diagram: 15, 24, 72, 36, 27, 122, 45, 56, 81, 63, 21 and 32.

Extension
Label the circles *Numbers divisible by 4* and *Numbers divisible by 5*. Try numbers such as: 15, 24, 72, 36, 27, 122, 45, 56, 81, 63, 21 and 32.

Decimals and fractions

33 Decimal additions

Ensure that the children have efficient strategies to add simple decimal numbers mentally (such as adding units, adding tenths, and then adding both numbers; looking for pairs that make whole numbers). Suggest they add the tenths first and then add them on to the units. Give them examples such as: 7.3 + 4.5 and 4.9 + 5.3.

Extension

Write on the board: 2.7 + 3.9 + 4.4. Remind the children of the strategies they could use. Then give further examples such as: 4.2 + 4.3 + 4.4 + 4.5; 1.7 + ? + 5.3 = 9.4; 4.0 + 9.0 + 6.0 + 5.0; 3.3 + 2.8 + ? = 8.9.

34 Decimal differences

Ensure that the children have efficient strategies to subtract simple decimal numbers mentally (including adding on from the lower number to the higher number). Suggest that they add the difference between the lower number and the next whole number and then add on the rest to the higher number. For example: for 8.6 − 3.7, the difference between 3.7 and 4 is 0.3, then add this to the difference between 4 and 8.6, (4.6), which gives 4.6 + 0.3 = 4.9.

35 Factors

Give the children a number and ask them to list as many factors of it as they can. For example: 12 (1, 2, 3, 4, 6, 12); 15 (1, 3, 5, 15); 20 (1, 2, 4, 5, 10, 20); 21 (1, 3, 7, 21); 17 (1, 17).

Extension

Focus on factor pairs. Write numbers on the board for the children to give you a pair of factors each time. For example: 12 would produce 6 and 2, 3 and 4, and 12 and 1.

Measurement

36 Conversions

Challenge the children to convert mm to cm, cm to m and m to km. Remind them to be careful with place value and the position of the zero as a place-holder. Ask questions such as: *How many millimetres are there in 2cm?*

Extension

Work on converting cubic mm to cubic cm, cubic cm to cubic m and cubic m to cubic km: *How many cubic millimetres are in 1cm³?   How many mm³ in 3cm³? How many cm³ in 1m³ and in 3m³?*

Geometry

37 Coordinate square practice

Give the children some quick-fire coordinate revision. Display a 10 × 10 square. Use letters on the horizontal axis and numbers on the vertical axis. Remind the children that the horizontal reference (letters) are given before the vertical reference (numbers). Place crosses or dots in a selection of squares and ask the children to give you the grid references.

Extension

Name some simple 2D shapes and ask the children to give you the grid references needed to construct them. Use shapes such as square, triangle, rectangle, pentagon and hexagon. Draw the shapes to check that they are accurate.

Oral and mental starters 38–39 continue on the CD-ROM.

Jumbled calculations (1)

■ Match each square to a circle and a triangle to make the calculations correct.

Square	Circle	Triangle
36 ÷	5	= 60
56 +	7.5	= 21
42 ÷	3	= 13
12 ×	30	= 1.4
2.8 ×	5	= 22
5.5 ×	6.6	= 10
4.4 ×	4	= 2
3.4 +	6	= 60

I can perform mental calculations.

How did you do?

Fraction calculations

■ Work out the following additions and subtractions involving fractions.

1. $\dfrac{1}{3} + \dfrac{1}{4} =$

6. $\dfrac{2}{5} + \dfrac{1}{2} =$

2. $\dfrac{1}{3} - \dfrac{1}{4} =$

7. $\dfrac{7}{9} - \dfrac{1}{6} =$

3. $\dfrac{3}{8} + \dfrac{1}{12} =$

8. $\dfrac{3}{8} + \dfrac{2}{5} =$

4. $\dfrac{3}{8} - \dfrac{1}{12} =$

5. $\dfrac{3}{5} + \dfrac{1}{2} + \dfrac{3}{4} =$

I can add and subtract fractions.

How did you do?

Mirror image

1. Reflect the shape ABCD in the vertical axis and the horizontal axis.

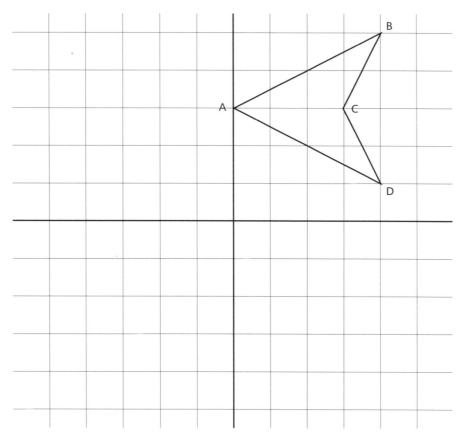

2. Reflect the shape PQRSTUVWX in the vertical axis and the horizontal axis.

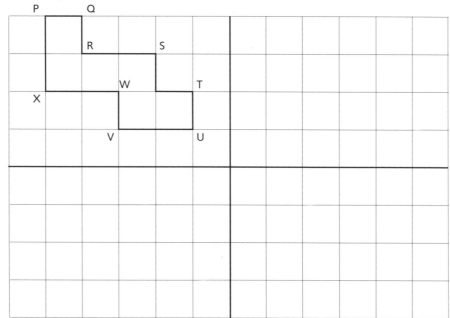

I can draw and translate simple shapes on the coordinate plane
and reflect them in the axis.

How did you do?

Mr Fixit

■ Mr Fixit has to build a new patio in the garden of *The Crossed Forks* restaurant. He has 60 one metre square patio slabs. What different rectangular patios can he make with his slabs? Which arrangement gives the greatest perimeter? Record your findings in this chart.

Length	Width	Perimeter

■ The restaurant owners have decided not to have a rectangular patio. Use either the grid below or a separate sheet of squared paper to find the compound shape that will give the greatest perimeter. The patio slabs must fit together side by side – they cannot overlap or join together with just the corners touching. What is the biggest perimeter you can find?

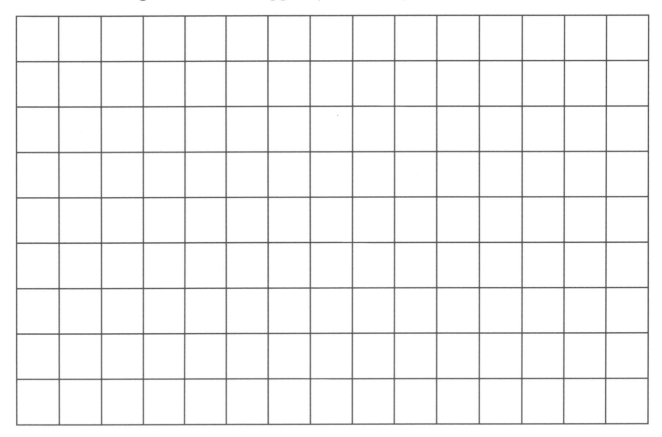

I can solve problems to find the perimeter of shapes.

How did you do?

PHOTOCOPIABLE   ■SCHOLASTIC
www.scholastic.co.uk

Calculating with large numbers

Expected prior learning

Children should be able to:

- calculate using all four operations
- use suitable written methods for multiplication and division.

Topic	Curriculum objectives	Expected outcomes
Addition, subtraction, multiplication and division	**Lesson 1**	
	To multiply multi-digit numbers up to four digits by a two-digit whole number using the formal written method of long multiplication.	Use long multiplication to perform calculations with large numbers.
	Lesson 2	
	To divide numbers up to four digits by a two-digit whole number using the formal written method of long division, and interpret remainders as whole number remainders, fractions, or by rounding, as appropriate for the context.	Use long division formally. Understand how to interpret remainders.
	Lesson 3	
	To perform mental calculations, including with mixed operations and large numbers.	Use a range of strategies to perform mental calculations. Solve problems using mental calculations.
	Lesson 4	
	To use their knowledge of the order of operations to carry out calculations involving the four operations.	Solve problems involving all four operations or a mixture of operations and involving large numbers.
	Lesson 5	
	To solve problems involving addition, subtraction, multiplication and division.	Solve multi-step problems, identifying the information needed and the calculations required.

Preparation

Lessons 2 and 3: write up the group-work and paired-work problems

Lesson 4: display an enlarged copy of 'Five steps to successful problem solving'; write up the whole-class and paired-work problems

Lesson 5: enlarge the top section of 'Paradise hotel' and prepare one copy of the full sheet for each child

You will need

Photocopiable sheets
'Paradise hotel'

General resources
'Five steps to successful problem solving'

Equipment
Individual whiteboards; number cards with a decimal point card; internet access and/or holiday brochures

Further practice

Photocopiable sheets
Eating out (1) and (2)'

Oral and mental starters suggested for week 1

See the bank of starters on pages 125 and 164. Oral and mental starters are also on the CD-ROM.

32 Venn division

41 Target number

43 Target 100

44 Tables count

46 Tables bingo (1)

Overview of progression

During this week the children will be developing the use of long division and long multiplication. They will use all four operations in calculations with large numbers, they will also be extending their ability to perform mental calculations with large numbers. By the end of the week they should be able to solve word-based problems using a mixture of operations with large numbers.

Watch out for

When working with large numbers, some children may not be fully confident with place value, so ensure that they check that they have the correct number of digits in their answers. Encourage them to approximate their answer before they complete the calculation formally, and to check that their answer makes sense.

Creative context

There are a number of opportunities to use this topic with large numbers in cross-curricular work, in particular in geography, looking at populations of various places across the world, both similar to and different from the children's own locality. Also look at the distances between the local area and the towns and cities investigated.

Vocabulary

long division, long multiplication, operation, remainder, rounding

■ SCHOLASTIC

Curriculum objectives

● To multiply multi-digit numbers up to four digits by a two-digit whole number using long multiplication.

Success criteria

● I can use long multiplication with calculations using large numbers.

You will need

Equipment

Individual whiteboards

Differentiation

Less confident learners

Children should work in a group with support. They may need to use the extended method for long multiplication.

More confident learners

Children could formulate their own multiplication problems and exchange them with partners.

Lesson 1 — Oral and mental starter 43

Main teaching activities

Whole-class work: Briefly recap multiplying large numbers.

Write 3543 × 38 on the board and work through the long multiplication:

```
        3543
    ×     38
   3543 × 30  =  106290
   3543 ×  8  =   28344
              134634
```

Remind the children about the importance of lining up the digits correctly. Then ask the children to calculate the following on their whiteboards: 4768 × 47; 9879 × 56 and 8034 × 78.

Progress check: Ask the children to hold up their whiteboards after the first calculation. Check the answer (224,096). If anyone has not calculated this correctly, invite volunteers to help you explain each step.

Whole-class work: Set the class this problem:

A football stadium has three stands, stand A has seating for 1355; stand B has seating for 2506; and stand C has seating for 5687. If there are 34 matches in the season and each one is a sell-out, how many tickets will they sell for each stand? (A: 46,070; B: 85,204; C: 193,358.)

Review

Check answers and discuss any difficulties encountered. Then ask the children to think of a problem where they would use multiplication with large numbers. Then invite a volunteer to challenge the rest of the class with their problem.

Curriculum objectives

● To divide numbers up to four digits by a two-digit whole number using long division, and interpret remainders as appropriate for the context.

Success criteria

● I can use long division to divide large numbers.
● I can interpret remainders as whole numbers, fractions or by rounding.

You will need

Equipment

Individual whiteboards

Differentiation

Less confident learners

Support children equating long division to other methods. Support their discussion on how to interpret the remainder.

More confident learners

Children should think of their own problems which involve dividing large numbers.

Lesson 2 — Oral and mental starter 41

Main teaching activities

Whole-class work: Remind the children that they have learned how to use long division in earlier lessons, but here you want them to especially think about how to deal with remainders. Go through this example: 6633 ÷ 36: 184 r 9, or 184.25, or 184 9⁄36, or rounded up to 185.

Elicit that we treat remainders differently depending upon the context. For example, if we were dividing money, we would use a decimal. If we were putting items in containers, we would need to round up.

Group work: Ask the children to calculate the following problems and discuss in their group how to deal with the remainder, if there is one:

- *2275 people are going on a trip. Each coach can hold 47 people. How many coaches do we need?* (48 r 4, so: 49.)
- *A syndicate of 34 people wins £6756 on the lottery. How much do they get each?* (£198.70, with 20p left.)
- *A bucket of 3000 marbles is shared between a class of 28. How many marbles does each child have?* (107, with 4 spare.)

Progress check: Check that the children agree on how to deal with the remainders. Why is each question dealt with in a different way?

Review

Discuss the three problems and check answers. Give the children a final question to test their understanding: *A visitor centre can accommodate 56 people at an information film. In one day, they have 2588 visitors. How many screenings must they give?* Establish that 46 screenings to 56 people would leave 12 people. How should the centre deal with this?

Curriculum objectives
● To perform mental calculations, including with mixed operations and large numbers.

Success criteria
● I can calculate mentally with mixed operations and large numbers.

You will need
Equipment
Individual whiteboards

Differentiation
Less confident learners
Help children to approach each problem in small steps.

More confident learners
Children should challenge each other with more complex problems.

Curriculum objectives
● To use their knowledge of the order of operations to carry out calculations involving the four operations.

Success criteria
● I can solve problems using all four operations by identifying the calculations needed and the order of operations.

You will need
General resources
'Five steps to successful problem solving'
Equipment
Individual whiteboards

Differentiation
Less confident learners
Make sure children are clear about place value.

More confident learners
Ask the children to pose each other further questions from the population figures.

Lesson 3 — Oral and mental starter 41

Main teaching activities

Whole-class work: Tell the children that in this lesson you will be asking them to work things out mentally, but say that they can use jottings

Give the children a little time to calculate 14 × 1999. Then ask them to say how they approached the problem. Establish that the easiest way is to round 1999 to 2000 and multiply by 14; using double 14 is 28 × 1000, and then subtract 14 × 1 to get 27,986.

Paired work: Give the children the following problems and ask them to try to solve them mentally.

- *A school wants to buy some new furniture. The price for chairs is £5.99 each, and the school needs 50 chairs. The budget is £350. How much money will the school have left?*
- *The price of exercise books is £1.99. The school needs to order 200. How much will they cost altogether?*

Progress check: Pause the children after the first question, and ask them which strategies they used. Which methods have been easiest to use?

Review

Invite a pair to share their word problem with the class. Discuss whether it is one that they can calculate mentally and what strategies they should use.

Lesson 4 — Oral and mental starter 45

Main teaching activities

Whole-class work: Tell the children that they will be solving problems using all four operations. Display 'Five steps to successful problem solving' from the CD-ROM and remind the children of each step. Recall BIDMAS (brackets, indices, division, multiplication, addition and subtraction) to recall in which order operations should be completed. Show the following problem:

A stadium has space for 16,500 people. Each of its 11 main sections has 29 rows which have 50 seats, which are all red. The remaining seats are in the executive section. How many seats are there in the executive section? There are 25 rows in the executive section. These seats are blue. How many seats are there in each row?

Ask the children how they should approach this problem: 29 × 50 × 11 = 15,950; then 16,500 − 15,950 = 550; and 550 ÷ 25 = 22.

Paired work: Provide the children with these figures for the population of four main cities in China: Shanghai 22,315,426, Beijing 18,827,000, Tianjin 11,090,314 and Shenzhen 10,357,938. Ask the children to work in pairs to calculate the following, remind them to approximate their answers first.

Round the populations to the nearest one hundred. If the populations of Tianjin and Shenzhen both increase by 2% in the next five years and the populations of Shanghai and Beijing increase by 4%, what will be the difference between the total population of the four cities in five years compared with now?
(64,665,260 − 62,590,600 = 2,074,660)

Round the answer to the nearest one hundred, if the rates of increase in population are the same in the following five years how much will the overall population of the four cities (rounded to the nearest hundred) increase by compared with now?
(65,958,606 − 62,590,600 = 3,368,006)

Progress check: Check the children are clear about place value when they are doing the calculations and that their figures are in the correct columns.

Review

Go through the answers, and recap on the order of operations. How accurate were their estimates? What figures did they use for their approximations?

Curriculum objectives
● To solve problems involving addition, subtraction, multiplication and division.

Success criteria
● I can solve problems involving addition, subtraction, multiplication and division.

You will need
Photocopiable sheets
'Paradise hotel'
Equipment
Individual whiteboards; internet access and/or holiday brochures (for extension)

Differentiation
Less confident learners
Support these children with identifying the correct options and with deciding on the order of operations.
More confident learners
Encourage children to research their own holiday choices and cost their own holidays, either from brochures or using the internet.

Lesson 5
Oral and mental starter 44

Main teaching activities

Whole-class work: Explain to the children that they are going to be exploring how to cost a holiday. Explain that different brochures show costs in a variety of ways. Display the top part of photocopiable page 166 'Paradise hotel'.

Departure dates	Jan 12–Mar 24 12 Nov–15 Dec	Mar 25–May 27 2 Oct–12 Nov	May 28–June 30 Sept 1–1 Oct	1 July–31 August	15 Dec–11 Jan
1 week					
Adult	£250	£279	£345	£425	£320
First child	£175	£180	£250	£299	£225
Additional children	£150	£155	£225	£260	£200
2 weeks					
Adult	£450	£520	£600	£775	£575
First child	£275	£345	£375	£400	£360
Additional children	£250	£295	£325	£350	£310
Rooms are for two adults and up to three children. Single room supplement add 25% of adult cost					

Ask the children to look carefully at the table, which shows prices for holidays at Paradise Hotel. Point out that in this example the dates are written across the top of the table, and information for accommodation (adults' price, then the price for the first child and the further child) is given on the left-hand side, with prices for one-week and two-week holidays.

Point out that it is important to read the 'small print' to find conditions for child discount and any supplements that may be payable.

Ask: *Who can tell me the price for two adults staying for one week with a departure of 14 December?* The answer £500 per person will probably be given. Ask: *What if just one adult went alone, what would the price be?* (£250 plus 25% of £250 = £312.50). Ask a child to explain why.

If the children need further clarification, ask some further questions such as: *How much for two adults and two children going for one week on 3 May?* (2 x £279 + 180 + 155 = £893)

Independent work: Hand out a copy of the photocopiable sheet to each child and ask them to complete it.

Progress check: Make sure that the children are identifying the relevant information and then using the correct order of calculation.

Review
Go through the answers and discuss any difficulties. Challenge the children to pose one or two other questions from the information given.

Multiplying and dividing decimals

Expected prior learning

Children should be able to:

- read and write decimal numbers as fractions
- recognise thousandths and relate them to tenths, hundredths and decimal equivalents
- round numbers to the nearest whole number and to one decimal place
- read, write, order and compare numbers with up to three decimal places
- solve problems involving numbers up to three decimal places.

Topic	Curriculum objectives	Expected outcomes
Fractions (including decimals and percentages)	**Lesson 1**	
	To multiply one-digit numbers with up to two decimal places by whole numbers.	Multiply one-digit numbers with up to two decimal places by whole numbers.
	Lesson 2	
	To multiply one-digit numbers with up to two decimal places by whole numbers.	Multiply one-digit numbers with decimal places by whole numbers and use the inverse operation to check.
	Lesson 3	
	To use written division methods in cases where the answer has up to two decimal places.	Use written division methods where the answer involves decimal numbers.
	Lesson 4	
	To multiply one-digit numbers with up to two decimal places by whole numbers.	Multiply and divide decimal numbers.
	Lesson 5	
	To multiply one-digit numbers with up to two decimal places by whole numbers.	Multiply decimal numbers by whole numbers.
	To solve problems which require answers to be rounded to specified degrees of accuracy.	Solve problems which require answers to be rounded accurately.

Preparation

Lesson 1: prepare sets of number cards with a decimal point card for each pair of children

Lesson 3: write up the calculations for independent work

Lesson 4: copy 'Be reasonable' for each child

Lesson 5: copy 'Sponsored walk' for each child

You will need

Photocopiable sheets

'Be reasonable'; 'Sponsored walk'

General resources

Interactive teaching resource 'Number sentence builder'; 'Number cards 0–9'

Equipment

Individual whiteboards; number cards with a decimal point card

Further practice

Use real life data such as travel brochures, population data or distances between locations to practice mental calculations.

Oral and mental starters suggested for week 2

See the bank of starters on pages 164 and 165. Oral and mental starters are also on the CD-ROM.

44 Tables count

46 Tables bingo (1)

47 Rounding decimals

48 What's the question?

Overview of progression

At the start of the week the children apply long multiplication methods to decimal numbers. Then they progress to dividing decimal numbers and rounding answers when necessary. As the week goes on, the children will practise using inverse operations to check their calculations and apply the multiplication and division methods to solving problems involving decimal numbers within measures.

Watch out for

It is important that children are clear about place value when they are using decimal numbers. When they are performing such calculations, they must take care to set out their work correctly so that the decimal point is in line throughout the process. Encourage the children to approximate answers first and to check their answers against their approximation for reasonableness.

Creative context

Take the opportunity to explore decimal numbers whenever there is the context for using money for economic awareness activities such as costing projects. Encourage the children to notice how decimal numbers are essential in cooking and how calculations are useful when changing quantities in food activities.

Vocabulary

decimal point, inverse, long multiplication, operation, recurring, round down, round up

Curriculum objectives
● To multiply one-digit numbers with up to two decimal places by whole numbers.
Success criteria
● I can multiply decimal places by whole numbers.

You will need
Equipment
Individual whiteboards; number cards and a decimal point card

Differentiation
Less confident learners
Ask children to multiply by a single digit initially, before helping them to move on.
More confident learners
When children are confident, they could move on to calculations with larger numbers.

Lesson 1

Oral and mental starter 44

Main teaching activities

Whole-class work: Tell the children that in this lesson they will be multiplying decimal numbers.

Ask the children to calculate 3.26×9 on their whiteboards. Advise them that, when they are multiplying a decimal number, the answer must have the same number of digits after the decimal point as the original decimal number has. After the children have had time to work out the example, take them through the steps:

3.26×9
$$3.00 \times 9 = 27.00$$
$$0.20 \times 9 = 1.80$$
$$0.06 \times 9 = \underline{0.54}$$
$$\underline{29.34}$$

Check the children reached the same answer, then ask them to calculate 5.98×7 in the same way (41.86), and invite a volunteer to demonstrate how the calculation was done.

Now move on to challenge the children to multiply 5.96×27. How would they tackle this? Explain that they can use long multiplication, which they were practising in last week's lessons:

5.96×27
$$5.00 \times 20 = 100.00$$
$$0.90 \times 20 = 18.00$$
$$0.06 \times 20 = 12.00$$
$$5.00 \times 7 = 35.00$$
$$0.90 \times 7 = 6.30$$
$$0.06 \times 7 = \underline{0.42}$$
$$\underline{171.72}$$

Finally, to double-check their learning, ask the children to calculate 4.85×7 (33.95) as quickly as they can.

Paired work: Each pair of children will need a set of number cards and a card with a decimal point. Explain that one child should generate a number by selecting and setting down one number card, then the decimal point and two further cards for the rest of the number. The second child should then select two number cards to find the number to multiply it by. Both children should do the calculation independently and then compare their result. The children should then reverse roles.

Progress check: Pause the children early on, particularly those you wish to assess or support, to check that they are generating suitable numbers and that their first calculations are correct. Remind them to approximate first to help them ensure that the decimal point is in the correct place.

Review

Invite the children to tell you some of their calculations and challenge the rest of the class with them. Ask the pairs who posed the question to confirm the class answer. Then ask everyone to do one more quick calculation: 8.28×36. (298.08.)

Curriculum objectives
● To multiply numbers with up to two decimal places by whole numbers.

Success criteria
● I can multiply decimal numbers by whole numbers.

You will need

General resources
'Number cards 0–9'; interactive teaching resource 'Number sentence builder'

Equipment
Individual whiteboards

Differentiation

Less confident learners
Focus first on statements given to one decimal place.

More confident learners
Children should use a decimal point in both numbers.

Lesson 2 — Oral and mental starter 48

Main teaching activities

Whole-class work: Tell the children that you are going 'keep it in the family' with decimal numbers. Revise the meaning of the word *inverse*. Use interactive teaching resource 'Number sentence builder' on the CD-ROM to show some simple examples. Show that, if $12 \times 9 = 108$ and $9 \times 12 = 108$, the inverse is also true that $108 \div 9 = 12$ and $108 \div 12 = 9$. Then show $3.56 \times 4 = 14.24$. Remind the children that the same rules apply to decimal numbers and that, if one member of the 'family' is known, we know the other three too: $4 \times 3.56 = 14.24$; $14.24 \div 4 = 3.56$; $14.24 \div 3.56 = 4$. Repeat with other examples.

Paired work: Ask the children to take turns to select number cards from a shuffled set and include a decimal point card to generate numbers. The children should devise questions with missing numbers for their partners to complete. Show the children that boxes should be used to indicate missing numbers: $6.45 \times 3 = \square$; $\square \times 6.45 = 19.35$; $19.35 \div \square = 6.45$; and $\square \div 6.45 = 3$.

Progress check: Visit pairs to check they are generating suitable questions and that the decimal point is being used correctly.

Review

Check some of the examples produced. Once the first family member was known, how quickly could the children complete the others? Using 'Number sentence builder' again, can the children start with a division fact and provide the other family members from there?

Curriculum objectives
● To use written division methods in cases where the answer has up to two decimal places.

Success criteria
● I can use written division methods with decimal numbers.

You will need

Equipment
Individual whiteboards

Differentiation

Less confident learners
Children may need adult support and if they are more comfortable with a different division method, allow them to use this.

More confident learners
Encourage children to devise their own real-life division problems with more than two decimal places.

Lesson 3 — Oral and mental starter 47

Main teaching activities

Whole-class work: Start off by giving the children a calculation like this one: *What is 87.64 divided by 7?* Approximate first: $84 \div 7 = 12$. Ask the children to help you solve the calculation using a written method:

```
7 │ 87.64
  − 70.00    10 × 7
    17.64
    14.00     2 × 7
     3.64
     3.50    0.5 × 7
     0.14
     0.14    0.02 × 7      10 + 2 + 0.5 + 0.02 = 12.52
     0.00
```

So, the answer to 87.64 divided by 7 is 12.52. Recap that it is important to keep the decimal points in line under each other. Then tell the children you want them to work out 56.25 divided by 5 in the same way. (11.25.)

Independent work: Write the following for the children to solve:

$459 \div 6$ (76.5); $689 \div 5$ (137.8); $729 \div 6$ (121.5); $125 \div 4$ (31.25).

$122.04 \div 3$ (40.68); $18.88 \div 8$ (2.36); $298.8 \div 8$ (37.35).

Progress check: Pause the children after the first set of questions. Remind them to make sure that when they move on to calculations with more than one decimal place in their answer, they line up the decimal points correctly.

Review

Check the children's answers and talk through any difficulties. Then tell the children you want them to divide 80 by 6. They will find that the answer is 13.33 rec. Establish that this is a recurring answer and in this instance the answer should be 'stopped' at two decimal places.

Curriculum objectives
● To multiply one-digit numbers with up to two decimal places by whole numbers.
● To use written division methods in cases where the answer has up to two decimal places.

Success criteria
● I can multiply decimal numbers.

You will need
Photocopiable sheets
'Be reasonable'
Equipment
Individual whiteboards

Differentiation
Less confident learners
Children may need support in deciding which approach to take to the questions.
More confident learners
Children devise questions involving more decimal places.

Lesson 4 — Oral and mental starter 48

Main teaching activities

Whole-class work: Talk the children through the following question as you write the details on the board: *A cake uses 0.4kg of flour. As I have 1½ kg of flour, can I make four cakes?* Let the children discuss the problem with their partners before you take feedback. Establish that, in this case, the best way of solving the problem is to multiply 0.4 × 4, which is 1.6kg, hence for four cakes 1.5kg is not enough flour.

Ask a second question: *Is it true that ten 20cm lengths of string can be cut from a piece 2m long?* Again, ask the children to offer an answer (Yes, it is true) and explain their reasoning. (2cm is 0.2m so 10 × 0.2 = 2.0.)

Independent work: Tell the children they are going to answer a selection of similar questions, for which they will need to explain their reasoning. Ask them to work through photocopiable page 167 'Be reasonable'.

Progress check: Pause the children after the first one or two questions. Check their understanding and make sure they are using appropriate methods. Remind the children that they should estimate where appropriate in order to check that their answer is feasible.

Review

Ask some children to share their answers and justify their reasoning. Ask the other children whether they agree or disagree, and why. Go over any difficulties.

Curriculum objectives
● To solve problems which require answers to be rounded.
● To multiply one-digit numbers with up to two decimal places by whole numbers.

Success criteria
● I can multiply decimal numbers by whole numbers.
● I can solve problems with accurately rounded answers.

You will need
Photocopiable sheets
'Sponsored walk'
Equipment
Individual whiteboards

Differentiation
Less confident learners
Encourage children to work together.
More confident learners
Invite children to make up some problems for others to solve.

Lesson 5 — Oral and mental starter 47

Main teaching activities

Whole-class work: Write 543 × 38 on the board. Invite a confident child to demonstrate the long multiplication method, as shown below. Remind the children that for calculations like this, it is often a good idea to approximate first, and then use the approximation to check the result is in the right area.

$$
\begin{array}{rl}
543 & \quad 543 \times 30 = 16290 \\
\times\ 38 & \quad 543 \times 30 = \underline{4344} \\
& \quad 20634
\end{array}
$$

Ask the children what the result of multiplying 54.3 × 38 would be. Point out that as 54.3 is ten times smaller than 543, the answer to the calculation 54.3 × 38 will be ten times smaller than 543 × 38, so: 2063.4. Ask: *What about 5.43 × 38?* Elicit that in this instance the answer will be 100 times smaller than 20,634, so: 206.34.

Independent work: Hand out photocopiable page 'Sponsored walk' from the CD-ROM for the children to work through independently if they can.

Progress check: Pause the children after the first section. If necessary, point out that some of the amounts are given as pence and some as pounds, so suggest that they put all the amounts as decimal parts of a pound. Check that they remember how to find the average (mean) cost.

Review

Discuss the methods the children used for multiplication. Ask: *Which calculations did you do mentally? Which methods did you use to check your answers?*

 SCHOLASTIC

Solving problems with percentages, fractions and decimals

Expected prior learning

Children should be able to:

- multiply and divide mentally by 10, 100 and 1000
- understand percentage as the number of parts in every 100
- find simple percentages
- halve and double numbers.

Topic	Curriculum objectives	Expected outcomes
Ratio and proportion	**Lesson 1**	
	To solve problems involving the calculation of percentages [for example, 15% of 360] and the use of percentages for comparison.	Understand *per cent* as number of parts per one hundred.
	Lesson 2	
	To solve problems involving the calculation of percentages [for example, 15% of 360] and the use of percentages for comparison.	Understand the application of percentages. Find and compare percentages.
	Lesson 3	
	To solve problems involving the calculation of percentages [for example, 15% of 360] and the use of percentages for comparison.	Find percentages by combining different simple percentages.
	Lesson 4	
	To solve problems involving the calculation of percentages [for example, 15% of 360] and the use of percentages for comparison.	Apply percentages to problem solving.
Fractions (including decimals and percentages)	**Lesson 5**	
	To recall and use equivalences between simple fractions, decimals and percentages, including in different contexts.	Convert fractions to decimals to percentages, and vice versa.

Preparation

Lesson 1: enlarge 'Hundred square' or have it available from the CD-ROM; copy and laminate a copy for each pair of children

Lesson 2: prepare sets of cards with amounts on and cards with percentages on for each pair; group them according to ability

Lesson 4: write on the board the information for paired work

Lesson 5: write the equivalences on the board for independent work

You will need

General resources
'Hundred square'

Equipment
Individual whiteboards and pens; marker pens; amounts cards (40, 50, 150 and so on); percentage cards; on-screen calculator; calculators

Further practice

Photocopiable sheets
'Discount electrics'

Oral and mental starters suggested for week 3

See the bank of starters on pages 164, 165 and 206. Oral and mental starters are also on the CD-ROM.

40 Tenths and hundredths

42 Halving and doubling

49 Order the fractions

50 Equivalent fractions

59 Percentage bingo

Overview of progression

At the start of the week children will be consolidating their understanding of the term *percentage*, then they will work on calculating percentages using different methods. They will come to understand that calculating a percentage of a quantity is the same as calculating a fraction of a quantity. They will learn to compare percentages and understand how percentages are used in context, particularly linked to discounts and increases up or down, in order to find the solution. Children then multiply a two-digit multiple of 10 by a one-digit number. They use table facts that they already know to find solutions. They move on to scaling up measures, such as increasing the amount of ingredients needed for two people, instead of just one. Finally, they solve word problems that bring together the learning for this week.

Watch out for

Some children will find it difficult to understand that percentages can be greater than 100%, so they might need to examine this in some detail. Some children might also become confused when using percentages with measures. Help them to distinguish between the two during problem-solving work.

Creative context

Explain that it is useful to understand percentages for everyday banking scenarios, for example interest on savings is usually quoted as a percentage. Similarly when people are borrowing money for mortgages or other purchases it is vital to be able to calculate the interest costs which will be quoted as percentages.

Vocabulary

discount, equivalent, hundredth, increase, per cent (%), percentage, recurring, rounding, tenth

Curriculum objectives

● To solve problems involving the calculation of percentages [for example, 15% of 360] and the use of percentages for comparison.

Success criteria

● I can calculate and compare percentages of whole numbers.

You will need

Equipment

Individual whiteboards; amounts cards; percentage cards

Differentiation

Less confident learners

Limit the percentages to 1%, 10%, 25% and 50%.

More confident learners

Include percentages over 100%.

Lesson 1   Oral and mental starter 40

Main teaching activities

Whole-class work: Remind the children what they have learned about percentages, ask the children when they have heard *100%* used; perhaps as a test score or that someone has 'given *100%*' effort. Ask some quick-fire questions:

- *If you scored 50% in a test with 100 questions, how many did you get right?*
- *If you scored 100% in a test with 20 questions, how many did you get right?*
- *If you scored 50% in a test with 20 questions, how many did you get right?*

Establish that to calculate a percentage, you can divide by 100 to find 1% and then multiply by the required per cent. To demonstrate, ask: *How do we find 34% of 150?* Elicit that $\frac{1}{100}$ of 150 is 1.5, so to find 34%, multiply 34 by 1.5 (51). So, 34% of 150 is 51. Go on to calculate 46% of 84 (38.64). Encourage a volunteer to demonstrate this and discuss each stage with the class.

Paired work: Children will need piles of digit cards with amounts on (50, 40, 150 and so on) and one pile of cards with percentages on. Explain that each child selects two or three digit cards to make an amount and also a percentage card. They should use the percentage as an operator on the amount, calculate the answer and then compare it with their partner: the highest amount is winner. So, if child A selects the amount 140 and a percentage card of 40%, and child B selects 80 and 75%, child A's answer would be 56 and child B's answer would be 60 so child B is the winner. Ask the children to keep a record of the calculations and the scores.

Progress check: Pause the children and ask one or two pairs to share their first example with the class. Check that the children appreciate that the answer is dependent upon the size of the percentage as well as the starting number.

Review

Ask: *Which is higher, 55% of 300 or 95% of 200? How did you work that out? Did anyone do it in a different way? What is higher, 59% of 200 or 75% of 160?*

Curriculum objectives

● To solve problems involving the calculation of percentages and the use of percentages for comparison.

Success criteria

● I can calculate different percentages by combining simple ones.

You will need

Equipment

Individual whiteboards; on-screen calculator; calculators

Differentiation

Less confident learners

Give children cards with the amounts: £50, 300m, £200 and 450cm. Ask them to use these amounts with the operators on the board.

More confident learners

When they finished let children suggest their own amounts and operators.

Lesson 2   Oral and mental starter 42

Main teaching activities

Whole-class work: Remind the children that they have been finding percentages of quantities. Write 600m on board and ask: *What is 10% of 600m?* Establish that 10% is 60m, then extend to 1%, 5% and 2.5 % (15m). Then ask: *How can we use this information to work out 35% of 600m?* Invite a child to demonstrate 3 × 60m + 30m = 210m. Similarly, go through 27.5% of 600m: 2 × 60m + 30m + 15m = 165m. Then ask: *How would you calculate 99% of £400?* Advise the children to find 1% (£4) and subtract this from 100%.

Paired work: Write the following amounts on the board: £54, 360m, £196, 465cm; and the operators: 99%, 17.5%, 51%, 11%, 49%. Explain to the children that one of them should select the amount and their partner should choose the operator. They then each work out the answer and record it.

Progress check: Pause the children and check one of the examples. Ask how they could check their answer. Suggest finding 1% and scaling up.

Review

Go through some of the examples with the children. Then challenge them to calculate 12% of 240 (28.8) and to use another method to check their answer. Ask: *How did you work that out? Did anyone do it in a different way?*

Curriculum objectives
● To solve problems involving the calculation of percentages and the use of percentages for comparison.

Success criteria
● I can calculate and compare percentages of whole numbers.

You will need

Equipment
Individual whiteboards

Differentiation

Less confident learners
These children may need support to identify the calculation for each percentage.

More confident learners
Suggest that these children may devise their own timetable of lessons for a day and calculate the percentage time spent on each lesson.

Lesson 3 — Oral and mental starter 42

Main teaching activities

Whole-class work: Tell the children that in this lesson they will be looking at how they spend the school day. If the day is from 8.30 until 3.30 (7 hours) with lunch from 12 to 1, they have 6 hours of lesson time. In one day lessons are: PE: ¾ hour; English: 1½ hours; Maths: 1 hour; Science: 1¼ hours; History: 50 minutes; RE: 40 minutes.

Ask the children what fraction of the day is spent on PE, elicit that as the lesson is ¾ hour that is 45 mins out of the total of 360 minutes for the day, hence it is 45/360 or 1/8. Remind the children that to convert the fraction to a decimal it is necessary to divide the numerator by the denominator, hence 0.125 which as a percentage is 12.5%.

Paired work: Ask the children to calculate the percentage of the school day of 6 hours that is spent on each subject, rounding to two decimal places. English 1½ hours (25%); Maths 1 hour (16.667%); Science 1¼ hours (20.83%); History 50 min (13.89%); *RE* 40 minutes (*11.11%*)

Progress check: Stop the children and ask if there are any percentages that they are having difficulty with, remind them that they should round the answers to two decimal places

Review

Go through the answers with the children and check the strategies that they have used. Ask how they have checked their answers, remind them that they should all total 100%.

Curriculum objectives
● To solve problems involving the calculation of percentages and the use of percentages for comparison.

Success criteria
● I can apply percentages to problem solving.

You will need

Equipment
Individual whiteboards

Differentiation

Less confident learners
Help children break down the percentage total into more manageable amounts, for example 26% is 10% × 2 + 5% + 1%.

More confident learners
When the children have finished the paired work, ask them to find an alternative method to work out the answer.

Lesson 4 — Oral and mental starter 59

Main teaching activity

Whole-class work: Tell the children that in the next two lessons they will be learning about how percentages are used in daily life, and they will be looking for the best ways to calculate and use percentages. Consider the best way to work out these examples:

- 11% of 200. (Find 10% and then 1%.)
- 52% of 1500. (Find 50% and then 2 × 1%.)
- 14% of 4500. (Find 10%, 5% and 1%.)
- 17½ of 3900 (Find 10%, 5%, then halve again to find 2½%.)

Examine the children's solutions. Which strategies did they find most useful?

Paired work: Ask the children to work out the total number of votes received by each party in the following elections:

- *Downtown*: Red Party 43%, Blue Party 31%, Green Party 26%. Total votes 15,000.
- *Upstate*: Red Party 63%, Blue Party 19%, Green Party 18%. Total votes 24,000.
- *Knoxville*: Red Party 72%, Blue Party 19%, Green Party 9%. Total votes 18,000.
- *Marston*: Red Party 32%, Blue Party 22%, Green Party 46%. Total votes 32,000.

Progress check: Pause the children and ask them how they have calculated the number of votes for Downtown. Suggest that they should check their answers by using a different strategy.

Review

Go through the children's answers. Ask questions such as: *Which amounts were more straightforward to find? How did you check your answers?*

Curriculum objectives
● To recall and use equivalences between simple fractions, decimals and percentages.

Success criteria
● I can find equivalences between fractions, decimals and percentages.

You will need

Equipment

Individual whiteboards; calculators

Differentiation

Less confident learners

Support children by going through the worked examples with them and advising them to use this as a structure to follow.

More confident learners

Encourage children to use more complex fractions as their starting point, especially those that may give a recurring decimal number. Ask them to think about why there are recurring numbers.

Lesson 5
Oral and mental starter 50

Main teaching activities

Whole-class work: Explain to the children that in this last lesson of the week they will be looking at the relationship between fractions, decimals and percentages. Remind them that they already know decimal equivalents for many common fractions. Ask them for the decimal equivalents of some common fractions, such as: ½ (0.5), ¼ (0.25), ¾ (0.75). Similarly, they will know that $\frac{3}{10}$ is equivalent to 0.3, so ask them for the decimal equivalent of $\frac{4}{10}$, $\frac{7}{10}$ and so on. Prompt the children to notice that $\frac{7}{10}$ is also equivalent to $\frac{70}{100}$ or $\frac{700}{1000}$.

Now write 0.265 on the board. Explain that this is the sum of 0.2 + 0.06 + 0.005. Ask:

- *What is 0.2 as a fraction? ($\frac{2}{10}$, which is equivalent to $\frac{20}{100}$ or $\frac{200}{1000}$.)*
- *What is 0.06 as a fraction? ($\frac{6}{100}$ which is equivalent to $\frac{60}{1000}$.)*
- *What is 0.005 as a fraction? ($\frac{5}{1000}$.)*

Go on to explain that, if we look at the decimal equivalents that are in thousandths, we can add them together. Hence:
$0.2 + 0.06 + 0.005 = \frac{200}{1000} + \frac{60}{1000} + \frac{5}{1000} = \frac{265}{1000}$.

Show the children that, to find the percentage equivalent for a decimal, it is necessary to multiply by 100, as *per cent* means 'out of a hundred'. Hence the percentage equivalent of 0.265 would be 26.5%.

Independent work: Ask the children to work independently to find the equivalent fraction, decimal or percentage for each of the following. Make sure the children understand that they need to provide *two* equivalences each time.

$\frac{3}{8}$; 0.3; 45%; $\frac{5}{8}$; 0.35; $\frac{3}{5}$; 22%; 0.4; 33⅓%

Progress check: Pause the children after a short time to check that they are confident with the task, and check the first few results. Then tell the children that, when they have completed the examples given, they should generate some full sets of three equivalences of their own.

Review

Write the fraction ⅓ on the board. Tell the children that you want them to use their calculators to work out the decimal. Ask: *What is shown in the calculator display?* Invite a volunteer to copy from their calculator onto the board (0.33333333). Explain that with some fractions, such as ⅓, there will not be an exact decimal equivalent because there would be an infinite number of 3s following the decimal point. We usually write decimals rounded to an agreed number of places, so, to two decimal places, for example, ⅓ would be 0.33.

Ask the children: *Can you work out ⅔ rounded to three decimal places?* (0.667). Help the children to notice that in this instance it was necessary to round *up*. Give some other examples for the children to convert, such as ⅗ and ⅕.

Simple formulae

Expected prior learning

Children should be able to:

- use common formulae such as (a) area of rectangle = l (length) × w (width).

Topic	Curriculum objectives	Expected outcomes
Algebra	**Lesson 1**	
	To express missing number problems algebraically.	Use and devise simple formulae.
	To use simple formulae.	
	Lesson 2	
	To express missing number problems algebraically.	Use and devise simple formulae.
	To use simple formulae.	
	Lesson 3	
	To use simple formulae.	Construct and use simple expressions and formulae in words then symbols.
	Lesson 4	
	To express missing number problems algebraically.	Find unknowns that will satisfy number sentences.
		Use simple formulae.
	Lesson 5	
	To find pairs of numbers that satisfy an equation with two unknowns.	Find two unknowns that will satisfy number sentences.

Preparation

Lesson 1: copy 'What's it worth?' for each child

Lesson 2: copy 'Formula 1' for each child

Lesson 3: copy 'Monty the match snake' for each child

Lesson 5: write the number sentences for independent work on the board

You will need

Photocopiable sheets
'What's it worth?'; 'Formula 1'; 'Monty the match snake'

General resources
Interactive activity 'Letter time'

Equipment
Individual whiteboards; matchsticks, or similar

Further practice

Interactive activity 'Letter time'

Oral and mental starters suggested for week 4

See the bank of starters on pages 125, 126 and 164. Oral and mental starters are also on the CD-ROM.

27 Jumping forwards and backwards

28 Number order

30 Quick additions

33 Decimal additions

43 Target 100

Overview of progression

During this week the children will be developing their understanding of algebra. They will revisit known formulae, practise using them and from there begin to construct formulae themselves. Later in the week they will use this understanding to solve problems where missing numbers are expressed algebraically.

Watch out for

Children often find it difficult to understand that symbols or letters can represent unknowns and that these can be different in different expressions, but that these unknowns can be found from the information in the rest of the sentence or calculation. Make sure that children are clear about arithmetical rules that relate to algebra in the same way as to number sentences with full digits, for example: $a + b = b + a$, and $2(a + b) = 2a + 2b$. Children also sometimes find it difficult to group terms. Help them to understand that, for example: $2y + x + 3y + 2x = 5y + 3x$.

Creative context

Algebra can be used across many areas where there are unknown values. Ask the children to look out for them in other topics across the curriculum and in real life, particularly in science.

Vocabulary

algebra, commutative property, formula, formulae, equation, expression, pattern, rule, **sequence**, term, unknown, variable

Curriculum objectives
● To express missing number problems algebraically.
● To use simple formulae.

Success criteria
● I can use simple formulae.
● I can express missing numbers algebraically.

You will need

Photocopiable sheets
'What's it worth?'

Equipment
Individual whiteboards

Differentiation

Less confident learners

Children should focus on the first part of 'What's it worth?'. They may need support with working on it.

More confident learners

Challenge children to write their own word problems and then make up simple formulae for solving them.

Lesson 1   Oral and mental starter 30

Main teaching activities

Whole-class work: Explain to the children that in mathematics, letters sometimes represent numbers, in cases where, for example, a number is not known or might change. Tell the children, if they have not heard of it already, that this is called *algebra*. Write up and talk through the following example: *If x = 4, what is 2 times x?* Encourage the children to offer suggestions for x, then show them that *2 times x* can also be written as 2x, where the multiplication is implicit, and the multiplication sign is therefore not needed. So, 2x = 8. Try these further examples: *If x = 4, what is 8x? ...12x? ...9x?*

When the children are showing good understanding, ask them how they could combine this technique with that of using letters to write formulae. Remind them of the formulae they know already. For example, the formula for calculating an area is length × width: $a = l \times w$, and for a perimeter is (length + width) × 2: $p = 2(l + w)$.

Next, show the children how to devise a simple formula or equation to help them work out a problem. Try an example such as: *If sweets cost 7p each, how can we work out the cost for any number of sweets?* Work through the process with the children, asking the following questions:

● *What do we want to find out?* The total cost, so call this c.
● *What do we know?* Sweets are 7p each, so c = [a number] × 7.
● *How many do we want?* We don't know – it's variable, so call the missing number n.
● So, the cost will be 7 pence × the number of sweets, or c = 7n.

Try out the formula together. Say: *I want 6 sweets. How much will this cost?* (c = 7n, so c = 7 × 6 = 42p.)

Now ask the children to write the formula or equation for the cost of sweets at 4p each. Elicit that c = 4n.

Then work on the following as a class:

● *What is the number of months in y years?* (m = 12y.)
● *What is the formula for finding the nth term of this sequence: 4, 8, 12, 16, 20?* (n = 4n.)
● *There are x carrots in a field. How many carrots will each rabbit get if there are 6 rabbits?* ($\frac{x}{6}$, or x ÷ 6.)

Independent work: Give out photocopiable page 'What's it worth?' from the CD-ROM to provide practice in basic algebra. Before the children work on their own, show and explain these additional algebra statements: n divided by 5 = $\frac{n}{5}$; $n \times n = n^2$; $a \times b = ab$; 3 × n = 3n.

Progress check: Pause the children when they have had enough time to work through Section 1. Check the first few answers. Talk through any difficulties and misconceptions, and make sure that the children are able to apply the statements above when necessary.

Review

Write the following formulae on the board and ask the children to explain what they mean: $\frac{x}{6}$; xy; 12n; p^2. Invite individuals to make up a question to go with each statement. Then ask the rest of the class to work through the question to see if the understanding of the algebra is correct.

■SCHOLASTIC

Curriculum objectives
● To express missing number problems algebraically.
● To use simple formulae.

Success criteria
● I can use simple formulae.
● I can express missing numbers algebraically.

You will need

Photocopiable sheets
'Formula 1'

General resources
Interactive activity 'Letter time'

Equipment
Individual whiteboards

Differentiation

Less confident learners
Children should work as a group with some support, discussing each question to make sure that they understand the concept. With support, they could work on interactive activity 'Letter time' first to help with this.

More confident learners
Challenge children to investigate other formulae, for example that for the circumference of a circle.

Main teaching activities

Whole-class work: Remind the children that in mathematics, relationships between numbers can be written using symbols – often letters of the alphabet – and that these symbols are often used in simple formulae to help us with certain rules and calculations.

Write up a simple example on the board, similar to the main one in lesson 1 and talk the children through it:

We could denote a packet of sweets by the letter p. The cost of each individual packet could be shown by the letter c. If we wanted to find the total cost (t) of a number of packets of sweets we could use the formula t = p × c or, in full: total cost (t) = number of packets (p) × cost of one packet (c).

Check understanding and go on to use another example. Establish first with the children that the area of a rectangle or square can be calculated by multiplying the length by the width. Invite a volunteer to confirm that in formula terms this could be written as a (area) = l (length) × w (width). Ask the children what other formulae could be developed from this. Look for responses using the inverse: l = a/w and w = a/l.

Then ask the children if they can give you a formula for finding the perimeter of a rectangle or square. Encourage them to produce several alternatives. They could use p = l + w + l + w in various forms, or p = (l + w) × 2, or p = 2(l + w). From this last example, emphasise that in these types of formulae, a letter and number next to each other with no visible operation sign always means multiply. So, for example: 2t = 2 × t, and 5n = 5 × n.

Independent work: Provide the children with photocopiable page 'Formula 1' from the CD-ROM to work through.

Progress check: Pause the children when they have had time to complete the first part of the photocopiable sheet, and check that they have understood each of the terms.

Review

Check through the calculations that the children have carried out on the photocopiable sheet and ensure figures have been correctly matched to letters in formulae. Select one of the formulae from the sheet and say: *Explain what this formula means?*

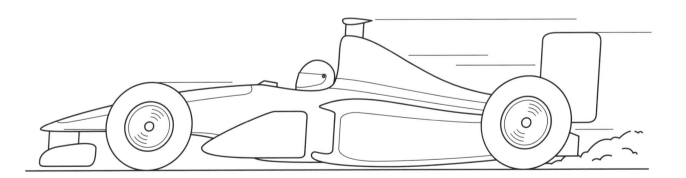

Curriculum objectives
● To use simple formulae.
Success criteria
● I can create and use simple formulae expressed in words and symbols.

You will need
Photocopiable sheets
'Monty the match snake'
Equipment
Individual whiteboards; matchsticks or similar (for support)

Differentiation
Less confident learners
Let children continue the pattern with matchsticks as a practical aid. Ask them to find the eighth, tenth and twentieth segments.

More confident learners
Challenge children to go on to investigate different shapes such as hexagons.

Main teaching activities

Whole-class work: Tell the children that they are going to investigate growing patterns and how they are generated. Draw these two patterns on the board:

Then ask the children to draw the next pattern on their whiteboards:

Check the children's patterns, then explain that pattern 1 (the first term) can be written as (3 × 1) + 2. How could the second and third terms be written? (3 × 2) + 2; (3 × 3) + 2. What is happening in the pattern? Ask: *What would be the tenth term?* (3 × 10) + 2 = 32. *And the thirtieth?* (3 × 30) + 2 = 92. *What about the hundredth?* (3 × 100) + 2 = 302. Elicit that this formula can be written as 3n + 2.

Paired work: Ask the children to construct a similar pattern, for example 6n + 4. Explain that, after the first three sequences, they should produce a formula. Ask the pairs to swap their patterns with another pair and find the tenth and hundredth terms.

Progress check: Choose one or two pairs to explain their growing patterns. Check that the children are able to find the nth term.

Independent work: Ask the children to work through photocopiable page 'Monty the match snake' from the CD-ROM.

Review

Discuss the formula needed to solve the problem of Monty's body. Elicit 4 + 3n; 4 being the head of the snake. Ask: *What is the total number of matches in the tenth term?* 4 + (3 × 10) = 34. Can the children work out the twenty-fifth and fiftieth terms?

Curriculum objectives
● To express missing number problems algebraically.
Success criteria
● I can solve missing number problems.
● I can express missing number problems algebraically.

You will need
Equipment
Individual whiteboards

Differentiation
Less confident learners
Children may need adult support to talk through each step.

More confident learners
Give children some further, more complex problems, such as: 3(a + 2) = 14 − a, to discuss as a group.

Main teaching activities

Whole-class work: Tell the children that they are going to work on some algebraic calculations. Write on the board: 15 − ? = 3. Ask the children what the missing number is? (12.) Establish that the missing number could be called 'a', then: if 15 − a = 3, then a = 12. Ask: *What if we have 15 − 2a = 3?* Then 2a is 12. Remind the children that 2a is 2 times a, hence a = 6.

Write these challenges on the board for the children to answer quickly on their whiteboards:

● *Find the value of y in y + 3 = 7.* (4.)
● *Find the value of b in 9 − b = 5.* (4.)
● *Find the value of p in 10 = 5 + p.* (5.)
● *Find the value of d in 2d − 4 = 6.* (5.)

Progress check: Go back to the first number sentence and ask: *If this were written as 3 + y = 7, what would the value of y be?* Children should recognise straight away that y = 4. Recap that y + 3 = 3 + y and that with addition the *commutative property* applies, the addition can be done in any order.

Review

Ask the children how they would solve the following: 3 + y + 9 + 2y = 18. Elicit that they should group like terms, so: 3 + 9 + y + 2y = 18. Invite a volunteer to demonstrate the next steps: 12 + 3y = 18, leading to 3y = 6, so y = 2.

Curriculum objectives
● To find pairs of numbers that satisfy an equation with two unknowns.

Success criteria
● I can find pairs of numbers in number sentences involving two unknowns.

You will need
Equipment
Individual whiteboards

Differentiation
Less confident learners

Give children more practice at finding many possible values for unknowns in expressions such as x + y = 20 before they attempt the independent work.

More confident learners

When children have completed the given examples, suggest they investigate more complex expressions and devise some questions of their own.

Lesson 5   Oral and mental starter 33

Main teaching activities

Whole-class work: Let the children know that in this lesson they will be continuing with algebraic calculations and problems, but that this time, there might be more than one 'unknown' number expressed as a letter and to be found.

To start off, write on the board: a + b = 12. Ask the children what possible values there could be for a and b. The children are likely to suggest 2 and 10, 3 and 9, and so on. Some may offer decimal numbers or negative numbers. Explain that there could be a wide range of numbers, but, in this case where there is no specific context, as long as the two numbers satisfy the expression, they are acceptable solutions.

Now add the criterion that a > b. Ask: *Now what are some possible values for a and b?* Again, the children should be able to generate quite a few suggestions. Establish that there is still a range of possible numbers that would satisfy the expression, as long as the value of a is greater than the value of b.

Next, write p + q = 15, and ask: *What is the value of p if q = 8?* Encourage the children to attempt an answer, then explain, or confirm, that in this expression, we can substitute the value of q (8), so we have p + 8 = 15, hence p = 7.

Independent work: Write the following on the board for the children to work out on their whiteboards:

- A + B = 9, what is the value of B when A = 2?
- B − A = 7, what is the value of A when B = 12?

Progress check: Check that the children have the found the correct values. Make sure that the children appreciate that the two expressions bear no relationship to each other; the terms A and B simply represent the unknowns in each individual expression.

Independent work: Continue by writing the following on the board and asking the children to find the unknown values:

- *8 = a − c. What is the value of c when a = 19?* (11.)
- *b + d = 8. What is the value of b when d = 3?* (5.)
- *p + s + p = 10. What is the value of p if s = 4?* (3.)
- *2c − a = 7. What is the value of c if a = 3?* (2.)

Review

Check the children's answers to the questions above. Go over any difficulties.

Then write on the board: 2(x + y) = 16. Ask: *What values could x and y have?* (Possible answers are 1 and 7; 2 and 6; 3 and 5.) Share answers and ask the children to explain their thinking. Point out to the children, if they have not already noticed, that 2(x + y) = 2x + 2y. Then add: *If we are then told that y = 5, what is the value of x?* Elicit the answer that x = 3, and check that the children realise that if one of the unknown values is given (y = 5), then there is only one value for the other (x must equal 3).

Measurement

Expected prior learning

Children should be able to:

- convert between different units of metric measure
- understand the use of equivalences between metric units and common imperial units.

Topic	Curriculum objectives	Expected outcomes
Measurement	**Lesson 1**	
	To use, read, write and convert between standard units, converting measurements of length, mass, volume and time from a smaller unit of measure to a larger unit, and vice versa, using decimal notation up to three decimal places.	Convert between standard units of measurement, using decimal notation up to three decimal places.
	Lesson 2	
	To use, read, write and convert between standard units, converting measurements of length, mass, volume and time from a smaller unit of measure to a larger unit, and vice versa, using decimal notation up to three decimal places.	Read, write and convert between standard units of measurement for length, mass and volume using decimal notation up to three decimal places.
	Lesson 3	
	To use, read, write and convert between standard units, converting measurements of length, from a smaller unit of measure to a larger unit, and vice versa, using decimal notation up to three decimal places.	Read, write and convert between standard units of length, using decimal notation up to three decimal places.
	Lesson 4	
	To solve problems involving the calculation and conversion of units of measure, using decimal notation up to three decimal places where appropriate.	Solve problems involving the calculation and conversion of units of measure, using decimal notation.
	Lesson 5	
	To calculate the area of parallelograms and triangles.	Calculate the areas of parallelograms and triangles.
	To recognise when it is possible to use the formulae for area and volume of shapes.	Recognise when to use formulae for area and volume of shapes.

■SCHOLASTIC

Preparation

Lesson 1: prepare a poster of metric abbreviations and conversions as a classroom resource

Lesson 3: copy 'Inch by inch' for each child

Lesson 4: enlarge 'European holiday' or have it available for display from the CD-ROM; prepare a copy for each child

Lesson 5: copy 'Areas' for each pair of children

You will need

Photocopiable sheets

'Inch by inch'; 'European holiday'; 'Areas'

Equipment

Individual whiteboards; rulers; tape measures; trundle wheels; weighing scales; jug; plastic cups; calculators; place value charts; metric abbreviations and conversions poster

Further practice

Photocopiable sheets

'New measures'

General resources

Interactive activity 'Perimeter and area'

Oral and mental starters suggested for week 5

See the bank of starters on pages 125, 126, 164 and 165. Oral and mental starters are also on the CD-ROM.

31 Multiplication rounds

36 Conversions

43 Target 100

47 Rounding decimals

52 Recording metric units

Overview of progression

At the start of the week the children will be reading, writing and converting between standard units of measurement. They will be converting measurements of length, mass and volume from a smaller unit to a larger unit, and vice versa. They will then apply this to real-life problems involving distance. At the end of the week they will develop their skills in finding the areas of triangles and parallelograms, as well as looking at calculating volume.

Watch out for

Children will have had some understanding about converting units of measure, but are sometimes confused by terms such as *milli* and *centi*. It is important that they have a real understanding of the sizes of units so that they can estimate and visualise the measurements. This will help to avoid or overcome confusion with the place value of units within measures.

Creative context

There are numerous opportunities to develop the creative context, especially with global education when children may be looking at different currencies. In practical situations, children may often come across mixed use of metric and imperial measures and need to be able to convert them easily, for example if planning a planting area or decorating their bedroom, or planning a holiday or excursion and exploring journey times and distances.

Vocabulary

about, approximately, centilitre (cl), centimetre (cm), foot (ft), estimate, gram (g), inch (in), kilogram (kg), kilometre (km), litre (l), measure, metre (m), mile, millilitre (ml), millimetre (mm), scale, table, tonne (t), yard (yd)

Curriculum objectives
● To use, read, write and convert between standard units, using decimal notation up to three decimal places.
Success criteria
● I can convert between standard units of measurement, using decimal notation.

You will need
Equipment
Individual whiteboards; various measuring equipment; place value charts

Differentiation
Less confident learners
Provide place value charts.
More confident learners
Children should challenge each other with real-life questions.

Lesson 1
Oral and mental starter 36

Main teaching activities

Whole-class work: Recap with the children that there are 1000m in a kilometre, 1000ml in a litre, 1000g in a kilogram, 1000mm in a metre and 100cm in a metre. Display a chart of metric abbreviations and equivalents.

Establish that 3kg 125g can be written in two other ways: by converting to grams (3125g) or as a decimal fraction of a kilogram (3.125kg). Notice that, as a decimal, only the kg unit is used, not the g. Ask the children to write 4723g in two other ways on their whiteboards. Then ask the children to try the same with the following, but stress the importance of place value:

- 2465m (2.465km or 2km 465m)
- 1.25l (1250ml or 1l 250ml)
- 76m (7600cm or 0.076km)
- 2km 5m (2.005km or 2005m)

Progress check: Invite children to come out and record their answers and explain their reasoning.

Independent work: Explain to the children that you want them to measure various items around the classroom or the school. They may choose to measure length, weight or capacity but must record their results on a table showing the measurement in at least two ways.

Review

Display a place value chart. Ask the children where they would place 1m, 10m, 100m and 1000m. Repeat the process for 1g, 10g, 100g and 1000g, and 1ml, 10ml, 100ml and 1000ml.

Curriculum objectives
● To use, read, write and convert between standard units using decimal notation up to three decimal places.
Success criteria
● I can read, write and convert between standard units of measurement for length, mass and volume using decimal notation up to three decimal places.

You will need
Equipment
Individual whiteboards; rulers, metre sticks, tape measures, trundle wheels

Differentiation
Less confident learners
These children may need support to decide which calculations they should be using for each conversion.
More confident learners
This group should be encouraged to calculate the decimal equivalents of larger units.

Lesson 2
Oral and mental starter 52

Main teaching activities

Whole-class work: Explain to the children they are now going to be working with units of time. Recap units of time: 60 seconds in a minute, 60 minutes in an hour, 24 hours in a day, 7 days in a week and so on. Point out that as these are not metric units we have to think more carefully about the calculations when we convert from smaller to larger units and vice versa. Ask: *How many seconds in 4½ minutes?* ($4 \times 60 + 30 = 270$ seconds.)

Ask: *How many seconds in 2 hours 25 minutes?* Elicit that this is ($2 \times 60 \times 60$) + (25×60) = 8700 seconds. Now try: *What is 6264 seconds in hours, minutes and seconds?* Work through this with the children. Ask: *What do we do first?* Divide by 60 to convert to minutes (104 r 24), then divide by 60 to convert to hours = 1 hour 44 minutes. Hence 6264 seconds is 1 hour, 44 minutes and 24 seconds.

Independent work: Ask the children to convert the following:

- 3 hours 45 minutes to minutes (225 minutes) and then to seconds (13500 seconds).
- 3 days 6 hours to hours (78 hours) and then to minutes (4680 minutes).
- 2 weeks 3 days 10 hours to days and hours (17 days 10 hours) and then to hours (418 hours).
- 34 hours to days (1.4167 days) and then to weeks (0.2024 weeks).

Progress check: Check the calculations the children are using for the second example. Make sure they realise that this is now converting from days to hours.

Review

Check the calculations that the children have completed, discuss any difficulties and compare strategies that the children have used.

Ask them to convert the following: 6 weeks, 5 days and 3 hours to hours (1131). Then convert 2910 minutes to weeks giving the answer to three decimal places (2.021 weeks).

 SCHOLASTIC

Curriculum objectives

● To use, read, write and convert between standard units, converting measurements of length from a smaller unit of measure to a larger unit and vice versa, using decimal notation.

Success criteria

● I can read, write and convert between standard units of measurement for length, using decimal notation.

You will need

Photocopiable sheets

'Inch by inch'

Equipment

Individual whiteboards; rulers, metre sticks, tape measures, trundle wheels

Differentiation

Less confident learners

Support children when they are calculating the conversions. Make sure, too, that they are confident and accurate when measuring.

More confident learners

Extend children to making conversions between feet and metres, and vice versa, encouraging them to use decimal numbers. For example: *Convert 6m into feet* (19.5ft). They could also investigate conversions between other metric and imperial measures.

Lesson 3

Oral and mental starter 31

Main teaching activities

Whole-class work: Encourage the children to give you examples of imperial units of measurement: inch, foot, yard, mile, pint, gallon and so on. Explain that, many years ago, people measured a distance by pacing out with their feet, but as feet are different sizes this had to be standardised to give 12 inches = 1 foot. Tailors measured cloth by holding it between the tip of their nose and the tips of their fingers, so again this needed to be standardised to 3 feet = 1 yard. Compare this with metric measurements which are based on units of 10.

Say to the children that, if 12 inches = 1 foot and 3 feet = 1 yard, how many inches are there in a yard? ($12 \times 3 = 36$in.) Write this on the board and help the children to recognise and understand the abbreviations and symbols: *in* ("), *ft* (') and *yd*.

Then write up the metric equivalents for imperial units:

- 1 inch = approximately 2.5cm.
- 1 metre = 39 inches (3' 3").

Explain that the conversions will not necessarily be completely accurate and there is usually a degree of approximation when converting between different types of unit. Check that the children understand these equivalents, then ask how they might be able to convert between these units. Elicit that if 1 inch = 2.5cm, they can multiply the number of inches by 2.5 to get the number of centimetres.

Ask the children to convert the following into centimetres on their whiteboards:

- 6 inches (15cm)
- 9 inches (22.5cm)
- 15 inches (37.5cm)

Check the children's answers, then ask them how they could convert from centimetres to inches. (Divide by 2.5.) Ask them to convert the following to inches:

- 24cm (9.6in)
- 14cm (5.6in)
- 30cm (12in)

Paired work: Set the children working in pairs to measure two or three objects around the classroom. Tell them to measure in either centimetres or inches and then convert their measurements to the metric/imperial equivalents.

Progress check: Ask the pairs to share some of their measurements with the class, and challenge the other children to work out the metric/imperial equivalents. Make sure that they are converting accurately, and talk through any misunderstandings as necessary.

Independent work: Give the children rulers and photocopiable pages 'Inch by inch' from the CD-ROM to complete. These provide practice in measuring and then converting their measurements from metric to imperial, and vice versa.

Review

Review some of the measurements that the children have done in their pairs, and ask the rest of the children to check the conversions. Then ask the class: *How many inches in 10cm?* (4.) *How many centimetres in 16 inches?* (40.)

Curriculum objectives
● To solve problems involving the calculation and conversion of units of measure, using decimal notation up to three decimal places.
Success criteria
● I can solve problems involving the calculation and conversion of units of measure, using decimal numbers.

You will need
Photocopiable sheets
'European holiday'

Differentiation
Less confident learners
Children work as a group.
More confident learners
Children calculate a route in both miles and kilometres.

Lesson 4   Oral and mental starter 47

Main teaching activities

Whole-class work: Explain that although many measurements in this country are in metric units, imperial units are still quite widely used. Ask the children where they have seen imperial units in use (height, which is often given in feet and inches, and travelling distances, which are more often in miles). Point out that our driving speed limits in the UK are given in miles per hour. Tell the children that, by contrast, when driving abroad it is sometimes necessary to convert from metric to imperial units. Speed limits are most often given in km per hour and distances in km. Display the table of driving distances from photocopiable page 'European holiday' from the CD-ROM and ask the children a few questions from it to check understanding.

Independent work: Give the children the photocopiable sheet to complete.

Progress check: Pause the children after they have decided which ferry ports to use, and make sure that they are using the correct conversion. Remind them that a mile is longer than a kilometre, so there will be fewer miles than kilometres.

Review
Check the children have rounded up or down correctly in the last part of the photocopiable sheet. Then ask the children to calculate how many kilometres are equivalent to 70 miles (113km). How did they calculate the answer? Ensure they understand: converting miles to kilometres, *divide* by 0.62; converting kilometres to miles, *multiply* by 0.62.

Curriculum objectives
● To calculate the area of parallelograms and triangles.
● To recognise when to use the formulae for area and volume of shapes.
Success criteria
● I can use formulae to calculate the area of parallelograms and triangles.

You will need
Photocopiable sheets
'Areas'
Equipment
Individual whiteboards

Differentiation
Less confident learners
Let children work as a group with support.
More confident learners
Ask children to devise their own challenges for each other, using other shapes.

Lesson 5   Oral and mental starter 43

Main teaching activities

Whole-class work: Revise with the children what they learned about finding the area of parallelograms and triangles last term (Week 6, Lessons 2 and 3). Show this diagram:

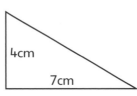

Ask the children to find the area of the triangle: ½ base × height (½ × 7cm × 4cm = 14cm²). Check that they understand that the answer must be in units *squared*. Then show the next triangle:

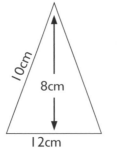

Ask the children to find the area. Elicit that they will need the base, length and the height. Area formula = ½ base × height = ½ × 12cm × 8cm = 48 cm².

Now ask the children how they could find the area of this parallelogram (below, right).

Elicit the formula area = base × height, so the area is 60 units².

Paired work: Hand out photocopiable page 'Areas' from the CD-ROM for children to calculate the remaining areas.

Progress check: Check that the pairs are identifying the correct calculations for the areas and that they are including the correct square units in the answers.

6cm
10cm

Review
Ask the children how they would find the volume of a cuboid with side lengths 5cm, 6cm and 9cm. Elicit that they would use the formula volume = length × width × height. So, the volume is 5cm × 6cm × 9cm = 270cms³. Check the children understand a volume like this is measured in units *cubed*.

Pie charts and line graphs

Expected prior learning

Children should be able to:

- interpret simple pie charts
- interpret and construct simple line graphs.

Topic	Curriculum objectives	Expected outcomes
Statistics	**Lesson 1**	
	To interpret and construct pie charts and line graphs and use these to solve problems.	Construct own pie charts and interpret them.
	Lesson 2	
	To interpret and construct pie charts and line graphs and use these to solve problems.	Construct and interpret straight line graphs.
	Lesson 3	
	To interpret and construct pie charts and line graphs and use these to solve problems.	Construct and interpret straight line graphs, including conversion graphs.
	Lesson 4	
	To interpret and construct pie charts and line graphs and use these to solve problems.	Construct and interpret line graphs, and set their own questions from them.
	Lesson 5	
	To interpret and construct pie charts and line graphs and use these to solve problems.	Construct and interpret curved line graphs.

Preparation

Lesson 1: draw the four different pie charts on the board

Lesson 3: make a note of current exchange rates to list on the board

Lesson 4: draw the data table on the board

Lesson 5: draw the data table and graph on the board

You will need

General resources

Interactive teaching resource 'Graphing tool'

Equipment

Individual whiteboards; rulers 360° protractors; squared paper; list of exchange rates

Further practice

General resources

Interactive teaching resource 'Graphing tool'

Oral and mental starters suggested for week 6

See the bank of starters on pages 164 and 165. Oral and mental starters are also on the CD-ROM.

41 Target number

47 Rounding decimals

51 Converting up and down

53 Get the point

Overview of progression

During this week the children will use their skills at interpreting and reading simple pie charts and line graphs to work on constructing them from given data. They will then move on to more complex graphs, including conversion graphs, which they will use to solve problems. They will collect, organise and interpret data in tables and present it on bar charts with the vertical axis marked in twos, fives and tens.

Watch out for

When children are working with representing data, they must be careful to use the correct scales and units. Make sure that they label the axes correctly on their graphs and input the data accurately. When children are working with pie charts they sometimes find it difficult to relate the sections of the pie chart to fractions or to angles as a proportion of 360°.

Creative context

Conversion graphs are often used in science and geography, as well as other data representations. If possible, provide opportunities for children to devise their own graphs from data they have collected in different contexts.

Vocabulary

chart, constant proportion, conversion graph, data, division, graph, horizontal axis, interval, line graph, origin, pie chart, scale, table, vertical axis

Curriculum objectives

● To interpret and construct pie charts and use these to solve problems.

Success criteria

● I can interpret and construct pie charts.

You will need

Equipment

Individual whiteboards; rulers; 360° protractors

Differentiation

Less confident learners

Suggest children work on pie charts with only ten sections.

More confident learners

Challenge children to make their own pie charts from blank circles, calculating their own angles and marking them using a 360° protractor.

Lesson 1   Oral and mental starter 47

Main teaching activities

Whole-class work: Tell the children that they are going to collect information to make their own pie charts. Remind them that the complete area of the circle of a pie chart represents all the data and that it is divided into sections, each showing different categories. Show examples on the board of four blank pie charts: 1: with 8 sections (45° angles); 2: with 10 sections (36° angles); 3: with 12 sections (30° angles); 4: with 24 sections (15° angles).

Explain to the children that pie charts can be divided into as many sections as they need. For eight sections the circle will need to be divided into segments with a 45° angle; ten sections will need a 36° angle and so on. Discuss possible topics that could be represented on such charts, including types of trees found in a park, a survey of favourite TV programmes.

Paired work: Children can choose a topic for their own pie chart. They should then collect data from their classmates, construct their own pie chart and write some questions to ask other children about their chart.

Progress check: Pause the children once they have constructed their charts, and check that they have worked out the sections of the pie chart correctly.

Review

Look at the pie charts that the children have produced. Let some of the pairs ask their questions and see if the class can answer them.

Curriculum objectives

● To interpret and construct line graphs and use these to solve problems.

Success criteria

● I can interpret and construct line graphs.

You will need

General resources

Interactive teaching resource 'Graphing tool'

Equipment

Squared paper

Differentiation

Less confident learners

Allow these children to work in a group and give them support in deciding which scale to use for their graph.

More confident learners

When children have completed their graph, ask them to make up questions about it to challenge the rest of the class.

Lesson 2   Oral and mental starter 41

Main teaching activities

Whole-class work: Use the interactive teaching resource 'Graphing tool' on the CD-ROM to draw the following graph: *Josh and Sarah take part in a cycle ride for charity. They cycle at a steady rate of 2km per half-hour. Plot the journey over 180 minutes.*

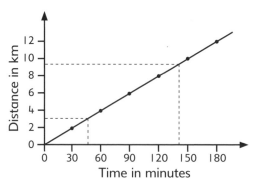

Ask: *How long did it take the riders to travel 11km?* Explain that this is a conversion graph to show the relationship between two units of measurement and that intermediary points between each marked division have values too.

Independent work: Say: *Jake also took part in the cycle ride. He left at 11am and cycled at a constant speed of 8km an hour for the first hour and a half. He then slowed-down to 5km an hour for the next hour and finished the ride at a speed of 10km an hour, reaching the end at 2pm.*

Ask the children to draw a graph of Jake's ride and then ask: *How far had Jake travelled by 12.30?* (12km); *How far did Jake travel altogether?* (22km); *How long did it take Jake to travel by 14km?* (1 hour 54mins)

Progress check: Check that the children are using the appropriate scale for the graphs and are able to read off the values correctly.

Review

Revisit the graph whole-class work. Say that another rider has joined the charity ride. Although she also travels at 2km per half-hour, she takes a 15-minute break after each hour. Ask the children how this would be plotted.

Curriculum objectives
● To interpret and construct line graphs and use these to solve problems.
Success criteria
● I can interpret and construct line graphs.

You will need
General resources
Interactive teaching resource 'Graphing tool'
Equipment
Individual whiteboards; squared paper; rulers; list of exchange rates

Differentiation
Less confident learners
Support the children with constructing the graphs, such as labelling axes, deciding on scale and marking the points.
More confident learners
Encourage children to make other examples of conversion graphs based on topics already worked on, such as converting kilograms to pounds and changing temperature from °C into °F.

Lesson 3 Oral and mental starter 51

Main teaching activities

Whole-class work: Remind the children that in the past they have looked at currency conversion graphs. Remind them about the Brown family and their camping holiday (which they worked on last week). Point out that all the countries that they were visiting are in Europe and use euros. Check the current exchange rate for sterling and euros and use the graphing tool to demonstrate a conversion graph for euros and sterling.

Emphasise that the graph must start at zero as at that point no money has been exchanged. Stress that this is a straight line graph as the amounts of currency increase by the same quantity each time. This is known as a graph of constant proportion.

Ask the children questions, such as:

- *How many euros will they get for 25 pounds?*
- *If a meal costs 55 euros, what is the sterling equivalent?*

Ask the children to come out and demonstrate how they have used the graph.

Independent work: Write up the current exchange rates for several currencies, including, for example, US dollars to pounds sterling and euros to sterling. Ask the children to choose an exchange rate and plot their own conversion graph on squared paper.

Progress check: Check that the children are using the exchange rate accurately and are able to represent it graphically. Check their labelling of axes. Remind the children that the starting point for both currencies will be at the origin (0).

Review

Ask the children to use the original graph to answer the following:

- *Change these pounds to euros: £2, £5, £8, £9, £25.*
- *Change these euros to pounds €3, €20, €60.*

Ask the children to explain what we mean by the phrase *constant proportion*.

Main teaching activities

Whole-class work: Show the children the following information: *Ben is cycling to his friend's house which is 50km away. He left at 4pm.*

Time in minutes	15	30	45	60	75	90
Distance in km	10	16	25	25	35	50

Independent work: Ask the children to plot line graphs from the information. Remind them of the following:

- Choose a suitable scale and number the axes in even 'jumps'.
- Label the axes.
- Plot the points from the table, then join them using a ruler.

When the children have completed their graphs, ask them to look at the different sections and write a narrative suggesting what might have happened in different parts of the race.

Progress check: Check that the children are using a suitable scale that will enable all the information to be shown.

Review

Invite the children to share their graphs. Then ask them to say what they think could have happened in different sections of the ride. The children's ideas will vary, but they should identify that Ben rested between 4.45 and 5.00pm.

Main teaching activities

Whole-class work: Tell the children that the graphs they have been working with have mainly had straight lines joining the points. However, some graphs may have curved lines. Give the children this scenario about a class experiment: *The children wanted to measure the rate at which a liquid cooled. They placed a beaker of hot liquid in a cold place and then measured the temperature every ten minutes. Here are their results:*

Time in minutes	0	10	20	30	40	50
Temperature in °C	90	50	40	32	30	30

Independent work: Provide squared paper, and ask the children to construct graphs from the information given and write some questions about them.

Progress check: Ask if they think they should use straight lines to join the points. Establish that the cooling would be continuous and there would therefore be no sharp bends in the line graph (which would mean stopping and restarting). So they should join the points with a sensible curve. Point out that as the line will be curved, the information interpreted from it will be approximate.

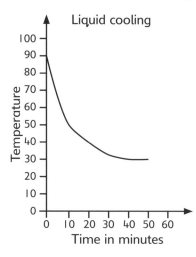

Review

This is the graph showing how the liquid cooled:

Ask the children to show their graphs. Compare them with the graph, noting that the line is slightly curved.

Curriculum objectives (Lesson 4)
- To interpret and construct pie charts and line graphs and use these to solve problems.

Success criteria
- I can interpret and construct line graphs.

You will need
Equipment
Squared paper; rulers

Differentiation
Less confident learners
Children should work as a group, and may need support when interpreting the graph.

More confident learners
Encourage children to go on to construct their own graphs, with a narrative explaining the different sections.

Curriculum objectives (Lesson 5)
- To interpret and construct line graphs and use these to solve problems.

Success criteria
- I can interpret and construct line graphs and use them to solve problems.

You will need
Equipment
Individual whiteboards; squared paper

Differentiation
Less confident learners
Support children by suggesting the scale they should use and the intervals (5 minutes, 5 degrees).

More confident learners
Encourage children to investigate other graphs that have curved lines, ideally linking with science and experiments such as melting ice.

Curriculum objectives
● To solve problems involving the calculation of percentages [for example, of measures].

You will need
1. Check
Oral and mental starter
40 Tenths and hundredths

2. Assess
'Discount electrics'

3. Further practice
Photocopiable sheets
'Percentages'

Solving percentage problems

Most children will understand the application of percentages and use them to make comparisons in real-life situations.

Some children will not have made such progress and will require more practice in finding percentages.

1. Check
40 Tenths and hundredths

Go through the starter, finding tenths and hundredths. Point out that this is calculating 10% and 1% of amounts. Then ask: *How can you then find 5%?*

2. Assess

Set the children to work on photocopiable page 168 'Discount electrics'. Make sure they are using appropriate strategies to find the discounts. Are they finding 1% and then multiplying, or finding 10% and scaling up or down, or a combination of both? Record the outcomes.

3. Further practice

Photocopiable page 208 'Percentages' will give further practice in calculating discounts by using either 1% or 10% as a starting point.

Curriculum objectives
● To use simple formulae.

You will need
1. Check
Oral and mental starter
27 Jumping forwards and backwards

2. Assess
'What's next?'

3. Further practice
General resources
Interactive activity 'Jumping frogs'

Using simple formulae expressed in words

Most children should be able to complete number sequences and make generalisations about them. They should also be able to express simple formulae in words.

Some children will need support in developing the ability to make and express generalisations.

1. Check
27 Jumping forwards and backwards

Ask the children to explain a sequence of numbers. For example: *If we start with 26 and we want to count backwards with an interval of 4, how do we know what the third term would be?* ($26 - (4 \times 3)$.) *How can we write what the nth term would be?* ($26 - 4n$.)

2. Assess

Ask the children to work on photocopiable page 169 'What's next?'. Make sure that they can explain the sequences and find the rule. Check that they are able to express the formula in words. Record the outcomes.

3. Further practice

The interactive activity 'Jumping frogs' on the CD-ROM gives practice in finding the rule for a number sequence and expressing it.

You will need
1. Check
Oral and mental starter
 Conversions

2. Assess
'New measures'

3. Further practice
Oral and mental starter
 Conversions

Converting units of measure

Most children should be able to convert between standard units, from a smaller unit of measure to a larger unit, and vice versa.

Some children will require support to develop their understanding of conversion rates and how to apply them.

1. Check
36 Conversions

Give the children a number of units to convert. Initially use a unit of length, such as mm to cm, cm to m, and m to km, and then move on to units of weight and then capacity. Ask the children what *kilo* and *centi* mean.

2. Assess

Work through photocopiable page 170 'New measures' with a group of children, checking that they are sure about the conversion rate they are using and about how to convert the amounts. Are the children clear about the difference between weight and capacity? Ask the children further questions which involve up to three decimal places, such as converting 3cm 5mm to m (0.035m); 235g to kg (0.235kg). Record the outcomes.

3. Further practice

Using the extension part of the 'Conversions' starter will reinforce the children's understanding of how to convert units.

Curriculum objectives
● To interpret and construct line graphs and use these to solve problems.

You will need
1. Check
Oral and mental starter
53 Get the point

2. Assess
Kilometres/miles conversion table, grid paper

3. Further practice
Photocopiable sheets
'How many koruna?'

Constructing line graphs

Most children should be able to construct a conversion graph and be able to use it effectively.

Some children will require support with constructing the graph and how to use it.

1. Check
53 Get the point

Use the starter to make sure that children can identify where to plot points for the line graphs. Tell the children to check the scale and be careful to plot the point accurately.

2. Assess

Show the children a kilometres/miles conversion table and ask them to draw their own line graph to be used for converting miles to kilometres, and vice versa. Make sure that they understand why the starting point will be 0,0. Ask the children how many more points they need to plot in order to draw the graph. (They only need one other point, but can use others to check.) When the children have drawn the graph, ask them to convert different numbers of miles to kilometres, and vice versa. Record the outcomes.

3. Further practice

Photocopiable page 171 'How many koruna?' is a fairly simple activity, particularly useful for giving less confident learners more practice.

If possible, encourage the children to research currency exchange rates on which to base their own conversion graphs. This will reinforce their understanding of how the graphs may be used.

Oral and mental starters

Number and place value

40 Tenths and hundredths

Tell the children that you want them to find one tenth of a certain amount. Give them an amount and ask them to write a tenth of it on their whiteboards. Try, for example: £895 (£89.50) and 583 (58.3).

Then ask the children to find hundredths. So, using the above examples, they should then divide by ten again to get £8.95 and 5.83.

Addition, subtraction, multiplication and division

41 Target number

Write a target number on the board, such as 48. Ask the children to think of as many ways as they can of generating 48 in the given time. Encourage them to use all four operations. Repeat with other numbers.

Extension

Include prime numbers and increasingly large numbers as targets.

42 Halving and doubling

Give children a starting number and ask them to either halve or double, chanting their answers together: 6, 12, 24, 48, 96 and so on or 76, 38, 19, 9.5.

43 Target 100

Give the children a starting number such as 19, and ask them to multiply it by another number to get as close to 100 as possible. (Try 5, in this instance.) Then ask the children to use a decimal number to get even closer (5.263). Repeat with other starting numbers, such as 37 and 41.

44 Tables count

Tell the children that you want them to count in multiples of 7 as far as they can go, starting from 0: 7, 14, 21. Repeat with other multiples.

Extension

Expect children to be able to go beyond the twelfth multiple.

45 Related facts

Ask the children to work out 6×18 (108), then ask them to write down as many related facts as they can in two minutes. For example: 6×1.8; $10.8 \div 6$. Repeat with other calculations.

Extension

Challenge the children by starting with calculations involving decimal numbers or fractions.

46 Tables bingo (1)

Tell the children to draw a 3×2 grid on their whiteboards and write in it eight numbers which are multiples of 5, 6 or 7. Then play 'Tables bingo'. Call out a multiplication from one of the chosen tables and say to the children that, if it is on their card, they can mark it off. The winner is the child who crosses off all their numbers first.

This can also be played with other times tables.

Decimals and fractions

47 Rounding decimals

Give the children decimal numbers and specify how they should be rounded. Suggest that the children round to the whole number first. For example: 8.8 (9), 14.3 (14) and 6.63 (7).

Finally move on to round to two decimal places, such as: 5.378 (5.38), 12.453 (12.45) and 25.624 (25.62).

48 What's the question?

Pose the following question: *The answer to a calculation is 0.48; what could the calculation be?* Give the children a limited amount of time (perhaps two minutes) to write down as many calculations as possible on their whiteboards. For example: 0.6 x 0.8. Repeat for other decimals such as 0.72, 3.6.

49 Order the fractions

Give the children a list of fractions to order. Start with three but extend to more. For example: ⅔, ¾, ⅗.

Extension

Include mixed numbers and improper fractions, and expect children to order at least four or five fractions.

50 Equivalent fractions

Give the children a fraction and ask them to write down as many fractions equivalent to it as they can in one minute. Examples might include: 3/4, 4/12, and 6/30.

Measurement

51 Converting up and down

Converting up: Write a list of measurements on the board and ask the children to convert them to larger units. For example: 2536m to km, 9125mm to m, 1532g to kg and 69450ml to l.

Converting down: Write a list of measurements on the board and ask the children to convert them to smaller units. For example: 13.5km to m, 93m to mm, 3.25kg to g and 65l to ml.

52 Recording metric units

Invite the children to suggest metric units of length, such as centimetre and kilometre. For each suggestion, ask the children to write the unit as a word on their whiteboards, and then in its abbreviated form. Repeat this for metric units of mass and capacity.

Geometry

53 Get the point

Show a grid on the board with labelled x- and y-axes. Mark points on the grid and ask the children to write down the coordinates of the points. Check these together as a class.

Paradise hotel

■ Show your working and answers on a separate piece of paper.

	12 Jan–24 Mar 12 Nov–15 Dec	25 Mar–27 May 2 Oct–12 Nov	28 May–30 June 1 Sept–1 Oct	1 July–31 August	15 Dec–11 Jan
1 week					
Adult	£250	£279	£345	£425	£320
First child	£175	£180	£250	£299	£225
Additional children	£150	£155	£225	£260	£200
2 weeks					
Adult	£450	£520	£600	£775	£575
First child	£275	£345	£375	£400	£360
Additional children	£250	£295	£325	£350	£310
Rooms are for 2 adults and up to 3 children. Single room supplement add 25% of adult cost.					

1. How much will it cost for Mr and Mrs Brown and two children to have a one-week holiday leaving on 1 June?

2. What will be the cost for Miss Smith to have a two-week holiday leaving on 3 October?

3. How much will it cost for the Singh family (mum, dad and three children) to have a two-week holiday leaving on 5 September?

4. Eight adult friends have saved £6500 between them and want to go to Paradise Hotel for one week in August. When they have paid for the holiday they will share the remaining money between them for spending. How much will each person have as spending money?

5. The Adams family (mum, dad and two children) have saved £2000 and would like a two-week holiday as close to July as possible. What would be their best choice?

I can solve problems involving all four operations.

How did you do?

Name: _____ Date: _____

Be reasonable

■ Read each question carefully to decide whether it is true or false. If it is false, work out the correct answer. Don't forget to estimate first.

1. A roll of wallpaper is 10.5m long. Derek the decorator works out that 6 lengths of paper, each one measuring 195cm long, can be cut from the roll. Is he correct?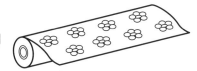

_____

2. At the gardening centre, compost is put into bags, each containing 3250g. Sam bags up 26kg of compost altogether, and produces 8 bags. Is this correct?

_____

3. If I make squash with 450ml of juice and 5 litres of water, I can pour 25 glasses each containing 225ml of squash. Am I right?

_____

4. Jaz saves £2.12 a week. At the end of the 18th week, he tells everyone he has saved £38.20. How do you know he is wrong?

_____

5. The groundskeeper at the local park is marking out the football pitches with his line machine: 1 litre of white marker produces 50m of line. He works out that he will need 20 litres to produce 1000m of line. Will he have enough marker?

_____

6. Skipping ropes are made with 225cm of rope. Leigh has a length of rope 67m long. She works out she will need 10cm more rope in order to make 30 skipping ropes. Is she correct?

_____

I can multiply decimal numbers.

How did you do?

Discount electrics

Tom has £200 to buy electrical equipment. It is sale time and he is looking for the best deals. He would like to buy an MP3 player and a digital camera. With any money he has left he will buy DVDs.

- How much does he spend on each item and how many DVDs can he buy?

SALE 30% DISCOUNT ON ALL ITEMS

HI-FI STORE SALE!

MP3 PLAYER	**£135**
Digital camera	**£99**

ELECTRO DISCOUNT STORE
lowest price anywhere!

MP3 player	**£99**
Digital camera	**£65**
DVDs sale price	**£9.99 each**

_____

_____

_____

_____

I can solve problems by calculating percentages of whole numbers.

How did you do?

PHOTOCOPIABLE

What's next?

■ Look carefully at each sequence. For each one, write down the next three numbers or letters in the sequence and explain the rule.

1. 17 22 28 35 ☐ ☐ ☐   The rule is _____

2. 98 50 26 ☐ ☐ ☐   The rule is _____

3. 25 36 49 ☐ ☐ ☐   The rule is _____

4. $\frac{1}{4}$ $\frac{2}{8}$ $\frac{4}{16}$ ☐ ☐ ☐   The rule is _____

5. A D H ☐ ☐ ☐   The rule is _____

6. 2 7 22 67 ☐ ☐ ☐   The rule is _____

7. Now write three sequences of your own and explain the rule for each.

a) ☐ ☐ ☐ ☐ ☐ ☐ ☐

The rule is _____

b) ☐ ☐ ☐ ☐ ☐ ☐ ☐

The rule is _____

c) ☐ ☐ ☐ ☐ ☐ ☐ ☐

The rule is _____

I can explain and complete a number sequence and write my own.

How did you do?

PHOTOCOPIABLE

New measures

■ Carry out the following conversions between metric units. You will need to use decimal numbers to give the answers.

Change from litres to centilitres:	**Change from centilitres to litres:**
11.5l _____	175cl _____
12.75l _____	215cl _____
18.5l _____	870cl _____
22.5l _____	1460cl _____
Change from kilograms to tonnes:	**Change from tonnes to kilograms:**
1275kg _____	$4\frac{1}{2}$ tonnes _____
3470kg _____	5.9 tonnes _____
5500kg _____	12.35 tonnes _____
12578kg _____	10.43 tonnes _____

I can convert between standard units of measurement.

How did you do?

PHOTOCOPIABLE

How many koruna?

- The Rashid family are going to Prague for the weekend. They will change their money before they go and expect to get 39.34 koruna to the pound.
- When they are there they want to be able to work out the cost of items so they would like to take a conversion graph with them.
- Draw a conversion graph for pound sterling to koruna.

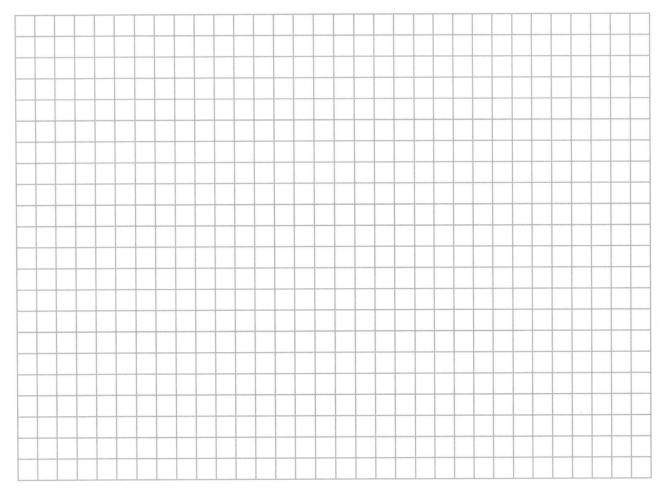

1. Their restaurant bill is 1288 koruna.

   Use your graph to find out how much that is in sterling. _____

2. Ali wants to change the pocket money he has saved.

   How many koruna will he get for £15.50? _____

I can draw a conversion graph and use it to solve problems.

How did you do?

Number, place value and rounding

Expected prior learning

Children should be able to:

- order and compare numbers to 1,000,000
- round decimal numbers to the nearest whole number.

Topic	Curriculum objectives	Expected outcomes
Number and place value	**Lesson 1**	
	To read, write, order and compare numbers up to 10,000,000 and determine the value of each digit.	Say, read and write numbers to 10,000,000 accurately. Know the values of each digit in a seven-digit number.
	Lesson 2	
	To round any whole number to a required degree of accuracy.	Round numbers to the nearest 10, 100 and 1000. Round decimal numbers.
	Lesson 3	
	To read, write, order and compare numbers up to 10,000,000 and determine the value of each digit. To round any whole number to a required degree of accuracy.	Find differences between positive and negative numbers.
	Lesson 4	
	To use negative numbers in context and calculate intervals across zero.	Find differences between positive and negative numbers.
	Lesson 5	
	To solve number and practical problems that involve all four operations.	Solve problems within familiar contexts involving rounding and estimating.

Preparation

Lesson 1: enlarge 'The place value game', or have it ready from the CD-ROM; make a copy for each child

Lesson 2: write the 'true or false' statements on the board

Lesson 3: copy 'True or false' for each child

You will need

Photocopiable sheets
'The place value game'; 'True and false'

General resources
'Number cards 0–9'

Equipment
Individual whiteboards; dice; number lines

Further practice

Photocopiable sheets
'Rise and fall'

Oral and mental starters suggested for week 1

See the bank of starters on pages 205 and 206. Oral and mental starters are also on the CD-ROM.

54 Counting steps

57 Multiples of 10

58 Ordering

Overview of progression

During this week the children will continue to practise and develop their ability to work with whole and decimal numbers to 10,000,000. This will include saying, reading and writing numbers to three decimal places and rounding to the nearest hundredth, tenth, whole number and multiples of ten. They will also be working with negative numbers in familiar contexts, including use of all four operations.

> ### Watch out for
> Children may have difficulty with decimal numbers. Focus on tenths, and link the decimal fraction with the fraction they should be familiar with, for example 0.1 and ¹⁄₁₀. You could provide place value charts that show tenths, ones, tens and hundreds and ask children to, for example, put their finger on 0.3, add one, multiply by 10, take away 20, divide by 10, and so on. Some children may have difficulty rounding decimals to the nearest tenth and whole numbers to the nearest 10, 100 or 1000. Provide number lines so that children can plot their number and see the number it is closest to.

Creative context

Encourage the children to look out for numbers in other contexts, for example in catalogues and on food packaging. They could make a note of these in words and figures. There is a good opportunity here to teach financial capability by examining the details on bank statements and financial transactions. If possible, develop this into giving children the financial responsibility of, for example, running a stall at the school fête.

Vocabulary

decimal, digit, estimating, hundred, hundreds, hundreds of thousands, million, millions, negative, ones, place value, place-holder, positive, rounding, tens, tens of thousands, thousand, thousands

Curriculum objectives
● To read, write, order and compare numbers up to 10,000,000 and determine the value of each digit.

Success criteria
● I know the value of each digit in a seven-digit number.
● I can say, read and write seven-digit numbers.

You will need
Photocopiable sheets
'The place value game'
General resources
'Number cards 0–9'
Equipment
Individual whiteboards; dice

Differentiation
Less confident learners
Adapt the sheet to show 1000, 100, 10 and 1.
More confident learners
Encourage children to make up their own rules for winning the game.

Lesson 1
Oral and mental starter 54

Main teaching activities
Whole-class work: Begin by revising previous work on place value and large numbers. Write 9,821,074 on the board. Ask: *What can you say about this number?* Encourage them to tell you what each number represents, for example, the 8 is 800,000, and that the zero is holding the place of the hundreds. Ask the children to use the digits from the number on the board to make up another seven-digit number on their whiteboards. Let the children show their numbers to their partners and explain what each digit is and what place the zero holds.

Say some large numbers (in words), such as, 6,207,453, for the children to write on their whiteboards in figures.

Then ask them to alter different digits. For example: *Change the 4 to a 3. Is the number larger or smaller now? By roughly how much smaller?*

Paired work: Demonstrate 'The place value game' on the photocopiable page from the CD-ROM by playing it with a volunteer. Then organise the children to play in pairs and hand out the number cards and dice.

Progress check: After each child has completed the first table on the sheet, check they are on the right track by asking: *What is the value of each digit in 3,420,014? What do we call the zeros? What is the job of the place-holder?*

Review
Invite some of the pairs to write the numbers they made on the board.

Play the game as a class. Invite a volunteer to pick cards with you. Ask the rest of the class to agree where to place each digit.

Curriculum objectives
● To round whole numbers accurately.

Success criteria
● I can round numbers to the nearest 10, 100 and 1000.
● I can round decimal numbers involving money.

You will need
Equipment
Individual whiteboards

Differentiation
Less confident learners
Work with the children, discussing each statement as a group.
More confident learners
Challenge children to make up their own true or false statements for each other. Encourage them to focus on rounding numbers with decimal points.

Lesson 2
Oral and mental starter 57

Main teaching activities
Whole-class work: Challenge the children to estimate different things, for example, the height of the door or another child, how long it will take to count to 50, the number of hairs on someone's head. Then revise rounding to the nearest 10, 100 and 1000 using numbers such as 124,259 (124,260, 124,300, 124,000). Invite children to read out their answers from their whiteboards.

Now write up a decimal, such as 145.26. Establish how to round it to the nearest tenth (145.3) and then whole number (145). Discuss that rounding is useful if you need to estimate quickly and don't need exact amounts. Say: *Lucy has £120. She wants to buy 10 CDs. Each CD costs £12.90. Does she have enough money?* Agree that £12.90 can be rounded to £13 and that, if this is multiplied by 10, the total cost is £130; more than Lucy has.

Paired work: Organise the children into pairs to decide which of these statements are true or false, and why:
- Ryan wanted a pair of shorts for £9.98 and a T-shirt for £13.15. He had £20. He didn't have enough money. (True.)
- Cherri rounded 156.23 to 157. She was correct. (False; 156.)
- Bobby had saved £185. He wanted a bike for £159.50 and a helmet for £24.99. He hadn't saved enough. (False; the cost was £184.49.)
- Charlie bought some toys costing £26.75. He paid with a £50 note. He thought he would have less than £25 change. (True; £23.25 change.)

Progress check: Check that the pairs agree on the calculations needed.

Review
Check answers and invite volunteers to explain their thinking. Ask children to suggest new statements; the class to decide if they are true and why.

Curriculum objectives

● To read, write, order and compare numbers up to 10,000,000 and determine the value of each digit.
● To round any whole number to a required degree of accuracy.

Success criteria

● I round numbers to the nearest 10, 100 and 1000.
● I can round decimal numbers to the nearest 10th and whole number.

You will need

Photocopiable sheets
'True or false'

Equipment
Individual whiteboards

Differentiation

Less confident learners
Work with these children during the task.

More confident learners
When they have finished, ask them to make up their own true and false statements.

Lesson 3 — Oral and mental starter 58

Main teaching activities

Whole-class work: Discuss the meaning of estimating and rounding. Ask the children to estimate different things, for example, the height of the door or another child, how long it will take to count to 50, the number of hairs on someone's head. Rehearse rounding to the nearest 10, 100 and 1000 using numbers such as 124,259 (124,260, 124,300, 124,000), 235,872 (235,870, 235,900, 236,000). The children write their answers on whiteboards and read them out. Repeat this for decimal numbers such as 145.26. They round these to the nearest tenth and then whole number (145.3, 145). Discuss when it is useful to round numbers in real life. Agree that rounding is useful if you need to estimate when you don't need to know exact amounts. Demonstrate using this scenario: *Lucy had £120. She wants to buy 10 CDs. Each CD costs £12.90. Does she have enough money?* Agree that £12.90 can be rounded to £13. If this is multiplied by 10 the cost is £130 which is more than she has. Repeat with similar scenarios.

Paired work: Explain the task that the children need to work on using the instructions on photocopiable page 'True or false' from the CD-ROM.

Progress check: Ask: *How would you explain rounding to someone who didn't know the term? Toni had 6 packets of sweets. There were 18 sweets in each packet. She thinks she has about 120 sweets. Is she right? Why?*

Review

Together discuss the statements from the activity. Invite volunteers to share what they thought and to explain their thinking. Invite the more confident children to share the statements they made up. The class should decide whether they are true or not and why.

Curriculum objectives

● To use negative numbers in context and calculate intervals across zero.

Success criteria

● I can find differences between positive and negative numbers.

You will need

Equipment
Individual whiteboards

Differentiation

Less confident learners
These children should make up single-step problems using amounts of money between −£100 and £100.

More confident learners
These children should make up multi-step problems using amounts of money between −£1000 and £1000.

Lesson 4 — Oral and mental starter 58

Main teaching activities

Whole-class work: Recap the work that the children have previously covered on positive and negative numbers. Ask them to give you five examples of each. Write these on the board and ask the children to order them from negative to positive on their whiteboards and show you. Select one of each type of number and ask the children to find the difference between them. Repeat this several times. Discuss when negative numbers are found in real life. Spend some time considering overdrafts as this links well with financial capability. Ask: *What is an overdraft? What is a bank statement? What does it mean to take out a loan? Why should people be careful if they do this?* Ask problems related to bank statements for example: *I had £150 in my bank account, I spent £275 on a bike, what will my bank statement say now?* Invite a volunteer to write a number sentence to describe this: £150 − £275 = −£125. Continue the scenario: *I was paid £425 for some work and I put it in the bank. How much did I have now?* (−£125 + £425 = £300) Repeat for similar scenarios.

Paired work: Ask the children to work in pairs of similar attainment to make up two-step problems for each other to solve similar to the example worked through in the lesson. They write these down and then give them to their partner to answer.

Progress check: Visit pairs to check that they are correctly finding the difference between their amounts. You could suggest to any having difficulty that they use a number line to find the differences.

Review

Invite pairs to share one of their problems. The class work out the answer on their whiteboards.

Curriculum objectives
● To solve number and practical problems that involve all four operations.

Success criteria
● I can solve word problems involving rounding and estimating.

You will need

Equipment

Individual whiteboards

Differentiation

Less confident learners

Ask children to make up problems involving amounts of money up to £100.

More confident learners

Ask children to make up problems that involve other forms of measurement including length and mass. Challenge them to create problems that require several steps and two or three of the main operations.

Lesson 5
Oral and mental starter 54

Main teaching activities

Whole-class work: Review the week. Ask the children to tell you what they have been thinking about over the week. Allow them some time to talk about the lessons in pairs, and ask them to make notes on their whiteboards. Remind them to include examples. Take feedback, and agree that they have been: reading, writing and ordering large numbers and decimal numbers, rounding and working with both positive and negative numbers.

Invite volunteers to write on the board some numbers in the millions. Ask other volunteers to read them aloud. Then work together as a class to, first, put them in order, and then round them to the nearest 10, 100 and 1000. Repeat the exercise for numbers with up to three decimal places.

Then invite children to write up some positive and negative numbers between 50 and −50. Pick one of each and challenge the class to find the difference between them. Repeat this a few times.

Recap when it is useful to round numbers up or down (for example when doing a quick estimate when shopping). Set this problem:

Courtney was in a café. She wanted to buy a pizza which cost £12.15 and salad which cost £4.90. She had £20. She wondered if she had enough money for a drink costing £2.50.

Without working out the exact answer, can you tell me whether Courtney will be able to afford the drink? What did you do to find out?

Agree with the children that they can round £12.15 to £12 and £4.90 to £5, and add them to give £17. Which leaves Courtney with about £3 spare, enough for the drink. Ask: *How can we be sure?* Elicit that they would need to calculate the exact total (£17.05). Repeat with similar problems.

Ask problems that involve multiplying, for example *Kipper works in the supermarket. He had a delivery of tins of beans. There were 23 crates and inside each crate were 68 tins. Tell me roughly how many tins were delivered.* Discuss the best way to make an estimate. If no one else does, suggest rounding 23 to 20 and multiplying by 68 (by multiplying by ten and then doubling: 1360). Ask: *What would we need to do to our estimate to find the actual answer?* (Add three multiplied by 68 giving a total of 1564) Continue this scenario: *Kipper needs to stack the beans on shelves. He has to put 28 on each shelf. Give me an estimate of how many shelves he will fill?* Again, encourage them to use rounding: 30 divided into 1500 (50). Next ask them to work out the answer using the formal written method, or, if they find this difficult grouping: 55 r 24. Ask the children to tell you what he could do with the remaining 24 (for example put them on another shelf or save them until there was space for them). Set similar problems for the children to answer on their whiteboards.

Paired work: Organise the children to work in similar-ability pairs to create and solve multi-step problems similar to Courtney's or Kipper's. Tell the children that the problems should involve rounding amounts of money to estimate answers first before finding the exact solution. Remind the children to be prepared to share these during the review.

Progress check: Visit the pairs, particularly those you wish to assess, and ask questions such as: *How would you round that amount? What would a good estimate of the answer be? Why do you think that? What operation do you need to use? How would you carry this out?*

Review

Invite pairs to share one of the problems they invented. Ask the rest of the class to work with their partners to find an estimate to the answer. Then work as a whole class to check the accuracy of the estimate by calculating the actual solution. Establish that rounding is a useful skill but that often it provides only a guide and the actual solution often needs to be found.

Adding and subtracting large and small numbers

Expected prior learning

Children should be able to:

- add and subtract using a variety of mental calculation strategies
- add and subtract using column methods.

Topic	Curriculum objectives	Expected learning outcomes
Addition and subtraction	**Lesson 1**	
	To perform mental calculations, including with mixed operations and large numbers.	Use a variety of mental calculation methods to solve problems.
	Lesson 2	
	To perform mental calculations, including with mixed operations and large numbers.	Use a variety of mental calculation methods to solve problems.
	Lesson 3	
	To solve addition and subtraction multi-step problems in contexts, deciding which operations and methods to use and why. To use estimation to check answers to calculations and determine, in the context of a problem, an appropriate degree of accuracy.	Add numbers using a variety of methods, including carrying. Check answers using estimation.
	Lesson 4	
	To solve addition and subtraction multi-step problems in contexts, deciding which operations and methods to use and why. To use estimation to check answers to calculations and determine, in the context of a problem, an appropriate degree of accuracy.	Subtract numbers using a variety of methods, including decomposition. Check answers using estimation.
	Lesson 5	
	To solve addition and subtraction multi-step problems in contexts, deciding which operations and methods to use and why.	Solve addition and subtraction problems within familiar contexts.

Preparation

Lesson 1: copy 'Shopping' for each child

Lesson 2: enlarge 'How much?' or have it ready from the CD-ROM; make a copy for each child

Lesson 5: write the amounts of money for display on the board

You will need

Photocopiable sheets
'Shopping'; 'How much?'

General resources
'Number cards 0–9'

Equipment
Individual whiteboards

Further practice

Photocopiable sheets
'Addition'

Oral and mental starters suggested for week 2

See the bank of starters on pages 205 and 206. Oral and mental starters are also on the CD-ROM.

55 Number lines

56 Rounding

59 Percentage bingo

60 Quick decimal addition

Overview of progression

During this week the children will continue to practise and develop their ability to add and subtract large whole numbers and decimal numbers. They will do this using mental calculation strategies and informal methods leading to the column written methods that involve carrying and exchanging. The lessons will prompt the children to make decisions as to the most appropriate method to use. They will also encourage the children to estimate answers and check calculated solutions using those estimations.

Watch out for

Children who do not have the conceptual understanding to carry out the more formal column written methods will need more practice in this. They will benefit from using practical equipment such as place-value counters or counting blocks to gain a deeper understanding of exchanging ones for tens, tens for hundreds, and vice versa.

Creative context

Let the children use catalogues or the internet to cost resources that they might like to buy for use in a particular area of the curriculum, such as PE, music or science. Give them budgets and ask them to 'go shopping', working out the total costs of several items within those budgets and then how much money they will have left.

Vocabulary

addition, calculate, calculation, **complementary addition**, decomposition, inverse, mental method, partitioning, **sequencing**, strategy, subtraction

Lesson 1 — Oral and mental starter 55

Main teaching activities

Whole-class work: Set this problem: *Tommy measured the length and width of the school field. The length was 25.25m; the width was 17.48m. How much longer is the length than the width? What is the total measurement?* Ask what calculations need to be done. Agree that we need to subtract the width from the length, then add them together to find the total. Encourage the children to use mental calculation strategies to work this out. For example, complementary addition for subtraction: 17.48 + 0.52 + 7.25, so the difference is 7.77m; partitioning for addition: 25.25 + 10 + 7 + 0.4 + 0.08, so the total is 42.73m; sequencing for both: 25.25 − 10 − 7 − 0.4 − 0.08. Ask: *How can we check the answers?* Agree to use inverse operations. For example: 7.77 + 17.48. Try similar problems for the children to answer on their whiteboards.

Now set another one: *Samir had saved £198. Yukesh had saved £297. How much more had Yukesh saved? How much had they saved altogether?* Again, consider the most appropriate strategy to use. Agree on rounding and adjusting. Establish that Yukesh had saved £99 more (£297 − £200 + £2), and the total saved is £495 (£297 + £200 − £2). Revise how to check using the inverse operation, and repeat with similar problems.

Independent work: Hand out photocopiable page 'Shopping' from the CD-ROM reminding the children to work out answers in their heads.

Progress check: After the first couple of shops, check progress by asking: *Which strategy do you think is the best to find the total? Why? How would you find the amount Sammy has left? Is there another way?*

Review

Check answers, and invite the children to share their strategies.

Curriculum objectives
● To perform mental calculations, including with mixed operations and large numbers.

Success criteria
● I can solve problems using mental calculation methods.

You will need
Photocopiable sheets
'Shopping'
Equipment
Individual whiteboards

Differentiation
Less confident learners
On the photocopiable sheet, ask children to focus on the cost and change when buying the clothes just at Clothes Etc. and Looking Good.

More confident learners
After the photocopiable sheet, challenge children to work out the cheapest way to buy the clothes, and then the most expensive.

Lesson 2 — Oral and mental starter 59

Main teaching activities

Whole-class work: Tell the children that this is a second lesson to practise mental calculation strategies. Set this problem: *Emma needs 4.5kg of flour to make some biscuits. She has 1.9kg. How much more flour does she need?* Explore methods for solving this. For example: count on from 1.9, add 0.1 to make 2 then add 2.5 to make 4.5kg. Emphasise the importance of checking, and suggest that a second method is used for this. Then set another problem: *Sandy has saved £165.50. She wants to buy a DVD player and needs another £99. How much is the DVD player?* Again, explore methods, such as: partitioning the last number, rounding £99 to £100 and taking away £1.

Write on the board a series of calculations that involve adding or subtracting near multiples of 10, for example: 6.7 + 5.9, 45.7 − 29.9. Ask the children to answer these on their whiteboards, and then share their methods.

Independent work: Hand out photocopiable page 'How much?' from the CD-ROM, working through the first problem together.

Progress check: As the children are working, ask questions such as: *How would you use rounding to find the total? Which strategy could you use to check?*

Review

Go through the photocopiable sheet together. Encourage children to explain their methods. Invite confident children to present their new problems, and answer them as a class.

Curriculum objectives
● As lesson 1.
Success criteria
● I can solve problems using mental calculation methods.

You will need
Photocopiable sheets
'How much?'
Equipment
Individual whiteboards

Differentiation
Less confident learners
Support children in reading each problem and extracting the numbers and calculations.

More confident learners
Once children have completed the photocopiable sheet, ask them to make up their own problems involving measurement with two decimal places.

Curriculum objectives
● To solve addition multi-step problems in contexts.
● To use estimation to check answers to calculations.

Success criteria
● I can solve addition problems.
● I can check answers by estimating.

You will need

General resources
'Number cards 0–9'

Equipment
Individual whiteboards

Differentiation

Less confident learners

Support children and restrict questions to three-digit whole numbers and numbers to one decimal place.

More confident learners

Encourage children to move on as quickly as possible to examples in which numbers have a large number of digits, including decimal numbers, and where a range of mixed amounts have to be added, such as 4.275kg + 84g + 1kg 257g.

Lesson 3 — Oral and mental starter 60

Main teaching activities

Whole-class work: Tell the children that they will be solving more real-life problems in this lesson. Try this one to start: Tina scored 6409 in the first round of a competition. In the next two rounds she scored 236 and 198 points. How many points did she score in total? Ask the children to discuss how they could find the answer. Elicit that they need to add all the numbers together. Invite the children to suggest ways of doing this. Briefly revise informal mental methods, such as, adding the most significant digits first, sequencing, rounding and adjusting, going through examples on the board.

Then tell the children that they are going to focus on formal written methods of column addition. Demonstrate on the board how to add numbers by transferring them from a horizontal 'sentence' position to vertical columns, ensuring digits are correctly positioned underneath each other. For example: 6409 + 236 + 198 becomes:

```
  6409
+  236
+  198
```

Then show how, during the calculation digits being carried are written underneath the answer line:

```
  6409
+  236
+  198
  6843
   1 2
```

Ask the children to check the answer by making an estimate by rounding, for example, 6400 + 200 + 200 = 7000. Practise this technique with further calculations.

Then extend the activity to include decimal numbers, pointing out that decimal points should line up under each other. Do this by setting a problem for the children to answer on their whiteboards, such as: Bertie spent £105.60 on a laptop, £74.27 on an external hard drive and £3.94 on a memory stick. How much did he spend?

```
   74.27
+   3.94
+ 105.60
  183.81
   1 1  1
```

Encourage the children to check their answer again by estimating.

Paired work: Let the children practise addition calculations using these column methods. Give each pair a set of number cards and decimal point cards. Ask them to work together to make a set of three or four numbers, then to each write a problem for their partner to solve. Remind the children to show their working out in full.

Progress check: Visit pairs you particularly wish to assess. Check that they understand how to use the column method by asking questions such as: *Why do you need to be careful when you set out your calculation? Which column will you start adding? What will you do if you get a two-digit number when you add the ones column? What do you need to remember next?*

Review

Ask some of the pairs to demonstrate the calculations they made up and answered. Encourage others to check the answers by quick estimation. Invite confident volunteers to share problems they made up, for the class to solve.

Curriculum objectives
- To solve subtraction multi-step problems in contexts.
- To use estimation to check answers to calculations.

Success criteria
- I can solve subtraction problems.
- I can check answers by estimating.

You will need
General resources
'Number cards 0–9'

Equipment
Individual whiteboards

Differentiation
Less confident learners
Ensure children are proficient at using the decomposition method with three-digit numbers before progressing.

More confident learners
Children to work with metric measures.

Lesson 4

Oral and mental starter 56

Main teaching activities

Whole-class work: Set this problem: *Araan scored 9576 points on the computer game he was playing. Harry scored 4092. How many more points did Araan score?* Ask the children how to work out the answer. Revise familiar mental calculation strategies, such as counting on (4092 + 8 + 900 + 4000 + 576), rounding and adjusting (9576 − 4100 + 8), sequencing (9576 − 4000 − 90 − 2).

$$\begin{array}{r} 9\overset{4}{\cancel{5}}\overset{1}{7}6 \\ -\ 4092 \\ \hline 5484 \end{array}$$

Write on the board the subtraction as shown in column form. Ask the children to explain how to solve this.

Ask the children to check the answer by rounding to estimate the difference, for example, 9500 − 4000. Set problems with different numbers of digits and decimal numbers.

Paired work: Organise pairs to challenge each other with their own problems with sets of numbers made from 'Number cards 0–9'. The children should practise the column method of subtraction, showing their working.

Progress check: Visit the pairs to ensure that they understand the standard written method.

Review

Share a selection of the children's calculations. Ask volunteers to explain the stages of the decomposition method. Revise any difficult parts if necessary.

Curriculum objectives
- To solve addition and subtraction multi-step problems in contexts.

Success criteria
- I can solve multi-step addition and subtraction problems.

You will need
Equipment
Individual whiteboards

Differentiation
Less confident learners
Help children to focus on adding and subtracting numbers with the same number of digits.

More confident learners
Challenge children to add three amounts of money and find the change from a budget of £5000. They will need to select their amounts to stay under budget!

Lesson 5

Oral and mental starter 56

Main teaching activities

Whole-class work: Ask the children how to solve this problem: *Kieran is saving to buy a laptop for £267.98 and a printer for £199.50. How much money does he need to save?* Go through the children's suggestions, then focus on a standard written method:

$$\begin{array}{r} £267.98 \\ +\ £199.50 \\ \hline £467.48 \\ {\scriptstyle 1\ \ 1\ \ 1} \end{array}$$

Discuss how they can check the answer is correct. Establish that they could add in a different order, use the inverse operation or an estimation. Write similar money calculations on the board for the children to answer. For each, invite a volunteer to demonstrate the standard written method.

Set this problem: *Maddie has saved £875.50. She wants to buy a new TV, costing £645.45. Does she have enough left to buy a games console costing £236?*

Ask the children to jot down an answer, then invite them to share their strategies, such as sequencing and complementary addition. Focus on this standard written method:

$$\begin{array}{r} £875.\overset{4}{\cancel{5}}\overset{1}{0} \\ -\ £645.45 \\ \hline £230.05 \end{array}$$

Independent work: Display the following amounts: £335.75; £2971.80; £3526.99; £145.50; £78.99; £40.98

Ask the children to choose two to make an addition calculation, then a subtraction calculation. Advise them to check their answers using a different strategy. Tell them to repeat this with other pairs of numbers. Then ask the children to make up some word problems to go with their calculations.

Progress check: Ask: *How would you explain how to add 1452 and 398? How would subtract these numbers? Which other methods could you use?*

Review

Invite volunteers to demonstrate the standard written method for calculations they have made up. Ask the rest of the class to check the answer.

Long multiplication and division

Expected prior learning

Children should be able to:

- multiply and divide using a variety of mental calculation strategies
- multiply and divide using written methods.

Topic	Curriculum objectives	Expected outcomes
Multiplication and division	**Lesson 1**	
	To multiply multi-digit numbers up to four digits by a two-digit whole number using the formal written method of long multiplication.	Use written methods to multiply.
	Lesson 2	
	To multiply multi-digit numbers up to four digits by a two-digit whole number using the formal written method of long multiplication.	Use formal written methods to multiply.
	Lesson 3	
	To multiply multi-digit numbers up to four digits by a two-digit whole number using the formal written method of long multiplication.	Calculate three-digit by two-digit numbers using long multiplication.
	Lesson 4	
	To divide numbers up to four digits by two digit whole numbers using the formal written method of long division and interpret remainders as whole number remainders, fractions or by rounding, as appropriate for the context. To use estimation to check answers to calculations and determine, in the context of a problem, an appropriate degree of accuracy.	Solve long division calculations. Estimate to check answers.
	Lesson 5	
	To divide numbers up to four digits by two digit whole numbers using the formal written method of long division and interpret remainders as whole number remainders, fractions or by rounding, as appropriate for the context. To use estimation to check answers to calculations and determine, in the context of a problem, an appropriate degree of accuracy.	Solve problems involving division with remainders. Check answers by estimating

■SCHOLASTIC

Preparation

Lesson 2: prepare ten multiplication questions for the children to answer during their activity

You will need

Photocopiable sheets
'Multiplication problems'; 'Division problems'

General resources
'Number cards 0–9'

Equipment
Individual whiteboards

Further practice

Photocopiable sheets
'Division'

Oral and mental starters for week 3

See bank of starters on pages 205 to 206. Oral and mental starters are also on the CD-ROM.

57 Multiples of 10

59 Percentage bingo

61 Multiplication and division facts

Overview of progression

During this week the children will continue to practise and develop their ability to multiply and divide numbers. They will do this using partitioning, the grid method and grouping which lead towards more efficient written methods such as a column method for multiplication and long division for dividing three-digit numbers by two-digit numbers. They will also be encouraged to estimate answers and check solutions using these estimations.

Watch out for

Some children may not have the conceptual understanding to carry out the more formal written methods. These children will need more practice using practical resources such as place value counters, counting blocks or Base Ten equipment to gain a deeper understanding of how these operations work.

Creative context

Ask the children to use shopping catalogues or the internet to find prices of items that they might like to buy. Give them budgets and ask them to work out total costs of several items within those budgets and then how much money they will have left.

Vocabulary

calculate, calculation, inverse, long multiplication, long division, partitioning, **product**, **quotient**, remainder, strategy

Curriculum objectives
● To multiply multi-digit numbers up to four digits by a two-digit whole number using the formal written method of long multiplication.

Success criteria
● I can use written methods to multiply.

You will need

Photocopiable sheets
'Multiplication problems'

Equipment
Individual whiteboards

Differentiation

Less confident learners
Ask the children to pick four digit-cards and make three-digit by single digit calculations.

More confident learners
Ask the children to pick eight digit-cards and make six-digit by two-digit calculations.

Lesson I

Main teaching activities

Whole-class work: Recap long multiplication by multiplying a four digit number by a two digit number using partitioning and the grid method, for example 5278 x 23. Estimate first, by working out that 5000 × 20 = 100,000. Next demonstrate the column method:

$$
\begin{array}{r}
5278 \\
\times \quad 23 \\
\hline
15834 \\
105560 \\
\hline
121394
\end{array}
$$

Ask the children: *What is the same about these methods and what is different?* Agree that they are three different ways to show the same calculation and that the column method is more compact. Remind the children that the answer to a multiplication calculation is the *product*.

Practise some examples, such as 4294 × 24, using the column method, encouraging the children to estimate the answer first. Continue this type of exercise, now for multiplying decimal numbers within the context of money. Say, for example: *A box of chocolates costs £14.76. How much will 13 boxes cost?*

$$
\begin{array}{rcr}
10.00 \times 13 & = & 130.00 \\
4.00 \times 13 & = & 52.00 \\
0.70 \times 13 & = & 9.10 \\
0.06 \times 13 & = & 0.78 \\
\hline
& & 191.88
\end{array}
$$

$$
\begin{array}{r}
£14.76 \\
\times \quad 13 \\
\hline
44.28 \\
147.60 \\
\hline
191.88
\end{array}
$$

Ensure that the children understand that the decimal points must line up under each other. Practise further examples using decimals in the context of measures, for example: *Bert, the farmer, wants to build a fence around a field. He needs to buy some fence panels. Each one is 10.75m long. He bought 36. What is the total length of the panels?* (40.32m.)

Independent work: Give each child a set of number cards. Tell them to pick seven to make a five-digit number which needs to be multiplied by a two-digit number. Explain that, once they have made and answered the first calculation, they should use the same cards in different combinations to make other numbers and calculations.

Progress check: Visit less confident learners to ensure they are able to use the column method correctly. If necessary, they should multiply their numbers in two stages: first by the ones number, then by the tens number and add the two together.

Review

Ask the following questions and discuss with the class: *Why are we focusing on the column method for multiplication? What important fact must we remember when we multiply numbers involving decimals?*

Curriculum objectives

● To multiply multi-digit numbers up to four digits by a two-digit whole number using the formal written method of long multiplication.

Success criteria

● I can answer multiplication calculations using a formal written method.

You will need

Equipment

Individual whiteboards

Differentiation

Less confident learners

Begin with problems that involve work on HTU × U.

More confident learners

Give children problems for seven-digit by two-digit multiplications.

Lesson 2 — Oral and mental starter 59

Main teaching activities

Whole-class work: Recap the column method of long multiplication with a four-digit number multiplied by a two-digit number, such as 3782 × 32. Ask the children to estimate first (4000 × 32 = 128,000) before working on the accurate column calculation on their whiteboards. Ensure that the children understand that when calculations are set out in columns, numbers of the same value must line up under each other.

```
      3782
 ×      32
   113460
     7564
   121024
```

Try a few examples together.

Paired work: Organise the children to work in pairs to make up their own calculations for each other which involve multiplying four-digit numbers by two-digit numbers. Encourage them for each calculation to make up a word problem to put it in context.

Progress check: Observe how confidently the children work through the calculations. Watch their steps, and prompt children that need assistance.

Review

Invite pairs to share one or two of their problems with the rest of the class. Challenge the class to answer them on their whiteboards.

Curriculum objectives

● To multiply multi-digit numbers up to four digits by a two-digit whole number using the formal written method of long multiplication.

Success criteria

● I can use a formal written method for long multiplication.

You will need

General resources

'Number cards 0–9'

Equipment

Individual whiteboards

Differentiation

Less confident learners

Help children to move on from the grid method. They may still need to multiply by single digits.

More confident learners

Expect children to multiply four-digit numbers by a two-digit number.

Lesson 3 — Oral and mental starter 61

Main teaching activities

Whole-class work: Set this problem: *Zabby had a collection of 3245 stamps. Liam had a collection 14 times the size. How many stamps did Liam have?* Ask the children to work out the calculation on their whiteboards using long multiplication. Then ask them to check using another method. Invite volunteers to demonstrate their methods. Remind the children how to 'carry' numbers across as they work along the columns. For example:

```
     245
 ×    14
    2450
     980
    3430
     ı ı
```

Now tell the children that they will practise long multiplication today with decimal numbers. Write some calculations on the board for them to answer on their whiteboards. For example: 254.65 × 14; 365.34 × 16; 674.89 × 23. Invite a few of the children to demonstrate and explain their workings.

Paired work: Let the children work in pairs to practise long multiplication by generating their own numbers using number cards.

Progress check: Check the children are on the right track and ask questions such as: *What is each digit in 3,420,014 worth? What do we call the zeros? What is the job of the place-holder?*

Review

Ask some of the pairs to demonstrate the calculations they made up and answered. Invite a confident pair to suggest one of their calculations to work through as a class.

Curriculum objectives

● To divide numbers up to four digits by two-digit whole numbers using the formal written method of long division.
● To use estimation to check answers to calculations.

Success criteria

● I can solve long division problems.
● I can check answers by estimating.

You will need

General resources
'Number cards 0–9'

Equipment
Individual whiteboards; counters

Differentiation

Less confident learners
Ensure children understand the formal method for division. Work with them using place value counters to demonstrate the process.

More confident learners
Expect children to be dividing four-digit numbers by two-digit numbers.

Curriculum objectives

● To divide numbers up to four digits by two-digit whole numbers and interpret remainders as whole number remainders.
● To use estimation to check answers to calculations.

Success criteria

● I can solve problems involving long division.
● I can check answers by estimating.

You will need

Photocopiable sheets
'Division problems'

Equipment
Individual whiteboards

Differentiation

Less confident learners
Provide adult support.

More confident learners
Adapt the photocopiable sheet so that children are dividing four-digit numbers by two-digit numbers.

Lesson 4

Oral and mental starter 61

Main teaching activities

Whole-class work: Set this problem: *India had 2370 beads. She wanted to use them to make necklaces to sell at the store. Each necklace needs 15 beads. How many necklaces can she make?* Ask the children to discuss with a partner how to work out the answer. Remind them that the answer to a division is called the *quotient*. Demonstrate this way of setting out the problem:

$$15 \overline{\smash{\big)}\ 2^2 3 8 7^{12} 0} \quad \begin{array}{r} 1\ 5\ 8 \end{array}$$

Remind the children that 15 divided into 2 can't be done so exchange the 2 thousands for hundreds making 23 hundreds altogether. 23 hundreds can be divided into one group of 15 with 8 hundreds left. Exchange these for tens to make a total of 87. Five groups of 15 tens can be made with 12 left. Move the 12 tens into the ones to make 120 ones. 120 can be divided into 15 eight times. Repeat this for other four-digit numbers divided by two-digit numbers up to 20. For any calculations that have a remainder, demonstrate to the children how to write this as a fraction of the divisor.

Paired work: Ask the children to use their number cards to generate three-digit numbers for their partners. Explain that they should then choose a number from 11 to 20 as the divisor. Set the children to practise dividing the numbers as shown earlier in the lesson. Ask the pairs to check each other's answers by a quick mental estimation.

Progress check: Visit children who you particularly wish to assess to ensure that they are managing to carry out this method.

Review

Work through a few of the children's calculations. Ask volunteers to explain the stages of this division method.

Lesson 5

Oral and mental starter 59

Main teaching activities

Whole-class work: Set this problem: Harry and his friends baked 2750 cakes for the school fair. They want to pack them in boxes of 25. How many boxes do they need? Revise the long division written method:

$$25 \overline{\smash{\big)}\ 2^2 7^7 5 5} \quad \begin{array}{r} 1 3 0 \text{ remainder } 5 \end{array}$$

Elicit that you can't divide two by 25 so the 2 thousands move to the hundreds to make 27 hundreds. You can make one group of 25 with two hundreds remaining. These move to the tens to make 75 tens. You can make three groups of 25 tens. You can't make groups of 25 from the five ones, so these are the remainder. Discuss what to do with the remaining five cakes and agree Harry needs another box for these, so he needs 131 boxes altogether. Set similar problems for the children to answer on their whiteboards.

Independent work: Explain the activity on photocopiable page 'Division problems' from the CD-ROM. Suggest to the children that, when they have completed the sheet, they make up their own problems in a similar way.

Progress check: Spend time with those you wish to assess. Ask questions such as: *How many groups of 25 can you make out of six hundreds? What do you need to do? How many tens will you have? How can you check your answer?*

Review

Invite volunteers to share any problems that they made up. Ask the rest of the class to estimate and then solve these problems.

Working with fractions

Expected prior learning

Children should be able to:

- add and subtract factions using simple equivalences
- turn improper fractions to mixed numbers, and vice versa.

Topic	Curriculum objectives	Expected outcomes
Fractions (including decimals and percentages)	**Lesson 1**	
	To add and subtract fractions with different denominators and mixed numbers, using the concept of equivalent fractions.	Add and subtract fractions by finding common denominators.
	Lesson 2	
	To multiply simple pairs of proper fractions, writing the answer in its simplest form.	Understand that multiplying fractions gives a smaller answer.
	Lesson 3	
	To multiply simple pairs of proper fractions, writing the answer in its simplest form.	Multiply pairs of fractions.
	Lesson 4	
	To divide proper fractions by whole numbers.	Understand that dividing fractions by whole numbers gives a larger answer.
	Lesson 5	
	To add and subtract fractions with different denominators and mixed numbers, using the concept of equivalent fractions.	Solve problems involving fractions.

Preparation

Lessons I and 3: produce domino sets, ideally copied onto card and laminated. You will need a set for each pair of children

Lesson 4: prepare strips of A4 paper cut width-ways about 2cm wide

Lesson 5: copy 'Would you rather...?' for each child

You will need

Photocopiable sheets
'Would you rather...?'
General resources
'Dominoes'
Equipment
Individual whiteboards; squared paper; strips of A4 paper; rulers

Further practice

Photocopiable sheets
'Equivalence dominoes'

Oral and mental starters suggested for week 4

See the bank of starters on pages 205 and 206. Oral and mental starters are also on the CD-ROM.

54 Counting steps

55 Number lines

58 Ordering

62 Quick division

Overview of progression

During this week the children will develop their knowledge and understanding of fractions. They will practise adding, subtracting, multiplying and dividing them. To perform these operations, the children will consider what they already know about them and also identify equivalent fractions that will help. They will work visually to develop their understanding of these concepts. They will look at number patterns to deepen their understanding of the 'rules' of adding, subtracting, multiplying and dividing fractions.

Watch out for

Some children will still be struggling with the conceptual understanding of fractions. Offer these children more practice using practical equipment such as fraction strips (see lessons 2 and 4). Their work during this week might involve reinforcing and consolidating work from previous years.

Creative context

Ask the children to find examples of fractions on the internet and in everyday life (including in more unusual 'non-mathematical' contexts such as a half marathon and the Jewellery Quarter, the thirds of a football pitch) and to explore what these are about.

Vocabulary

common denominator, denominator, equivalent, improper fraction, mixed number, numerator, proper fraction, reduced, sharing

■✦SCHOLASTIC

Lesson 1 — Oral and mental starter 54

Main teaching activities

Whole-class work: Recap with the children what they know already about fractions. Draw out particularly that *denominator* is the number that an object or quantity must be shared into and the *numerator* is the number of resultant parts that are needed. Elicit that the larger the denominator, the smaller the fraction (if the numerators are the same). Ask, for example, which is larger, $\frac{1}{4}$ or $\frac{1}{6}$? Or, $\frac{2}{3}$ or $\frac{2}{5}$?

Go on to discuss briefly improper fractions (such as $2\frac{1}{4}$, $3\frac{5}{8}$), mixed numbers ($4\frac{1}{3}$, $12\frac{7}{8}$) and reducing fractions (that $\frac{9}{12} = \frac{3}{4}$, $\frac{8}{16} = \frac{4}{8} = \frac{1}{2}$). Then move on to focus on equivalent fractions. Ask the children to write some equivalent fractions on their whiteboards. Then take feedback by inviting children to write some of theirs on your board for the class.

Next, write a calculation such as this on the board: $\frac{1}{2} + \frac{1}{5} = \frac{2}{7}$. Ask the children: *Do you think I am correct? Why/why not? How can we add these two fractions? What do you think we need to do?* Establish that $\frac{2}{7}$ is smaller than both $\frac{1}{2}$ and $\frac{1}{5}$, so the answer must be wrong. On a separate part of the board, remind the children that adding $\frac{1}{2}$ and $\frac{1}{4}$ gives an answer of $\frac{3}{4}$ because $\frac{1}{2}$ is the same as $\frac{2}{4}$, and $\frac{2}{4} + \frac{1}{4}$ is $\frac{3}{4}$. Establish that, for $\frac{1}{2} + \frac{1}{5}$, therefore, they need to find an *equivalent fraction* to turn $\frac{1}{2}$ and $\frac{1}{5}$ into. Agree they can both be turned into tenths ($\frac{5}{10}$ and $\frac{2}{10}$). Demonstrate that, when changing a fraction into an equivalent, they need to multiply *both* the numerator and denominator by the number that makes the new fraction. To make $\frac{1}{2}$ into tenths, for example, multiply each part by 5 ($\frac{5}{10}$). To make $\frac{1}{5}$ into tenths, multiply both parts by 2 ($\frac{2}{10}$). These can now be added to give the answer $\frac{7}{10}$.

Repeat the activity with similar examples, such as $\frac{3}{4}$ and $\frac{1}{3}$ ($\frac{9}{12} + \frac{4}{12} = \frac{13}{12} = 1\frac{1}{12}$). Look again at this answer, reminding the children that if the numerator is larger than the denominator (an improper fraction), they actually have a whole number and a fraction (a mixed number).

Next, work through the same process to *subtract* decimals with different denominators. Begin with the examples you used for addition. So: $\frac{1}{2} - \frac{1}{5}$ becomes $\frac{5}{10} - \frac{2}{10} = \frac{3}{10}$.

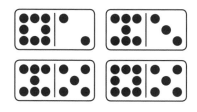

Paired work: Give each pair a set of domino cards from the photocopiable sheet. Explain that they should each pick two dominoes and place them vertically together to make two proper fractions. Ask them to add them together, by finding the common denominator, and then do the same to subtract one from the other.

Progress check: Visit pairs as they work to ensure that they can find the common denominators.

Review

Invite pairs to share the fraction addition and subtraction calculations they made, but without revealing the answers. Work with the rest of the class to work out the answers to both.

Recap on the important things that the children need to remember about adding and subtracting fractions: finding a common denominator, then multiplying both the numerator and denominators.

Curriculum objectives
- To multiply simple pairs of proper fractions.

Success criteria
- I can multiply by halves and quarters.

You will need
Equipment
Individual whiteboards; squared paper

Differentiation
Less confident learners
Support children as they focus on multiplying by a half.

More confident learners
Once children have made up some of their own examples, ask them to explore multiplying by an eighth.

Lesson 2

Main teaching activities

Whole-class work: Write a series of number sentences like this on the board: $4 \times 1 = 4$; $3 \times 1 = 3$; $2 \times 1 = 2$; $1 \times 1 = 1$; $\frac{1}{2} \times 1 = ?$. Ask the children to predict what the answer to the last number sentence will be. Encourage them to look at the pattern in the answers. Elicit that the answers are getting smaller, so the answer to $\frac{1}{2} \times 1$ must be somewhere between 0 and 1. Explain that if you have $\frac{1}{2}$ once, then the answer will be $\frac{1}{2}$. Write $\frac{1}{2} \times \frac{1}{2} = ?$ on the board. Ask the children to talk to a partner about what this means and therefore what the answer will be. Establish that this means you have a half times a half, which is the same as half of a half. Agree that half of a half is $\frac{1}{4}$. Repeat for $\frac{1}{4} \times \frac{1}{2} = ?$ Establish that this is half of a quarter, which is $\frac{1}{8}$. Demonstrate using this model of fraction strips:

$\frac{1}{2}$				$\frac{1}{2}$			
$\frac{1}{4}$		$\frac{1}{4}$		$\frac{1}{4}$		$\frac{1}{4}$	
$\frac{1}{8}$	$\frac{1}{8}$	$\frac{1}{8}$	$\frac{1}{8}$	$\frac{1}{8}$	$\frac{1}{8}$	$\frac{1}{8}$	$\frac{1}{8}$

Use the strips shown above to work out what $\frac{1}{2} \times \frac{1}{4}$ or one quarter of a half is.

Paired work: Give the children squared paper and ask them to explore multiplying the following fractions: $\frac{1}{3} \times \frac{1}{2}$, $\frac{1}{3} \times \frac{1}{4}$, $\frac{1}{5} \times \frac{1}{2}$, $\frac{1}{5} \times \frac{1}{4}$, $\frac{1}{6} \times \frac{1}{2}$, $\frac{1}{6} \times \frac{1}{4}$. Encourage them to draw fraction strips in the same way that you modelled above to work out what halves and quarters of the fractions are. If any of the children finish quickly, challenge them to explore finding halves and quarters of other numbers.

Progress check: Observe how confidently pairs of children can find halves and quarters of the fractions. Support any that need assistance.

Review

Invite some pairs to demonstrate, drawing fractions strips on the board if preferred, how they multiplied the fractions. Similarly, write these on the board (inviting the children to suggest the answers as you write):
$\frac{1}{2} \times \frac{1}{2} = \frac{1}{4}$; $\frac{1}{2} \times \frac{1}{4} = \frac{1}{8}$; $\frac{1}{3} \times \frac{1}{2} = \frac{1}{6}$; $\frac{1}{3} \times \frac{1}{4} = \frac{1}{12}$ and $\frac{1}{5} \times \frac{1}{2} = \frac{1}{10}$.
Ask the children what they notice each time. Prompt them to see that the numerators (in this case always 1) and denominators are multiplied together to give the answer: $\frac{1}{2} \times \frac{1}{2}$: $1 \times 1 = 1$, $2 \times 2 = 4$, so the answer is $\frac{1}{4}$.

Curriculum objectives
● To multiply simple pairs of proper fractions.
Success criteria
● I can multiply fractions.

You will need
General resources
'Dominoes'
Equipment
Individual whiteboards

Differentiation
Less confident learners
Children should focus on multiplying the dominoes with 3 and 4 as denominators by ½.
More confident learners
Ask children to use the extra dominoes, so that they have sevenths and eighths to multiply.

Lesson 3
Oral and mental starter 55

Main teaching activities

Whole-class work: Recap on the work from Lesson 2 and then focus on the multiplying aspect discussed in the Review. Work through examples to reinforce the fact that you can multiply numerators and then denominators to multiply fractions together. Write this example on the board: ½ × ¾ = ?. Ask the children how they could find the answer. Elicit that what they need to find is three-quarters *of* a half. They know ¼ of ½ is ⅛, so ¾ must be ⅜. Now multiply the numerators and then the denominators to confirm that the answer is the same. Repeat this with a few other examples, asking the children to multiply the numerators and the denominators: ⅓ × ¾; ⅕ × ¾; ⅔ × ¾. Each time, reinforce what the question is asking.

Paired work: Give each pair a set of domino cards. Ask them to pick two at a time and multiply them together. Tell them to record their work in fraction number sentences.

Progress check: Visit pairs, particularly those you wish to assess, and ask: *What is your multiplication asking you to do? How would you do this?*

Review

Ask pairs to demonstrate the fraction multiplications they made up and answered. Challenge the children to work out: ½ × ¼ × ⅛. Invite a volunteer to explain how they worked out the answer (½ × ¼ = ⅛, then ⅛ × ⅛ = ¹/₁₆). Repeat with a few other examples.

Curriculum objectives
● To divide proper fractions by whole numbers.
Success criteria
● I can divide fractions by whole numbers.

You will need
Equipment
Individual whiteboards; strips of A4 paper; rulers

Differentiation
Less confident learners
Ask children to focus on dividing the fractions by two.
More confident learners
Expect children to go on to divide fractions that are not unit fractions, such as ¾ and ⅔.

Lesson 4
Oral and mental starter 58

Main teaching activities

Whole-class work: Remind the children that *sharing* is dividing an amount into equal groups and that they can use this to divide fractions by whole numbers.

Give each child four strips of paper. Ask them to keep one whole and fold the others to show halves, quarters and eighths (see Lesson 2). Ask them to label each section with the appropriate fraction. They should then lay them down in order from largest to smallest.

Write on the board: ½ ÷ 1 = ?. *If we share one half into one group, what would we have?* Agree they would still have half. Now write: ½ ÷ 2 = ?. Again, focus on the half and imagine what two equal parts would be. Agree that ½ ÷ 2 = ¼. Repeat this for ½ ÷ 4. Invite a volunteer to complete the number sentence: ½ ÷ 4 = ?. (⅛.) Ask the children to find ¼ ÷ 2, then ¼ ÷ 4. Ask: *What do you notice about the answer?* Agree that the denominator is multiplied by the whole number.

Paired work: Give the children four more strips of paper each. Ask them to use a ruler to mark where the folds would go to make thirds, then sixths, then fifths and tenths. Write these calculations on the board for the children to solve: ⅓ ÷ 2; ⅓ ÷ 4; ⅙ ÷ 2; ⅙ ÷ 4; ⅕ ÷ 2; ⅕ ÷ 4; ¹/₁₀ ÷ 2; ¹/₁₀ ÷ 4. The children can use their strips to help. Then ask them to check their answers by multiplying the denominator and the divisor.

Progress check: Visit the pairs to ensure they can divide by two and four, using their strips if needed.

Review

Go through the calculations. Recap that to divide a whole number into a fraction, sharing is used, and a quick way is to multiply the denominator of the fraction by the divisor.

Curriculum objectives
● To add and subtract fractions with different denominators and mixed numbers, using the concept of equivalent fractions.
Success criteria
● I can solve problems involving addition of fractions.

You will need
Photocopiable sheets
'Would you rather...?'
Equipment
Individual whiteboards

Differentiation
Less confident learners
Adapt the photocopiable sheet so that children are adding halves and quarters.
More confident learners
Adapt the photocopiable sheet so that children are working with more complex fractions.

Lesson 5

Main teaching activities

Whole-class work: Recap the week's work on fractions. Begin with simple adding and subtracting (see Lesson 1 for details). Ask the children to add and subtract a variety of quick-fire fractions on their whiteboards, for example: $\frac{1}{2} + \frac{1}{10}$ and $\frac{3}{4} + \frac{2}{5}$. Move on to multiplying and then dividing. For each operation, recap with the children what they need to do to solve the calculation. Set some similar calculations to those in Lessons 3 and 4 for the children to answer quickly on their whiteboards.

Then give the children this problem: *Zoe ate ¾ of a pepperoni pizza and ⅓ of a four-cheese pizza. What fraction of the two pizzas did she eat?* Give the children a short amount of time to talk about this with their neighbours. Then agree that in order to find the answer, the children needed to add the two fractions. Invite them to do this on their whiteboards and hold them up. Establish that they can find equivalent fractions by making both fractions into twelfths: $\frac{9}{12} + \frac{4}{12}$, which equals $\frac{13}{12}$. Zoe therefore ate 1 whole pizza and $\frac{1}{12}$.

Set another two or three similar problems. Then tell the children that their next task involves solving similar word problems.

Independent work: Distribute the photocopiable page 'Would you rather...' and explain to the children what they need to do. Tell them that, once they have solved the problems on the sheet, you would like them to make up some similar word problems of their own.

Progress check: Visit the children after they have completed the first two or three problems on the sheet. Spend some time with those children you wish to assess. Ask questions such as: *What do you need to do to solve this problem? What fraction can you change both of these into? What must you remember to do to both the numerator and denominator?*

Review

Invite volunteers to demonstrate how they solved the problems and to share any problems that they have made up. Work with the rest of the class to solve these. Ask the children to assess their confidence in adding fractions.

Fractions, decimals and percentages

Expected prior learning

Children should be able to:

- find percentages of numbers
- find equivalences between simple fractions, decimals and percentages.

Topic	Curriculum objectives	Expected outcomes
Fractions (including decimals and percentages)	**Lesson 1**	
	To recall and use equivalences between simple fractions, decimals and percentages, including in different contexts.	Find percentages of amounts of money.
	Lesson 2	
	To recall and use equivalences between simple fractions, decimals and percentages, including in different contexts.	Know equivalences between fractions, decimals and percentages.
Ratio and proportion	**Lesson 3**	
	To solve problems involving the calculation of percentages [for example, of measures, and such as 15% of 360] and the use of percentages for comparison.	Know equivalences between fractions, decimals and percentages.
	Lesson 4	
	To solve problems involving the calculation of percentages [for example, of measures, and such as 15% of 360] and the use of percentages for comparison.	Solve problems involving percentages.
	Lesson 5	
	To solve problems involving the calculation of percentages [for example, of measures, and such as 15% of 360] and the use of percentages for comparison. To recall and use equivalences between simple fractions, decimals and percentages, including in different contexts.	Solve problems involving percentages.

Preparation

Lesson I and 2: make enough sets, ideally laminated, of the 'Equivalence dominoes' for each pair of children; copy the sheet, for the instructions, for each pair

Lesson 3: copy 'Percentages' for each child

Lesson 4: copy 'Percentage clocks' for each child

You will need

Photocopiable sheets
'Percentages'; 'Equivalence dominoes'; 'Percentage clocks'

Equipment
Individual whiteboards

Further practice

Photocopiable sheets
'Equivalence dominoes'

Oral and mental starters suggested for week 5

See the bank of starters on pages 205 and 206. Oral and mental starters are also on the CD-ROM.

57 Multiples of 10

59 Percentage bingo

60 Quick decimal addition

61 Multiplication and division facts

Overview of progression

During this week the children will develop their knowledge and understanding of equivalences between fractions, decimals and percentages.

Watch out for

Some children may not quite understand the concept of percentages. Encourage them to find examples of percentages in newspaper and magazine articles and advertisements and discuss with them what these figures are showing.

Creative context

Ask the children to make a poster of the percentages that they find on food packaging. Tie this in with examining the quantities in the nutritional information panels on food packets to help in making healthy food choices. Look at, for example, the amount of salt or sugar per 100g, convert them to percentages and find out whether they are low or high levels according to health guidelines.

Vocabulary

decimal, decimal fraction, decimal point, decimal place, equivalent, fraction, percentage, per cent (%)

Curriculum objectives

● To recall and use equivalences between simple fractions, decimals and percentages.

Success criteria

● I know equivalences between fractions, decimals and percentages.

You will need

Photocopiable sheets

'Equivalence dominoes'

Equipment

Individual whiteboards

Differentiation

Less confident learners

Throughout the lesson, let children focus on tenths and link these to percentages and decimals, $3/10 = 0.3 = 30\%$.

More confident learners

After the game, ask children to explore equivalences such as $3/4 = 0.75 = 75\%$; $5/8 = 0.625 = 62\frac{1}{2}\%$; $2/5 = 0.4 = 40\%$, and make dominoes for these.

Lesson 1   Oral and mental starter 57

Main teaching activities

Whole-class work: Write $1/2$ on the board. Ask the children to tell you another way to express this. Encourage equivalences such as $4/8$ and $5/10$, decimal notation (0.5) and percentages (50%). Link decimals to money (50 pence = £0.50) and measures (5mm = 0.5cm; 50cm = 0.5m). Repeat for tenths and hundredths, again linking to money and measures. For example: $1/10 = 0.1$ (£0.10 and 0.1m); $1/100 = 0.01$ (£0.01 and 0.01m). Ask the children to talk about where they might see 50% in real life and what it means (for example on a half-price item in a sale). Recall the fact that 50% can be recorded as $1/2$ or 0.5.

Ask the children to write on their whiteboards, and then share with the class, other equivalent fractions, decimals and percentages, such as $1/10 = 10\% = 0.1$; $7/10 = 70\% = 0.7$; $5/100 = 5\% = 0.05$.

Challenge the children to prove that 0.6 is more than 50% and less than $7/10$.

Group work: Distribute the sets of photocopiable page 209 'Equivalence dominoes' and go through how to play the game, matching equivalences.

Progress check: Visit groups that you particularly wish to assess and ask questions such as: *How else can you write $5/10$? Is there another way? How else can you write 25%? Is there another way? Where do we see decimals in real life? Where else? What about percentages? Which is the largest $9/10$, 15%, 0.3? How do you know?*

Review

Write sets of fractions, decimals and percentages on the board, such as: 0.8, 60%, $7/10$. Ask the children to order them from smallest to largest on their whiteboards. Prompt them to explain how they did it.

Curriculum objectives

● To recall and use equivalences between simple fractions, decimals and percentages.

Success criteria

● I know equivalences between fractions, decimals and percentages.

You will need

Photocopiable sheets

'Equivalence dominoes'

Equipment

Individual whiteboards

Differentiation

Less confident learners

Limit the number of dominoes that children play with.

More confident learners

Challenge children to find more than two equivalences where possible.

Lesson 2 | Oral and mental starter 59

Main teaching activities

Whole-class work: Recap, from lesson 1, that a percentage is a special fraction, that 1% of something is $\frac{1}{100}$ of it, and 100% is the whole amount of it. Ask the children to write down different percentages and their fraction equivalences, such as 72% = $\frac{72}{100}$. Highlight these if the children suggest them: ½ = 50%; ¼ = 25%; ¾ = 75% and $\frac{1}{10}$ = 10%; $\frac{2}{10}$ = 20% and the other tenths. Write them on the board and ask the children to work out why they are equivalent. For example: 50% = $\frac{50}{100}$, which is equivalent to $\frac{5}{10}$ and therefore ½.

Paired work: Give pairs of children a set of 'Equivalence dominoes' from page 209. Ask them each to pick one at a time and to write down two equivalences for each fraction, decimal or percentage on the domino.

Progress check: Visit pairs you particularly want to assess to check they can find all the types of equivalence (from fraction to decimal, from fraction to percentage, and vice versa) and ask questions such as: *What fraction is equivalent to 50%? Can you think of another?*

Review

Ask the pairs to share some of the equivalences they made. For some, let the pair give the first equivalence and challenge the rest of the class to suggest another. See if the suggestion is the same as the pair's original. (For example, for 80%, there could be 0.8, $\frac{8}{10}$ and $\frac{4}{5}$.)

Curriculum objectives

● To solve problems involving the calculation of percentages [for example, of measures, and such as 15% of 360] and the use of percentages for comparison.

Success criteria

● I can compare amounts using percentages.

You will need

Photocopiable sheets

'Percentages'

Equipment

Individual whiteboards

Differentiation

Less confident learners

Support them in extracting the calculations from the word problems.

More confident learners

Once they have completed the photocopiable sheet, ask children to work in pairs to set each other similar problems, starting from a larger amount of money.

Lesson 3 | Oral and mental starter 59

Main teaching activities

Whole-class work: Set this problem: Georgie wanted to buy a jumper. It cost £48.50. In the sale there was a 20% discount. How much was it in the sale?

Discuss how to find 20%. Agree to find 10% first and double for 20%. Establish that the discount is £9.70, the jumper will cost £38.80.

Ask the children to find as many percentages as they can from this information: 100% is £350. Encourage them to work out 10% first and then use doubling, halving, addition and subtraction to find others. Take feedback, the children share how they found their percentages. Set similar problems to Georgie's.

Focus on the equivalences between percentages, fractions and decimals. Agree that a percentage is out of 100, so 50% is $\frac{50}{100}$ or ½ and 0.5. They write as many as they can think of in one minute. Take feedback, listing their suggestions on the board.

Paired work: Distribute photocopiable page 208 'Percentages' and explain what the children need to do.

Progress check: Visit children who you particularly wish to assess and ask questions such as: *How would you explain what a percentage is to someone who doesn't know? Is there another way to explain? How would you find 19% of an amount?*

Review

Invite children to share the percentages that they found. Draw a web on the board as on the photocopiable sheet and add the percentages offered by the children. Work through the word problems together, identifying any areas that need clarification. Ask the children to assess how confident they are at finding percentages of numbers.

 SCHOLASTIC

Curriculum objectives

● To solve problems involving the calculation of percentages [for example, of measures, and such as 15% of 360] and the use of percentages for comparison.

Success criteria

● I can solve problems involving percentages.

You will need

Photocopiable sheets

'Percentage clocks'

Differentiation

Less confident learners

Ask children to focus on different ways to shade 50%, 25% and 75% and multiples of 10%.

More confident learners

Ask children to find more complex percentages and their fraction and decimal equivalences, such as 12½%.

Lesson 4 — Oral and mental starter 60

Main teaching activities

Whole-class work: Invite a volunteer to write the per cent symbol on the board. Then set this problem: *Lucas is on a cycling trip around Cuba. Yesterday he rode 45km in one hour, which is 10% of the total distance he will ride. How far will this be?* Elicit that they know 10%, so they need to work out 100%: 10 × 45km = 450km. Set similar problems for the children to solve on their whiteboards.

Ask: *If it took Lucas 15% of an hour to travel two kilometres, how many minutes is this?* Agree that they need to work out 15% of 60 minutes. Prompt them to work out 10% first and then halve to find the extra 5%. Conclude that Lucas took 9 minutes (10% + 5%) to ride two kilometres.

Now compare percentages in similar problems. For example: *Of Lucas' cycling group, 68% were boys and the rest were girls. What percentage were girls? Were there more girls or boys? If there were 50 children in total, how many were there of each?*

Paired work: Distribute photocopiable page 'Percentage clocks' from the CD-ROM and explain to the children what they need to do.

Progress check: Visit children you particularly wish to assess and ask: *How would you explain what a percentage is to someone who doesn't know? Is there another way to explain? How would you find 15% of an amount?*

Review

Take feedback from the task. Invite children to share the percentages they made describing how they worked them out. Compare the percentages they found by working out how many minutes each is worth. Ask them to assess their confidence at finding percentages of amounts and shape.

Curriculum objectives

● To solve problems involving the calculation of percentages and the use of percentages for comparison.
● To recall and use equivalences between simple fractions, decimals and percentages.

Success criteria

● I can solve problems involving percentages.

You will need

Equipment

Individual whiteboards

Differentiation

Less confident learners

Work with children to help them write their problems. Prompt them to use simple numbers, such as 10% and £50.

More confident learners

Expect children to create and solve more complex problems.

Lesson 5 — Oral and mental starter 61

Main teaching activities

Whole-class work: Recap the week's work on percentages and their equivalent fractions and decimals. Begin by writing, for example, *100% is £450* and asking the children to find as many percentages as they can in two minutes. Remind them that a good start is to find 10% first (£45) and then double, halve, add, subtract and multiply and divide by 10 to make others. Write the children's ideas on the board. Then ask them to change the percentages on the board to decimals and fractions, reducing these as appropriate ($\frac{40}{100}$ to $\frac{2}{5}$).

Set this problem: *Tia bought a large flat screen TV in a sale. It was £850 but had been reduced by 42 ½%. How much did Tia pay for her TV?* Talk about this with your partner. Invite them to do this on their whiteboards. Take feedback. Establish that 40% of £850 is four lots of 10% which is £340. They find 1% and double this to make 2% (£17). They divide the 1% by two (£4.25) and add these altogether. They take £361.25 away from £850 leaving £488.75. Set two or three similar problems.

Paired work: Tell the children that their task is to make up word problems for their partners to solve, similar to those worked through as a class.

Progress check: Visit each pair to ensure they are making up problems involving percentages. Ask the children to check each other's answers.

Review

Invite pairs to share one or two of their problems for the rest of the class to work out on their whiteboards.

Ratio and proportion

Expected prior learning

Children should be able to:

- solve problems involving fractions
- find equivalences between simple fractions, decimals and percentages
- solve problems involving the calculation of percentages [for example, of measures and such as 15% of 360] and the use of percentages for comparison.

Topic	Curriculum objectives	Expected outcomes
Ratio and proportion	**Lesson 1**	
	To solve problems involving the relative sizes of two quantities, where missing values can be found by using integer multiplication and division facts.	Understand what a proportion is and how it is represented.
	Lesson 2	
	To solve problems involving the relative sizes of two quantities, where missing values can be found by using integer multiplication and division facts. To solve problems involving unequal sharing and grouping using knowledge of fractions and multiples.	Understand what a ratio is and how it is represented.
	Lesson 3	
	To solve problems involving similar shapes where the scale factor is known or can be found. To solve problems involving unequal sharing and grouping using knowledge of fractions and multiples.	Find a variety of ratios.
	Lesson 4	
	To solve problems involving the relative sizes of two quantities, where missing values can be found by using integer multiplication and division facts. To solve problems involving unequal sharing and grouping using knowledge of fractions and multiples.	Solve problems involving ratio and proportion.
	Lesson 5	
	To solve problems involving the relative sizes of two quantities, where missing values can be found by using integer multiplication and division facts. To solve problems involving unequal sharing and grouping using knowledge of fractions and multiples.	Solve problems involving ratio and proportion.

Preparation

Lesson 1: collect 10p and 1p coins in tubs for the children to share; copy 'Proportion', for each child

Lesson 2: copy 'Recipe' for each pair of children

Lesson 3: find a class photograph or photographs of the children; make a collection of photographs of famous buildings; collect maps or atlases for the children to study

You will need

Photocopiable sheets

'Proportion'; 'Recipe'; 'Recipe template'

Equipment

Individual whiteboards; 10p and 1p coins; blue and red counters

Further practice

Photocopiable sheets

'Paint blobs'; 'Ratio problems'

Oral and mental starters suggested for week 6

See the bank of starters on pages 205 and 206. Oral and mental starters are also on the CD-ROM.

56 Rounding

58 Ordering

59 Percentage bingo

62 Quick division

63 Digit investigation

Overview of progression

During this week the children will have plenty of opportunities to solve problems involving proportion and ratio, particularly as ways to compare quantities. The children will learn that proportion is an amount out of a whole and that it can be expressed as a fraction. They will learn that a ratio is an amount directly compared with another amount. They will solve real-life problems involving both of these.

> ## Watch out for
> Some children will find it difficult to scale up and down to find ratios. In order to help overcome this, encourage them to use doubling, halving and simple addition or subtraction for this.

Creative context

Provide opportunities for the children to cook. The exploration of quantities in recipes offers an ideal chance for scaling up, to suit the number of children in the class for example. Lesson 5 involves paint-mixing, which could be extended to an art activity experimenting with different shades of one colour in, for example, a sunset.

Vocabulary

fraction, one for every, proportion, ratio, scale

Curriculum objectives
- To solve problems involving the relative sizes of two quantities.

Success criteria
- I understand what is meant by proportion.

You will need

Photocopiable sheets
'Proportion'

Equipment
Individual whiteboards, 10p and 1p coins

Differentiation

Less confident learners
Adapt the photocopiable sheet so that children are working on a suitable amount. Help them identify a proportion as a fraction.

More confident learners
Adapt the photocopiable sheet so that children are working on more challenging amounts.

Lesson 1 — Oral and mental starter 58

Main teaching activities

Whole-class work: Showing the appropriate coins, say to the children: *In my wallet I have four 10p coins and eight 1p coins. What proportion of my money is 10p coins? What proportion is pennies?* From this, discuss what is meant by proportion. Establish that it is a part of a whole amount and it is also a comparison of two or more parts. Putting the figures on the board, help the children to apply this knowledge to the question you just put to them. Agree that the whole, in this case, is the total number of coins (12). There are four 10p coins, so this proportion is $\frac{4}{12}$. The proportion of pennies is $\frac{8}{12}$. Look at how else these fractions can be represented – in their simplest reduced form: $\frac{1}{3}$ and $\frac{2}{3}$. Agree that the mathematics involved in proportion, therefore, is fractions.

Repeat with one or two more similar problems.

Then give the children piles of coins and ask them to work out the proportion of 10p and 1p coins they have, and to write these proportions on their whiteboards.

Next, set some problems similar to this one: *$\frac{3}{5}$ of a class have packed lunches; the rest eat a hot meal at school. What proportion eats a school meal?* Agree on $\frac{2}{5}$. Ask how many children that is. Establish that there is not enough information – the number of children could be any multiple of five. Ask the children what additional information is needed. (The number of children in the class.) So, say that there are 30 children in the class. Elicit that 12 children have a school meal, and 18 have a packed lunch.

Independent work: Ask the children to work through the problems on photocopiable page 'Proportion' from the CD-ROM. When they have finished, encourage the children to make up some similar problems of their own.

Progress check: Observe the children during the activity, assessing their understanding of proportion. Ask questions such as: *What is meant by proportion? Show me an example. Try to explain it in another way.*

Review

Take feedback from the activity by asking different children to share their answers from the photocopiable sheet, with explanations as to how they found them.

Curriculum objectives
- To solve problems involving the relative sizes of two quantities.
- To solve problems that involve unequal sharing and grouping.

Success criteria
- I understand what is meant by ratio.

You will need
Photocopiable sheets
'Recipe'; 'Recipe template'
Equipment
Individual whiteboards; blue and red counters

Differentiation
Less confident learners
Adapt the 'Recipe template' so that children work on a ratio of 1:2.
More confident learners
Adapt the 'Recipe template' so that children work on a more complex ratio, such as 1:2.25.

Lesson 2   Oral and mental starter 56

Main teaching activities

Whole-class work: Ask the children what they think is the meaning of *ratio*. Explain that a ratio is another way of comparing amounts. Recap that proportion shows the comparison of amounts within a whole. In a fruit bowl, for example, ⅓ of the whole amount is apples, ⅔ of the whole amount are bananas. Explain that ratio is different in that it shows the relative sizes of two or more values. Demonstrate using one blue counter and three red ones. Explain there is one blue counter for every three red ones, so the ratio of blue to red is 1:3. Repeat the demonstration for two blue counters and five red. Then show a different number of each colour counter for the children to write the ratio on their whiteboards. Invite a volunteer to explain how they got their answer. Repeat the activity a few times.

Discuss how the number of counters could be changed but give the same ratio. Agree that they could double each quantity. For example, in the case of one blue for every three red, it would be two blue for every six red: 2:6, which can be reduced to 1:3. Establish that if both quantities are multiplied by the same number there will be an equivalent ratio. Demonstrate examples using the counters. Talk about ratios in real life, for example when adapting recipes or mixing paints.

Paired work: Let the children work in pairs on photocopiable page 'Recipe' from the CD-ROM.

Progress check: Visit the pairs to assess their understanding. Can they explain ratio?

Review

Invite pairs to share their new recipe quantities and to explain how they did this. Ask the children how they could write a recipe for 6, 15 and 16 people.

Curriculum objectives
- To solve problems involving similar shapes where the scale factor is known or can be found.
- To solve problems that involve unequal sharing and grouping.

Success criteria
- I can find different ratios.

You will need
Equipment
Individual whiteboards; photographs

Differentiation
Organise the class into mixed ability groups of four. Encourage the children to work together and support each other during the task.

Lesson 3   Oral and mental starter 59

Main teaching activities

Whole-class work: Show the photographs of the children. Explain that the pictures are of them but that they look smaller than the children actually are. Find out if anyone knows what has happened to them. Agree that the pictures have been scaled down. Discuss other things that are scaled down in size. For example, models or pictures of cars, bridges or buildings, maps. Show the photographs of the buildings to illustrate this. Explain that to describe how much something has been scaled down or up we often use ratio. Give pairs or small groups a map. Ask them to look for the scale. Explain that if the scale says, for example, 1cm:100km it means that for every centimetre in length on the map the distance is actually 100 kilometres. Set this problem: *A tennis court is 7m wide and 21m long. A scale plan of it is drawn with a width of 3.5cm. What is its length?* Agree that 7m has been divided by 100 to become centimetres and then halved. The same must therefore be done with 21m to give 10.5cm. Repeat with a similar scenario.

Group work: The children work in a small group to make 2D drawings of objects in the classroom. They measure heights and widths of their objects and then scale them up. They decide their own ratio for scaling down, for example, 1:2 or 1:3.

Progress check: Visit each group to ensure they understand what to do and that they are scaling up or down correctly.

Review

Invite the children to share with the class their drawings. The class predicts the ratios used for scaling.

Curriculum objectives
● To solve problems involving similar shapes where the scale factor is known or can be found.
● To solve problems that involve unequal sharing and grouping.

Success criteria
● I can solve problems involving ratio.

You will need
Equipment
Individual whiteboards

Differentiation
Organise the class into mixed-ability groups of about four. Encourage the children to work and support each other during the task.

Lesson 4
Oral and mental starter 62

Main teaching activities

Whole-class work: Recap the work done in the previous lesson on scaling. Remind the children that often maps, drawings and plans of real things are scaled down. Ask when things are scaled up. Encourage them to think of examples such as looking at small organisms through a microscope. Ask the children to draw a line of 2cm on a piece of plain paper. They then draw a line which has been scaled up to be 4 times as long. They write the ratio on the paper (1:4). Repeat this a few times with different lengths and different ratios to scale up by. Write a:b on the board. Ask the children what this could mean. Establish that a and b represent different numbers. Ask them to draw lines and scale them up and then write down what their values for a and b are.

Paired work: The children work with a partner. They each draw a selection of polygons on plain paper. When they have drawn about five they pass their shapes to their partner who scales each shape up by a ratio of their choice.

Progress check: Visit each pair to ensure they understand how to scale their shapes up. Ask: *What is meant by ratio? By what ratio are you scaling your shape up?*

Review

Invite pairs to share the shapes they drew and explain the ratios used to scale them up. Finish the lesson by recapping what is meant by ratio and the differences and similarities between ratio and proportion.

Curriculum objectives
● To solve problems involving the calculation of percentages [for example, of measures and such as 15% of 360] and the use of percentages for comparison.

Success criteria
● I can solve problems involving percentages.

You will need
Equipment
Individual whiteboards; protractors

Differentiation
Organise the class into mixed-ability groups of about four. Encourage the children to work together and support each other during the task.

Lesson 5
Oral and mental starter 63

Main teaching activities

Whole-class work: Ask the children to tell you what they know about pie charts. Agree that they are a way of displaying data. Draw this on the board:

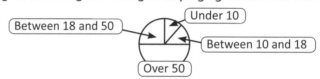

Tell the children that this represents 360 people who live in a village. Ask them to work out what fraction each part is and then how many people are within each age range. Discuss how it is possible to construct an accurate pie chart. Elicit that because a circle has a total of 360 degrees, they could draw round a circle and make the parts a percentage of 360. Give each child a protractor and a piece of plain paper. Set this scenario: there were 360 children in the school. 30% of them have packed lunches. 55% have school dinners and the rest go home for lunch. Ask the children to draw an accurate pie chart to show this information. Invite a volunteer to share what they did. Agree 108 of the children have packed lunches, 198 have school dinners and 54 children go home. Repeat the exercise with a similar scenario.

Group work: The children work in a small group to make up scenarios similar to those worked on during the lesson. They base their scenarios around 360 people. Once they have made up their story they draw pie charts to show the information.

Progress check: Visit each group to ensure they understand how to find the percentages of 360 and also how to construct their pie charts.

Review

Invite groups to share their stories. The rest of the class work out the percentages and volunteers show these percentages on pie charts that they draw on their whiteboards.

SCHOLASTIC

You will need

1. Check

Oral and mental starter

54 Counting steps

2. Assess
'Number cards 0–9'

3. Further practice

Photocopiable sheets

'What value?'

Place value

Most children should be able to recognise the value of each digit in a seven-digit number.

Some children will require additional practice at making and exploring large numbers.

1. Check

54 Counting steps

Count in steps of thousands and tens and hundreds of thousands. Point to places between divisions on the counting stick and ask the children to tell you what they think will go there. Ask:

- *What number would be halfway between 10,000 and 20,000?*
- *What number is halfway between 200,000 and 250,000?*
- *Say a number between 70,000 and 80,000. Tell me another?*

2. Assess

Give each child a set of number cards. Ask the children to make 38, then 238, 2389, 72,389, 724,389, 1,724,389. Ask them to show you the card that shows how many hundreds there are, then hundreds of thousands and so on. Ask the children to make other seven-digit numbers and to read them to you. Record the outcomes.

3. Further practice

Photocopiable page 210 'What value?' provides the opportunity for the children to show their understanding of the place value of numbers. They should work on this in pairs but independent of other support.

You will need

1. Check

Oral and mental starter

60 Quick decimal addition

Individual whiteboards

2. Assess
'Number cards 0–9'

3. Further practice

Oral and mental starter

56 Rounding

Photocopiable sheets

'Addition'

Addition

Most children should be able to add large numbers using the column method.

Some children may not have made such progress and will need to focus on smaller numbers and perhaps use partitioning.

1. Check

60 Quick decimal addition

During this starter, include whole numbers and numbers that lend themselves to specific mental calculation strategies, such as adding a multiple of 10 and adjusting, and near doubles. Ask:

- *What is 124 + 119? How did you work that out?*
- *What is 36 + 38? How do you know? Is there another strategy you could use?*

2. Assess

Give each child a set of number cards. Ask them to make two four-digit numbers and then add them. Watch which strategy they use. Ask them to check their answer using a different one. Ensure they use the column method as one of their strategies. Repeat this several times. Record the outcomes.

3. Further practice

Photocopiable page 211 'Addition' asks the children to practise addition calculations. Encourage them to use the column method where they can, and to check their answers by partitioning or sequencing. They should work on this independently. Oral and mental starter 'Rounding' offers another way of checking that answers are in the right area.

Curriculum objectives
● To divide numbers up to four digits by two digit whole numbers using the formal written method of long division.

You will need
I. Check

Oral and mental starter
62 Quick division

2. Assess
'Number cards 0–9'

3. Further practice

Oral and mental starter
63 Digit investigation

Photocopiable sheets
'Division'

Curriculum objectives
● To add and subtract fractions with different denominators and mixed numbers, using the concept of equivalent fractions.

You will need
I. Check

Oral and mental starter
55 Number lines

2. Assess
'Equivalence dominoes'

3. Further practice

Oral and mental starter
69 Fractions

Division

Most children should be able to divide using the formal methods, including long division.

Some children will not have made such progress and need support in dividing by two-digit numbers.

I. Check

62 Quick division

Use 'Quick division' to assess how well the children can use known number facts to work out answers to division calculations. Ask:

- What is $0.32 \div 4$? How can you find out if you don't know?
- What is $3.5 \div 5$? How can you find out if you don't know?
- How can you check that you are right?

2. Assess

Give each child a set of number cards. Ask them to pick three to make a three-digit number. They then pick a fourth to be the divisor. Ask them to divide the three-digit number by the divisor. Observe them as they do this, then challenge them to make a four-digit number to be divided by a two-digit divisor. Record the outcomes.

3. Further practice

Use the oral and mental starter 'Digit investigation' to remind the children of the operation inverse to division, and so useful for checking answers.

Photocopiable page 212 'Division' is designed to assess how efficiently and successfully the children are using the column method. Encourage them to check their answers by using either multiplication or another division method.

Adding fractions

Most children should be able to successfully add fractions by converting them to those with a common denominator.

Some children will need to focus on adding fractions that they are familiar with, for example halves, quarters and eighths.

I. Check

55 Number lines

As you work through 'Number lines', ask the children to convert the decimals plotted on the line to fractions. Ask:

- What is 0.2 as a fraction? How do you know?
- What is 0.75 as a fraction? How do you know?

2. Assess

Give each child a set of photocopiable page 209 'Equivalence dominoes'. Ask them to select two and add them together by finding the common denominator first. Record the outcomes.

3. Further practice

The oral and mental starter 'Fractions' allows you to assess how confident the children are at adding and multiplying fractions.

Oral and mental starters

Number and place value

Counting steps

Show the counting stick and explain that one end of the stick is zero, and the other end is 90. Ask the children: *What steps should we count in to get from 0 to 90?* Agree on 9. Together, count from 0 to 90 and back in steps of 9. Then place your finger on different divisions and ask: *What number would be found here?* Put your finger on the fifth interval and say that this is zero this time. Together, count in steps of 9 from 0 to one end (45). Then back to the other (−45).

Extension
Repeat the activity for other step sizes including fractions and decimal fractions.

Number lines

Draw three number lines on the board, marked in divisions of 10. Label the first from 3 at one end to 4 at the other, the second 3.1 to 3.2, and the third 3.11 to 3.12. Indicate various points on the number lines and ask the children to give you the number that would be positioned at each. Invite volunteers to write these on the lines on the board. Each time, encourage them to tell you the value of each digit.

Next, without any visual clues, ask the children to write down decimal numbers lying between numbers you give them. For example: *Write down a decimal number that comes between 6.12 and 6.13.*

56 Rounding

Draw this table on the board:

0.86	4.02	1.08
3.75	8.63	6.19
1.51	2.74	1.18

Ask the children to copy a blank version on their whiteboards. Ask them to round each number to the nearest whole number, writing the answer in the corresponding space on their blank table.

Extension
Repeat the activity, rounding to the nearest tenth.

Addition, subtraction, multiplication and division

Multiples of 10

Say a three-digit number, for example, 529. Ask the children to multiply it by 10, then 100, and then 1000. Then talk about what has happened. When multiplying by 10, the number is ten times bigger, so the digits move one place to the *left*, and a place-holder (0) is put in the units/ones position.

Next, ask the children to *divide* the same number by 10, 100 and 1000. Encourage the children to explain what has happened: the number is ten times smaller, so the digits move one place to the *right*, making 52.9.

Extension
Let children repeat the activity in pairs, challenging each other with four-digit numbers.

Percentages, decimals and fractions

58 Ordering

Tell the children that you will write four decimal numbers on the board. Ask the children to order the numbers from smallest to largest on their whiteboards and then hold them up. Write sets of numbers with similar digits, such as: 6.21, 1.26, 6.61, 1.63; 54.3, 54.5, 66.6, 65.6, and sets with negative decimals as well: 1.5, −2.5, 3.1, −2.3. You could also include money and measures: £2.40, £1.50, £3.20, £2.20; 4.7cm, 17.4cm, 7.4cm, 3.2cm.

59 Percentage bingo

Ask the children to draw a 4 × 2 bingo-card grid on their whiteboards and to fill it with multiples of 5 up to 100. Play a game of percentage bingo by asking questions that have answers which are multiples of five, for the children to cross off on their bingo cards. For example: *What is 20% of 50? What is 10% of 700? What is 1% of 500?*

60 Quick decimal addition

Practise quick-fire questions where the children add three and then four decimals, for example: 4.3 + 2.7 + 5.8 and 5.8 + 7.2 + 3.1 + 1.6. Let the children make jottings on their whiteboards, adding the whole numbers first and then looking for decimals that total whole numbers to add on to their total. For example: 4 + 2 + 5 = 11, 0.3 + 0.7 = 1, so 11 + 1 + 0.8 = 12.8.

61 Multiplication and division facts

Challenge the children to use knowledge of place value, doubling and halving and multiplication facts to 12 × 12 to derive related multiplication and division facts involving whole numbers and decimals. Write a multiplication fact on the board, such as 8 × 7 = 56. Ask the children to write down as many other multiplication facts as they can from this (they can introduce zero): 80 × 7 = 560, 80 × 70 = 5600, 80 × 35 = 2800, 0.8 × 7 = 5.6, 0.08 × 7 = 0.56, 5.6 ÷ 7 = 0.8. Do the same for a division such as: 48 ÷ 6 = 8: 4.8 ÷ 6 = 0.8, 0.48 ÷ 6 = 0.08, 96 ÷ 6 = 16.

62 Quick division

Set quick division questions for the children to answer on their whiteboards. The questions should be able to be answered with knowledge of multiplication and corresponding division facts. For example:
- Divide 8.1 by 9. (0.9.)
- Divide 320 by 40. (8.)
- What do I have to divide 72 by to get 8? (9.)
- A box of 24 eggs is divided into 4 cartons. How many are in each? (6.)
- What is one twentieth of 640? (32.)

63 Digit investigation

Write the digits 6, 5 and 9 on the board. Ask the children to arrange them as a U.t × U calculation to make as near to a whole number as possible (9.5 × 6 and 9.6 × 5 give whole-number answers). Put up three more digits to investigate, such as 1, 4 and 7. Repeat as required.

Extension

Ask: *In order to make an exact whole number, what digits are needed?* Elicit that a 5 and an even number are needed as the multiplier and the tenth.

Name: _____   Date: _____

Rise and fall

- Solve these temperature problems. Use the number line to help you.

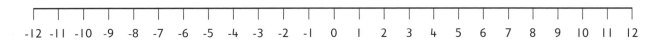

-12 -11 -10 -9 -8 -7 -6 -5 -4 -3 -2 -1 0 1 2 3 4 5 6 7 8 9 10 11 12

1. Gabby measured the temperature one December morning. It was −8°C. During the day, the temperature rose by 12 degrees. What was the temperature after it had risen?

_____

2. Sam measured the temperature one January afternoon. It was 9°C. During the evening, it dropped by 15 degrees. What was the temperature after it had dropped?

_____

3. India noticed that the temperature had risen by 8 degrees to 3°C. What was the temperature before it had risen?

_____

4. Harry was really surprised. The temperature during the day had reached 12°C. During the evening, it dropped by 17 degrees. What was the temperature after it had dropped?

_____

- Now make up some temperature problems of your own.

I can find differences between positive and negative numbers.

How did you do?

Percentages

■ Imagine that 100% is £260. Write down other percentages of this amount of money. See how many you can find in two minutes!

$100\% \approx £460$

■ Find the answer these problems. Show how you worked them out.

1. My friend bought a TV in a sale. Its original cost was £235. It had been reduced by 24%. How much has it been reduced by? _____

What is the new cost? _____

_____

2. Another friend bought a coat in a sale. It originally cost £260. In the sale it had been reduced by $17\frac{1}{2}$%. How much did it cost in the sale? _____

_____

3. Archie had saved £195. He gave 47% of his savings to charity. How much did he give to charity? _____

How much did he have left? _____

_____

I can calculate percentages.

How did you do?

PHOTOCOPIABLE

Name: _____   Date: _____

Equivalence dominoes

I. Cut out and shuffle the dominoes.

2. Deal seven dominoes to each player, and place the rest face down in a pile on the table.

3. The first player turns over the top domino of the pile. They look at their dominoes to see if they can match one end to one end of the domino placed face up. If they can, they put it in position. If they can't, they pick up another domino and try again.

4. The next player has their turn.

5. Keep playing until all the dominoes have been used or no one has a match.

6. The winner is the player with the fewest dominoes left.

$\frac{1}{10}$	0.3	$\frac{3}{10}$	20%	$\frac{2}{10}$	0.5
50%	0.6	$\frac{6}{10}$	80%	0.8	0.2
$\frac{5}{10}$	0.9	$\frac{9}{10}$	10%	0.1	30%
0.3	0.7	$\frac{7}{10}$	0.2	90%	40%
$\frac{4}{10}$	0.8	$\frac{8}{10}$	0.4	40%	0.5
$\frac{5}{10}$	0.6	60%	$\frac{7}{10}$	70%	$\frac{1}{10}$
10%	$\frac{3}{10}$	30%	0.9	90%	$\frac{5}{10}$
0.5	10%	0.1	$\frac{9}{10}$	30%	$\frac{8}{10}$

What value?

1. Read this number to a friend:

■ 4,507,328

a. What number does the 5 represent? _____

b. What number does the 3 represent? _____

c. What number does the 7 represent? _____

d. What is the job of the zero? _____

2. Write this number in words:

■ 2,896,190

_____

3. Make up a seven-digit number of your own.

a. Write it here: _____

b. Now write it in words:

_____

I can read and write numbers up to 10,000,000 and understand the value of each digit.

How did you do?

PHOTOCOPIABLE   ■SCHOLASTIC
www.scholastic.co.uk

Name: _____   Date: _____

Addition

- Add these numbers using one method.
- Check your answer using a different method.
- Show your working.

Numbers	Addition	Check
2538 + 3199		
8792 + 4874		
6382 + 1945		
7233 + 1999		
38,731 + 18,000		
41,354 + 32,845		
258,736 + 27,982		
4,132,897 + 2,713,890		

I can solve addition problems using a variety of methods.

How did you do?

Division

- Answer these division calculations using the column method.
- Check your answers using multiplication or a different division method.
- Show your working.

Division	Your calculation	Your check
356 ÷ 7		
1429 ÷ 8		
4536 ÷ 16		
6498 ÷ 22		
8897 ÷ 12		
3763 ÷ 14		
2829 ÷ 15		
7326 ÷ 28		

I can divide numbers with up to four-digits by two-digit whole numbers.

How did you do?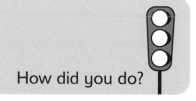

SCHOLASTIC
www.scholastic.co.uk

Solving problems involving large numbers

Expected prior learning

Children should be able to:

- add and subtract large numbers using a column method
- use a variety of mental calculation methods to carry out all four operations.

Topic	Curriculum objectives	Expected outcomes
Addition, subtraction, multiplication and division	**Lesson 1**	
	To multiply multi-digit numbers up to four digits by a two-digit number using the formal written method of long multiplication. To use estimation to check answers to calculations and determine, in the context of a problem, an appropriate degree of accuracy.	Multiply by formal methods. Estimate to check or predict answers.
	Lesson 2	
	To divide numbers up to four digits by a two-digit number using the formal written method of long division. To use estimation to check answers to calculations and determine, in the context of a problem, an appropriate degree of accuracy.	Divide numbers by a two-digit number using formal methods. Estimate to check or predict answers.
	Lesson 3	
	To solve addition and subtraction multi-step problems in contexts, deciding which operations and methods to use and why.	Solve problems using addition and subtraction.
	Lesson 4	
	To perform mental calculations, including with mixed operations and large numbers.	Choose and use appropriate mental calculation strategies to solve problems.
	Lesson 5	
	To solve problems involving addition, subtraction, multiplication and division. To use estimation to check answers to calculations and determine, in the context of a problem, an appropriate degree of accuracy.	Solve problems within familiar contexts.

Preparation

Lesson 1: write the calculations on the board

Lesson 2: prepare a set of number cards for each child; prepare sufficient place value counters for your demonstration and for each child to use

Lesson 4: copy 'Mental, not column' for each child

You will need

Photocopiable sheets
'Mental, not column'

General resources
'Number cards 0–9'; 'Place value counters'

Equipment
Individual whiteboards

Further practice

Photocopiable sheets
'What value?'

Oral and mental starters suggested for week 1

See the bank of starters on pages 246 and 247. Oral and mental starters are also on the CD-ROM.

65 Tables bingo (2)

69 Fractions

71 Decimal ordering

72 Factors

Overview of progression

During this week the children will continue to practise and develop their ability to add, subtract, multiply and divide large numbers. There is a focus on formal written methods including those set out in columns. There is also an emphasis on times when these are not as formal and where mental calculation strategies are more appropriate. The children are encouraged to check using estimation, inverse operations and alternative strategies. They will then use a compact form of column addition and subtraction, using this to solve word and missing number problems. They will estimate their answers and use inverse operations to check the accuracy of their work.

Watch out for

Children may have difficulty with long written methods. Help children to move on from portioning for addition, counting on for subtraction, the grid method for multiplication and grouping on a number line for division.

Creative context

Ask the children to explore shopping catalogues and use the information in them to make up word-based shopping problems for each other, involving all four operations.

Vocabulary

carrying, **complementary addition**, inverse, jotting, mental calculation method, partitioning, product, **quotient**, remainder, **sequencing**, strategy

Lesson 1   Oral and mental starter 69

Main teaching activities

Whole-class work: Recap multiplication methods the children know. Ask the children to multiply 2465 by 19 on their whiteboards, using the grid method. Then ask them to check their answer by estimating. (It will be just under 49300, from 2465 × 20.) Repeat this for 3824 × 14. Next, ask them to multiply 2458 by 16 using partitioning. When they have done this, revise the formal column method, beginning with the least significant digit:

$$\begin{array}{r} 2458 \\ \times \quad 16 \\ \hline 14748 \\ {\scriptstyle 2\ 3\ 4} \\ \underline{24580} \\ \underline{39328} \end{array}$$

Write one or two more four-digit by two-digit multiplications on the board for the children to practise. Check the answers by estimating as a class.

Independent work: Ask the children to work on these calculations using the column method: 2546 × 17 (43,282); 8964 × 16 (143,424); 3867 × 14 (54,138); 2785 × 17 (47,345)

Progress check: Pause the children after a short while to check they understand how to use short and long multiplication.

Review

Discuss when a written method like this might be the most efficient to use. Aim for an answer such as when the calculations are too difficult to answer using a mental method.

Lesson 2   Oral and mental starter 71

Main teaching activities

Whole-class work: Write 455 ÷ 13 on the board and ask the children to answer it on their whiteboards. Which method do they use? Invite children to demonstrate their working. Show four 100 place value counters. Agree that these cannot be divided into thirteen groups, so exchange them for tens. Demonstrate that the 45 tens can be divided into three groups of 13, with 6 tens left.

$$13\overline{)4\,{}^{4}5\,{}^{6}5}\;\;{}^{3\,5}$$

Next, exchange these for ones, giving a total of 65 which can be divided into five groups of 13, giving an answer of 35. Repeat for other examples.

Independent work: Give each child a set of number cards and place value counters. Explain that they should pick five cards and swap them around to make several calculations dividing a four-digit number by a two digit number. Let them use the place value counters as demonstrated. Each time they checking each time with an estimate.

Progress check: Visit pairs and ask: *What calculation have you made? How are you going to answer it? Explain each step you will take?*

Review

Invite the children to share their calculations and solutions.

Curriculum objectives
● To solve addition and subtraction multi-step problems in contexts, deciding which operations and methods to use and why.
● To use estimation to check answers to calculations and determine levels of accuracy.
Success criteria
● I can solve problems involving addition and subtraction.

You will need
General resources
'Number cards 0–9'
Equipment
Individual whiteboards

Differentiation
Less confident learners
Children should make up three-digit numbers to add and subtract.
More confident learners
Children should make up five-digit numbers. Ask them to add three sets of five-digit numbers and subtract two sets.

Lesson 3 · Oral and mental starter 71

Main teaching activities

Whole-class work: Set this problem for the children:

Hope counted 2575 cars driving down the high street of the town where she lives one morning. She counted 1387 in the afternoon. How many cars did she count altogether? How many more did she count in the morning?

Discuss how to answer it. Agree that we need to add to find the total and subtract to find the difference. Go through the calculation on the board, reminding the children to align the units, tens and so on under each other and to include any carried numbers in the next step of the calculation each time. Write some more examples on the board, including four-digit numbers, for example: 4674 + 8938 and 6856 − 3887. Encourage the children to check the answers by estimating.

Paired work: Give each pair two sets of number cards. Ask them to make two four-digit numbers to add and subtract using the column method. Remind them to check each other's answers using estimation. Tell them that, after two calculations, they should make up a word problem for each other that involves addition and subtraction.

Progress check: Visit the pairs after the calculations and say, for example: *Explain the column method for addition. What about for subtraction?*

Review

Invite pairs to share their problems with the class who answer them on their whiteboards. Finish the lesson by discussing when a written column method is useful. Aim for when a mental calculation strategy is too difficult to be efficient.

Curriculum objectives
● To perform mental calculations, including with mixed operations and large numbers.
Success criteria
● I can use mental calculation to solve problems.

You will need
Photocopiable sheets
'Mental, not column'
Equipment
Individual whiteboards

Differentiation
Less confident learners
Adapt the photocopiable sheet so that children work with more suitable numbers.
More confident learners
When children check their answers, ask them to do this by the column method too.

Lesson 4 · Oral and mental starter 72

Main teaching activities

Whole-class work: Write these calculations on the board: 2310 + 2315; 4369 − 1998; 245 × 14 and 650 ÷ 15. Ask the children to talk to a partner about how they could solve these using a mental calculation method, writing their solution on their whiteboards. Agree that near doubling is probably the most formal way to answer the addition, and rounding and adjusting for subtraction. Suggest doubling and doubling again for the multiplication, and dividing by 10 and doubling for the division. Encourage volunteers to demonstrate each by explaining with reference to jottings on the board.

Write a few more calculations on the board so that the children can practice these strategies.

Independent work: Explain the activity on photocopiable page 'Mental, not column' from the CD-ROM. Emphasise to the children that they should check their answers using a method different from the one they used to solve the problem, which could be using the inverse operation or a different mental calculation strategy.

Progress check: Spend time with children you particularly wish to assess. Ask: *Which strategy do you think is best for this problem? Why? Can you explain how you will use this strategy? How will you check?*

Review

Together, work through the four problems from the photocopiable sheet. Invite volunteers to demonstrate how they checked their answers. Ask a confident child to share one of their new problems. Work out the answer as a class.

Curriculum objectives

● To solve problems involving addition, subtraction, multiplication and division.
● To use estimation to check answers to calculations and determine levels of accuracy.

Success criteria

● I can solve word problems involving all four operations.

You will need

General resources

'Place value counters'

Equipment

Individual whiteboards

Differentiation

Less confident learners

Give children place value counters to help them with division. Ask them to make up problems involving two- or three-digit numbers to be multiplied and divided by single-digit numbers.

More confident learners

Ask these children to make up individual problems that involve all four operations.

Lesson 5   Oral and mental starter 65

Main teaching activities

Whole-class work: Give the children this problem:

Ava scored 1289 points on her computer game. Her brother scored 2837 points. How many points did they score altogether? (4126.) How many more did her brother score? (1548.)

Discuss the most appropriate method to find the total and difference in scores for these amounts. Aim towards the written column method and ask the children to solve the problem using this on their whiteboards. Invite a volunteer to demonstrate their working on the board. Ask the class to help you check the answer is in the right area by using approximation by rounding the numbers to the nearest 100 in their heads (1300 + 2800 = 4100; 2800 − 1300 = 1500).

Set a few more similar problems for the children to solve on their whiteboards. Again, check answers as a class.

Now set this next problem:

Bill works in a car factory. He was given 14 boxes of car parts. In each box there were 2445 bolts. How many bolts were there altogether? Bill had to sort these into containers with 15 bolts in each. How many containers did he need?

Again identify the calculations that need to be done and discuss the appropriate formal method. Look towards long multiplication and long division. Ask the children to solve both parts of the problem on their whiteboards. Give children the place value counters to help in modelling the division. Invite volunteers to demonstrate both calculations on the board. Check the answers as a class by approximating: the first answer will be between 2445 × 10 and 2445 × 20, the second will be just over the first answer divided by 10. (Actual answers are: 34,230 bolts to be put into 2,282 containers.) Repeat the exercise with similar multi-step problems.

Paired work: Organise the children to work in similar-ability pairs to work together to make up problems similar to those set during the lesson. Explain that the problems should involve each operation (some for multiplication and division and others that might include addition or subtraction too). Tell the children that, once they have made up a problem, they should work together to solve it. The children should be prepared to share these during the review.

Progress check: Visit the pairs as they work, particularly those you wish to assess, and pause them to ask questions such as: *What is your problem asking you to find out? How will you check that your solution is sensible?*

Review

Invite pairs to share one of the problems they made up. Ask the rest of the class to work with their partners to find the solution.

Recap the methods of addition, subtraction, multiplication and division that have been practised this week, identifying and working through any particular areas of difficulty.

Algebra

Expected prior learning

Children should be able to:

- recognise and use simple formulae
- calculate simple statements where a letter represents a number.

Topic	Curriculum objectives	Expected outcomes
Algebra	**Lesson 1**	
	To express missing number problems algebraically.	Solve possibilities problems and link to formulae.
	Lesson 2	
	To express missing number problems algebraically. To use simple formulae.	Find the values of letters in calculations.
	Lesson 3	
	To generate and describe linear number sequences.	Make and describe number sequences.
	Lesson 4	
	To find pairs of numbers that satisfy an equation with two unknowns. To enumerate all possibilities of combinations of two variables.	Identify unknown numbers in algebraic sentences.
	Lesson 5	
	To generate and describe linear number sequences.	Investigate and identify patterns in number sequences.

Preparation

Lesson 1: copy 'Sports kit' for each pair

Lesson 2: copy 'What's the letter?' for each pair

Lesson 3: prepare a set of number cards and 'Number sequences' for each pair

You will need

Photocopiable sheets

'Sports kit'; 'What's the letter?'; 'Number sequences'

General resources

'Number cards 0–9'; interactive activities 'Letter time' and 'Jumping frogs'

Equipment

Individual whiteboards; counters, squared paper or interlocking cubes

Further practice

General resource

Interactive activity 'Letter time'

Oral and mental starters suggested for week 2

See the bank of starters on pages 246 and 247. Oral and mental starters are also on the CD-ROM.

69 Fractions

70 Reach the target!

71 Decimal ordering

72 Factors

Overview of progression

During this week the children will develop their knowledge and understanding of algebra. They will be investigating how to find all the possible answers to certain problems expressed in words. They will be answering and also devising calculations where letters represent numbers. They will go on to make and extend number sequences.

Watch out for

Children may have difficulty with finding unknown numbers. It may help to take them back to work they have previously covered where a missing number was represented by a square or a question mark.

Creative context

Ask the children to investigate number sequences and patterns in other contexts, such as in nature. For example, they could explore the reflective and rotational symmetry of different plants and animals. They could investigate the number of sepals and petals on different flowers and find the patterns. They could look at shells and see if they can identify the Fibonacci sequence inside them. If they don't have the real items, they could search for pictures in library books or on the internet.

Vocabulary

algebra, ascending order, descending order, equation, formula, integer, linear, pattern, puzzle, symbol, triangular number, unknown

Curriculum objectives
● To express missing number problems algebraically.
Success criteria
● I can use a formula to solve a problem.

You will need
Photocopiable sheets
'Sports kit'
Equipment
Individual whiteboards

Differentiation
Less confident learners
Ask children to concentrate on the first part of the photocopiable sheet, which has fewer possibilities and requires a less sophisticated table.
More confident learners
Ask children to concentrate on the final part of the photocopiable sheet, which will need a more organised approach.

Lesson 1   Oral and mental starter 72

Main teaching activities

Whole-class work: Give the children the following problem:

In a local football league, there are six teams. If each team plays each other once, how many games will be played?

Ask the children to work in pairs to find the solution and then share their answer. Establish that there will be 15 games. Ask the children how they made sure that all the games were included. Prompt them to explain their methods. If not elicited, demonstrate two possible methods:

● Teams cannot play themselves, so 6 teams × 5 teams = 30, then halve this because teams only play each other once.
● A systematic method such as:

1 v 2, 2 v 3, 3 v 4, 4 v 5, 5 v 6

1 v 3, 2 v 4, 3 v 5, 4 v 6

1 v 4, 2 v 5, 3 v 6

1 v 5, 2 v 6

1 v 6.

Discuss the importance of tabulating all possibilities when finding solutions to problems like this. Ask the children to give you the rule for what is happening as indicated in the first method. Agree that there are six teams; this number is multiplied by one less than itself and then halved. Demonstrate writing the calculation in this way:

$$\frac{6 \times (6 - 1)}{2}$$

Tell the children that there is a formula for working this out and using the formula will mean they can answer any similar problems. Demonstrate using n as the number of teams:

$$\frac{n \times (n - 1)}{2}$$

Ask the children to use the formula to work out the number of games that will be played if there are 10 teams (45). Repeat with different numbers of teams.

Paired work: Distribute photocopiable page 'Sports kit' from the CD-ROM. Tell the children they must find out all the possibilities available for a group of sports teams who are buying new kit. In order for all possible outcomes to be listed, they should design a table to list results. The majority of the class should start on question 2.

Progress check: Visit pairs early on to check they understand what to do and how to do it by asking questions such as: *How are you going to work out all the possibilities? How will you know when you have them all?*

Review

Share a selection of the children's tables and discuss the different layouts used. Decide on the most effective and discuss how easy it is to read the information to check that all possibilities have been included.

Use the tables to check answers as a class. Work through any difficulties encountered.

Curriculum objectives
● To express missing number problems algebraically.
Success criteria
● I can solve calculations that have letters instead of numbers.

You will need
Photocopiable sheets
'What's the letter?'
General resources
Interactive activity 'Letter time'
Equipment
Individual whiteboards

Differentiation
Less confident learners
Ask children to concentrate on the first 12 questions on the photocopiable sheet.
More confident learners
When they have completed the photocopiable sheet, set them to work on interactive activity 'Letter time' on the CD-ROM.

Lesson 2   Oral and mental starter 69

Main teaching activities

Whole-class work: Remind the children of the formula they used in lesson 1 to find the number of football games played. Use the formula to work out how many games would be played between 15 teams. Ask: *Can anyone think of another occasion when we have used a formula?* Lead the children towards measuring perimeter and area. Write on the board: p = 4s. Say that p is perimeter and ask the children to explain the rest. Agree that s means side and, as there are four, it must be the perimeter of a square shape. Give some measurements for s and ask the children to find the perimeters. Then write: a = l × w and ask what this is. Agree it is the formula for the area of a rectangle. Give various lengths and widths and ask the children to find the areas.

Now write 2x + 4 = 10. Ask the children how to find the value of x. Agree that what you do to one side of the equals sign you must do to the other to keep everything equivalent. So take 4 from both sides (2x + 4 − 4 = 10 − 4) to give 2x = 6. Next divide both sides by 2 to give x = 3.

Paired work: Distribute photocopiable page 'What's the letter?' from the CD-ROM for the children to work in pairs on problems similar to the last example above.

Progress check: Visit pairs to check their understanding. Ask: *How are you going to find x?*

Review

Work through the photocopiable sheet together. Ask confident children to help you go through the interactive activity 'Letter time' with the class.

Curriculum objectives
● To generate and describe linear number sequences.
Success criteria
● I can describe and devise number sequences.

You will need
Photocopiable sheets
'Number sequences'
General resources
'Number cards 0–9'; interactive activity 'Jumping frogs'
Equipment
Individual whiteboards

Differentiation
Less confident learners
Work with the children on sequences that have a single operation.
More confident learners
Give children the interactive activity 'Jumping frogs' which extends to sequences that have more than one rule.

Lesson 3   Oral and mental starter 70

Main teaching activities

Whole-class work: Ask the children to give you three single-digit numbers. Write them in order on the board. Then, ask the children to work out a sequence from these numbers. Explain that it can use any rule, for example: for 4, 6, 9, the sequence could be + 2, + 3... Ask the children to continue the rule, so extending the sequence on their whiteboards. Invite children to explain their sequences. Repeat with other numbers.

Then write this sequence on the board: 25, 50, 75, 100. Ask the children to continue it on to 125 and back to − 125. Ask them to discuss in pairs what the tenth positive number in the sequence would be. Establish they would multiply 25 by 10. Elicit how they could find any positive number in the sequence: multiply the chosen number by 25. Ask them to work out numbers of their choice within this sequence. Repeat for other sequences.

Paired work: Organise pairs to work on photocopiable page 'Number sequences' from the CD-ROM with a set of number cards. Go through the example as a class first.

Progress check: Visit pairs to see how well they are creating number sequences. Ask: *What is the rule to your sequence? What will the 20th number in your sequence be?*

Review

Invite volunteers to share their sequences. See if the rest of the class can identify the pattern and extend the sequence further. Finish the lesson with this sequence: 18, 27, 36, asking the children what the tenth number in the sequence would be. (The sequence begins on the second multiple of 9, so the tenth number will be the eleventh multiple of 9.)

Curriculum objectives
● To find pairs of numbers that satisfy an equation with two unknowns.
● To enumerate all possibilities of combinations of two variables.

Success criteria
● I can work out unknown numbers in number sentences involving letters.

You will need
Equipment
Individual whiteboards

Differentiation
Less confident learners
Let children work with whole numbers and focus on addition and subtraction.

More confident learners
Challenge children to work on number sentences that involve multiplication and division including fractions and decimals.

Lesson 4   Oral and mental starter 71

Main teaching activities

Whole-class work: Write this on the board: $a + b = -6$. Ask the children to work with partners to find as many possible answers to this as they can in two minutes. Ask them to write their ideas on their whiteboards. Then invite pairs to share their suggestions, checking them as a class. Repeat this with other number sentences, such as: $a - b = 45$, $a \times b = 24$, $a \div b = 2$. Encourage the children to use positive and negative integers, decimals and fractions. Draw out the fact that there is an unlimited number of possible solutions.

Paired work: Organise the children to work in pairs. Explain that you want one partner to make up algebraic number sentences with two 'unknown' letters, as in the main activity, and give them to their partner to solve. Ask them to work out 10 possible solutions to each sentence.

Progress check: Spend time with those pairs you particularly wish to assess. Pause them to ask questions such as: *How are you going to work out what the possible answers could be? Is there another way?*

Review

Invite the pairs to share their number sentences. Challenge the rest of the class to find a given number of possible answers as quickly as they can.

Curriculum objectives
● To generate and describe linear number sequences.

Success criteria
● I can investigate and see patterns in number sequences.

You will need
Equipment
Individual whiteboards; counters, squared paper or interlocking cubes

Differentiation
Less confident learners
Suggest to children that they focus on some of the lower pairs of consecutive triangular numbers when adding.

More confident learners
Challenge children to continue with the pattern of triangular numbers so that they are dealing with three-digit numbers.

Lesson 5   Oral and mental starter 70

Main teaching activities

Whole-class work: Provide the children with counters, squared paper or other suitable apparatus, such as interlocking cubes. Ask them to make the pattern shown here, either using the equipment or drawing on the paper.

Ask the children to add the next row. *How many counters are needed? What about the next row?* Continue until ten rows have been created. Ask the children to list how many counters they have used row by row to create the following sequence: 1, 3, 6, 10, 15, 21, 28, 36, 45, 55. Explain that these are triangular numbers. Ask: *How does the pattern increase?* (Add 2, add 3, add 4, add 5...) *What are the next two numbers in the sequence.* (66 and 78.)

Paired work: Ask the children in pairs to write the first 20 triangular numbers, by adding 11 to 55, then adding on 12, 13 and so on. Then ask them to choose any two consecutive numbers from the list and add them together. They should try this at least four times.

Progress check: Visit the pairs to check how they are progressing through the task. Ask questions such as: *What do you notice about your answers? Have you seen these numbers before?*

Review

Ask the children to explain what they have discovered when adding pairs of adjacent triangular numbers. Elicit that two adjacent triangular numbers add up to a square number. Check some of the pairs to prove the statement.

Fractions, decimals and percentages

Expected prior learning

Children should be able to:

- add and subtract simple fractions
- find simple percentages of numbers
- find equivalences between some fractions, decimals and percentages.

Topic	Curriculum objectives	Expected outcomes
Fractions (including decimals and percentages)	**Lesson 1**	
	To add and subtract fractions with different denominators and mixed numbers, using the concept of equivalent fractions.	Add and subtract fractions by finding common denominators.
	Lesson 2	
	To multiply simple pairs of proper fractions, writing the answer in its simplest form.	Multiply proper fractions. Reduce fractions to simplest forms.
	Lesson 3	
	To divide proper fractions by whole numbers.	Solve problems involving dividing fractions by whole numbers.
Ratio and proportion	**Lesson 4**	
	To solve problems involving the calculation of percentages [for example, of measures, and such as 15% of 360] and the use of percentages for comparison.	Use percentages for comparison.
	Lesson 5	
	To solve problems involving the calculation of percentages [for example, of measures, and such as 15% of 360] and the use of percentages for comparison.	Solve problems involving percentages. Make comparisons involving percentages.

Preparation

Lesson 1: make a set of number cards for each child

Lesson 2: make a set of dominoes for each pair

Lesson 4: copy 'Percentage problems' for each child

You will need

Photocopiable sheets
'Percentage problems'

General resources
'Number cards 0–9';
'Dominoes'

Equipment
Individual whiteboards

Further practice

Photocopiable sheets
'What percentage?'

Oral and mental starters suggested for week 3

See the bank of starters on pages 246 and 247. Oral and mental starters are also on the CD-ROM.

67 Operation problems

69 Fractions

71 Decimal ordering

73 Algebra practice

Overview of progression

During this week the children will develop their ability to work with fractions, decimals and percentages. They will gain further practice in adding, subtracting and multiplying fractions and dividing fractions by whole numbers. They will also identify equivalences between fractions and between fractions and decimals, and use this understanding to solve problems. They will also be calculating and comparing percentages in problem-solving contexts.

Watch out for

Some children might still struggle with a conceptual understanding of fractions. It would be worth spending time demonstrating halves and quarters with counters, shapes and fraction strips to stress the sharing aspect. Help children to understand too that a percentage is also a fraction of a whole, expressed in a different way.

Creative context

Ask the children to look for and collect percentages and decimals from newspaper stories and advertisements. These could include interest rates for different credit cards, the Chancellor's twice-yearly Budget statements or discounts on holidays.

Vocabulary

decimal, decimal fraction, decimal place, decimal point, equivalent, fraction, per cent (%), percentage

Curriculum objectives

● To add and subtract fractions with different denominators and mixed numbers, using the concept of equivalent fractions.

Success criteria

● I can add and subtract fractions by finding common denominators.

You will need

General resources

'Number cards 0–9'

Equipment

Individual whiteboards

Differentiation

Less confident learners

Ask children to make fractions where only one needs changing into the equivalent of the other, for example halves and quarters, thirds and sixths, quarters and eighths.

More confident learners

When children are adding fractions, ask them to add three or four together.

Lesson 1 — Oral and mental starter 69

Main teaching activities

Whole-class work: Find out how much the children can remember about adding and subtracting fractions from the first half of this summer term. You may need to recap on the key idea of converting fractions to those with a common denominator. Discuss with the children how they can find these. Agree that they need to find the smallest multiple that is the same for each denominator. Write sets of unit fractions on the board for the children to find the common denominator of, for example: $\frac{1}{3}$, $\frac{1}{5}$, $\frac{1}{4}$ and $\frac{1}{6}$.

Once they have the common denominator (24), ask the children to convert the fractions so that they are equivalent to each other. Write this calculation on the board: $\frac{3}{4} + \frac{2}{3} = ?$. And ask the children to rewrite it on their whiteboards using equivalent fractions. Take feedback, and invite a child to demonstrate their answer on the board. Agree that the lowest common denominator is 12 and that $\frac{3}{4}$ is the same as $\frac{9}{12}$ and $\frac{2}{3}$ is $\frac{8}{12}$. So, the total would be $\frac{17}{12}$ which is an improper fraction that can be changed to the mixed fraction of $1\frac{5}{12}$.

Next, subtract the same set of fractions to give $\frac{1}{12}$.

Discuss with the children how they could check using the inverse operation. This is a tool that works for whole numbers; does it work for fractions? Agree that it does.

Repeat additions and subtractions with a selection of fractions, such as $\frac{4}{7}$ and $\frac{1}{3}$.

Independent work: Ask the children to use number cards to generate fractions, one card representing the numerator and the other the denominator. Then ask them to choose three to add together. Once they have done this, ask them to subtract pairs of fractions to find the three possible differences. Demonstrate one or two examples on the board first.

Progress check: Visit those children you particularly wish to assess. Pause them to ask questions such as: *How are you going to add these two fractions together? How do you know what the denominator will be? What will you need to do to find the numerators?*

Review

Invite children to share the fractions they added and subtracted and to demonstrate what they did on the board. Ask the children to assess how confident they are at adding and subtracting fractions. Work through any difficulties.

Curriculum objectives
• To multiply simple pairs of proper fractions, writing the answer in its simplest form.

Success criteria
• I can multiply simple fractions.

You will need
General resources
'Dominoes'

Equipment
Individual whiteboards

Differentiation
Less confident learners
Let children focus on multiplying fractions that have 2, 3 and 4 as denominators.

More confident learners
Use the extra dominoes, so that children have sevenths and eighths to multiply together and divide by whole numbers.

Lesson 2   Oral and mental starter 69

Main teaching activities

Whole-class work: Recap multiplying fractions. Draw on the model from the main teaching activity of summer 1, week 4, lesson 2, and demonstrate $\frac{1}{2} \times \frac{1}{2}$ as you did in that lesson. Ask the children: *Do we need to find the common denominator for fractions when we multiply them? Why not?* Agree that they don't, because they are finding a fraction of a fraction. Ask the children what they *do* need to do to multiply fractions. Agree that they need to multiply the numerators by each other and the denominators by each other. Write this on the board: $\frac{7}{8} \times \frac{3}{4}$, and ask the children to solve it on their whiteboards ($\frac{21}{32}$). Write some more similar examples on the board for the children to multiply.

Paired work: Give each pair a set of 'Dominoes' from the CD-ROM. Tell them to take it in turns to pick two, placing them vertically to make two proper fractions. Explain that they should multiply them together as in the main part of the lesson. Once they have done this for around 10 multiplications, ask the pairs to work together to compare different answers using the less than and more than (< and >) symbols.

Progress check: Visit the pairs to ensure they understand the multiplication process.

Review

Invite pairs to share the fraction multiplications and divisions they made. As a class, work out the answers to both. Do the class answers match the pairs'? Taking the answers one at a time, ask the children to tell you quickly whether each is less than or more than the previous one.

Curriculum objectives
• To divide proper fractions by whole numbers.

Success criteria
• I can solve problems involving dividing fractions.

You will need
Equipment
Individual whiteboards

Differentiation
Less confident learners
Ask children to divide simple unit fractions by whole numbers to five.

More confident learners
Ask children to divide fractions with numerators higher than one by whole numbers to 20.

Lesson 3   Oral and mental starter 71

Main teaching activities

Whole-class work: Ask the children: *How do we divide fractions by a whole number?* You may find it helpful to revisit Summer 1, Week 4, Lesson 4. Demonstrate by drawing a rectangle on the board, divide it into thirds and shade one. Divide the one third again, into three, and establish that $\frac{1}{3}$ divided by 3 is $\frac{1}{9}$. Remind the children that the denominator can be multiplied by the divisor. Now ask the children what they think will happen if they divide $\frac{2}{3}$ by 3. Work through this together on the board and agree that the numerator is also multiplied by 3.

Write some fractions on the board for the children to divide by different whole numbers, for example: $\frac{3}{4} \div 7$, $\frac{4}{5} \div 6$.

Then set this problem: *Marie has a pizza. She has divided it into quarters. She wants to divide each quarter by 3. What fraction is each piece now? How many slices of pizza does she have now?* You could ask the children to draw this on their whiteboards. Check the children's whiteboards, and agree that $\frac{1}{4}$ divided by 3 is $\frac{1}{12}$, so she now has 12 slices of pizza.

Paired work: Ask the children to challenge each other with some problems that involve dividing fractions by whole numbers to 10. Prompt the children to check each other's answers.

Progress check: Visit pairs you particularly want to assess and pause them to ask: *How would you divide a fraction by a whole number? Why do you multiply by the whole number?*

Review

Invite children to share some of the problems they made up and challenge the class to solve them.

■SCHOLASTIC

Curriculum objectives

● To solve problems involving the calculation of percentages [such as 15% of 360] and the use of percentages for comparison.

Success criteria

● I can compare amounts using percentages.

You will need

Photocopiable sheets

'Percentage problems'

Equipment

Individual whiteboards

Differentiation

Less confident learners

Adapt 'Percentage problems' so that the children are working with percentages and amounts suitable to their level of attainment.

More confident learners

Adapt 'Percentage problems' so that the children are working with more complex numbers. Expect children to have time to make up similar problems.

Lesson 4 — Oral and mental starter 67

Main teaching activities

Whole-class work: Draw the per cent sign on the board, and ask: *Where would you see this sign in real life?* For example, shop sales, clothing labels, food packaging, test scores.

Give the children this problem: *There were 200 children in the school hall. 55% of them were girls. How many were boys?* Discuss how to find out. Agree that the whole amount is 100%, so, if 55% are girls, the rest of the whole must be boys. Therefore, 45% are boys. To find 45%: 10% of 200 = 20. 20 × 4 = 80, giving you 40%. And 5% = 5. So 45% = 85. Compare the percentages and the amounts and agree that there are 20 more girls than boys.

Repeat with similar problems for different percentages. For example: *In a field of 80 animals, 30% are cows, ¼ are sheep and the rest are horses. What percentage are horses? How many of each animal are there?* Agree that there are 24 cows ((10% of 80) × 3), 20 sheep (½ 80 and ½ again) and 36 horses (45%). Compare the percentages and agree that most of the animals are horses and the animals that make up the least are sheep (25%).

Independent work: Distribute photocopiable page 248 'Percentage problems' from the CD-ROM and explain to the children what they need to do. Afterwards, ask them to make up their own problems.

Progress check: Visit children you wish to assess and ask: *How can you compare the percentages? How would you find 42%?*

Review

Go through 'Percentage problems' together by inviting children to explain how they found their answers. Ask those that made up their own problems to share them with the class. Work together to solve them.

Curriculum objectives

● To solve problems involving the calculation of percentages [such as 15% of 360] and the use of percentages for comparison.

Success criteria

● I can solve problems using percentages.
● Make comparisons with percentages.

You will need

Equipment

Individual whiteboards

Differentiation

Less confident learners

Ask children to make up simpler problems where they find percentage reductions of one item.

More confident learners

Ask children to make up problems involving finding percentage reductions of three items.

Lesson 5 — Oral and mental starter 73

Main teaching activities

Whole-class work: Recap the week's work on fractions, decimals and percentages. Write up: *100% is £360* and ask the children to make up as many other percentages of this amount as they can in three minutes. Suggest they begin with 10% and use this to make others. Make a list on the board.

Set a few problems similar to this one: *Derry was looking at two bikes in a sale. One was £225, but had been reduced to £157.50. The other was £200 and had been reduced to £150. Which is the best value in terms of percentage saving?* Give the children a moment to talk with partners about how to approach this. Establish that we need to find the percentage by which each bike had been reduced. Explain that to do this, find out what percentage of the whole amount the new price is and then find the difference between that and 100%. Ask the children to try it on their whiteboards. Establish that 50% of £225 is £112.50, 20% is £45, so 70% is £157.50. The first bike has been reduced by 30%. Then, £150 is ¾ or 75% of £200, so the second bike has been reduced by 25%. The best buy is the first bike.

Paired work: Organise the children to work with partners to devise problems similar to the ones in the lesson. Then arrange for each pair to swap with another pair to solve and check each other's problems.

Progress check: Pause each pair after one or two problems to ensure they are including the different steps.

Review

Invite one or two pairs to share one of their problems. Ask the rest of the class to work out the answer on their whiteboards.

Properties of shapes

Expected prior learning

Children should be able to:

- identify various polygons and know some of their properties
- recognise various 3D shapes.

Topic	Curriculum objectives	Expected outcomes
Geometry: properties of shapes	**Lesson 1**	
	To compare and classify geometric shapes based on their properties and sizes and find unknown angles in any triangles, quadrilaterals, and regular polygons.	Draw and describe the properties of triangles and quadrilaterals.
	Lesson 2	
	To illustrate and name parts of circles, including radius, diameter and circumference and know that diameter is twice the radius.	Name parts of a circle and find relationships between them.
	Lesson 3	
	To recognise, describe and build simple 3D shapes, including making nets.	Identify and make 3D shapes. Describe the properties of different 3D shapes.
	Lesson 4	
	To recognise, describe and build simple 3D shapes, including making nets.	Draw different nets of a 3D shape. Use nets to make a 3D shape.
	Lesson 5	
	To recognise angles where they meet at a point, are on a straight line, or are vertically opposite, and find missing angles.	Estimate and measure angles. Calculate unknown angles.

ꕥSCHOLASTIC

Preparation

Lesson 1: copy 'Triangles and quadrilaterals' for each child. Make cut-outs of the shapes on the sheet (for support)

Lesson 3: collect a wide selection of 3D shapes (see vocabulary list); copy '3D shapes' for each pair

Lesson 5: copy 'Angle problems' for each pair

You will need

Photocopiable sheets
'Triangles and quadrilaterals'; '3D shapes'; 'Angle problems'

Equipment
Individual whiteboards; collection of 3D shapes; rulers; squared paper; string; plain paper; card; scissors; sticky tape; protractors; calculators (for extension)

Further practice

Photocopiable sheets
'3D shapes'

Oral and mental starters suggested for week 4

See the bank of starters on pages 85, 165, 246 and 247. Oral and mental starters are also on the CD-ROM.

26 In the net

53 Get the point

64 Dividing by 9

66 Measuring time

70 Reach the target!

Overview of progression

During this week the children will extend their knowledge and understanding of 2D and 3D shapes. They will be looking in depth at circles, triangles and quadrilaterals. They will then move on to draw and use nets of different 3D shapes. They will explore angles, measuring them accurately using protractors and finding missing angles from their knowledge of the total angles inside triangles and quadrilaterals.

Watch out for

Some children will have difficulty visualising. It would be worth spending time helping them to 'see' simple 2D shapes and drawing what they see. They could then move on to simple 3D shapes.

Creative context

Ask the children to explore 3D shape in art, for example in the sculptures of artists such as Barbara Hepworth and Damien Hirst. Encourage them to identify 3D shapes that could be used to make them and then go on to make their own versions of the sculptures.

Vocabulary

acute angle, apex, cone, cube, cuboid, circumference, cylinder, diameter, dodecahedron, dynamic angle, equilateral triangle, hemi-sphere, heptagon, hexagon, irregular, isosceles triangle, **kite**, **parallelogram**, oblong, obtuse angle, octagon, octahedron, parallel, pentagon, perpendicular, polygon, polyhedron, prism, pyramid, quadrilateral, radius, regular, right angle, rhombus, sector, segment, semicircle, sphere, static angle, tetrahedron, three-dimensional, **trapezium**, two-dimensional scalene triangle, vertices, 2D, 3D

Curriculum objectives
● To compare and classify geometric shapes based on their properties and sizes.

Success criteria
● I can draw and describe the properties of polygons, including different triangles and quadrilaterals.

You will need
Photocopiable sheets
'Triangles and quadrilaterals'
Equipment
Individual whiteboards

Differentiation
Less confident learners
Give children cut-outs of the shapes on the photocopiable sheet. They should identify each one and then copy it into the appropriate place.

More confident learners
When children have completed the photocopiable sheet, ask them to label the parallel and perpendicular sides.

Lesson 1   Oral and mental starter 70

Main teaching activities

Whole-class work: Tell the children that they will be looking at shapes this week. Ask them: *What is a polygon?* Elicit that a polygon is a two-dimensional shape with three or more straight sides. Encourage the children to give examples, and draw up a vocabulary list on the board. Ensure the children include triangle, quadrilateral, pentagon, hexagon, heptagon, octagon and decagon along with any others.

Invite a volunteer to explain, with examples, the meanings of *regular* and *irregular* shapes. Confirm that regular shapes have all sides equal and all angles equal. So, a rectangle, for instance has equal angles but not all equal sides, so is an irregular shape. Establish too that the number of lines of symmetry is equal to the number of sides of the shape. For example:

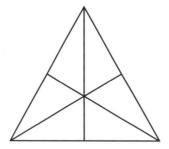 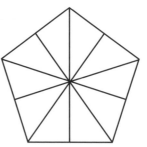 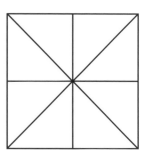

Ask the children to draw on their whiteboards the different shapes listed on the board. Encourage them to draw two of each shape – one regular and one irregular.

Now focus specifically on triangles. Ask the children to draw an equilateral triangle, two isosceles triangles – one with a right angle – and two scalene triangles – one with a right angle. For the right angles, encourage them to use the corner of a ruler, book or piece of paper; the other angles don't need to be completely accurate. Ask the children to talk in pairs to describe the properties of their triangles in terms of names, sizes of angles and lengths of sides.

Next, focus on quadrilaterals. Ask the children to give you the names of quadrilaterals. Highlight them if listed on the board, or add them to the list. Expect, or prompt: square, rectangle, trapezium, parallelogram, rhombus and kite. Ask the children to sketch an example of each, in random order, for their neighbours to identify before sharing as a class.

Finally, discuss the meanings of *parallel* and *perpendicular* sides. Ask the children to identify the quadrilaterals that have these properties (for example, rectangle, square, trapezium).

Independent work: Distribute photocopiable page 'Triangles and quadrilaterals' from the CD-ROM and make sure that the children understand what they need to do. (Angles don't have to be precise.)

Progress check: Visit the children as they work, particularly those you wish to assess. Check their work on the photocopiable sheet so far, and ask questions such as: *What is a polygon? Can you give some examples? What is the difference between regular and irregular shapes? What do we mean by* parallel? *What shapes have parallel sides? What is meant by* perpendicular? *Which shapes can have perpendicular sides?*

Review

Take feedback from the work on the photocopiable sheet. Invite some of the children to draw their triangles and quadrilaterals on the board. When they have, ask the rest of the class to describe their properties. Discuss what the square, rectangle and rhombus have in common. Establish that they all have two pairs of parallel sides and are therefore also parallelograms.

Curriculum objectives

● To illustrate and name parts of circles, including radius, diameter and circumference.

Success criteria

● I can name parts of a circle and find relationships between them.

You will need

Equipment

Individual whiteboards; rulers; squared paper; plain paper; string; scissors; calculators (for extension)

Differentiation

Less confident learners

Help children when they measure the circumferences of their circles. They may need support when finding the approximate relationship between this and the diameter.

More confident learners

Encourage children to divide the length of the diameters of their circles into the circumferences using a calculator to get a more accurate relationship between the two.

Lesson 2 — Oral and mental starter 64

Main teaching activities

Whole-class work: Ask the children: *Is a circle a polygon?* Establish that it is not because polygons have three sides or more. A circle doesn't have any. Explain to the children that a circle is made from all the points that are a given distance from a fixed point which is the centre of the circle. Demonstrate this on the board by drawing several radii of the same length from a point. Give the children a piece of squared paper each and ask them to do the same. Tell them to make a central point where a vertical and horizontal line cross. They should then draw radii of 5cm following the lines on the paper, and then make diagonals from the point, and finally radiating lines between those drawn. Then show them how to join the ends of the radii to form a circle:

Now ask the children if they can tell you anything about the lines of symmetry in a circle. Help them to understand that there are an infinite number of points from the centre of the circle and that is why a circle has an infinite number of lines of symmetry.

Ask the children to name and describe the parts of the circle that they know, for example: *circumference, diameter* and *radius*. Invite volunteers to highlight these on a circle on the board. Then ask the children to tell you, and show you, what a semicircle is. Agree that it is half a circle. Introduce or recall the terms *sector*, explaining that it is a section between two radii; and *segment* which is any section of a circle:

 Sector

 Segment

Paired work: Tell the children that they will be investigating the relationship between the radius and diameter and the diameter and circumference of circles. Give the children different-sized circles to draw around on plain paper. Once they have drawn around them, they should measure and note down the radius and diameter each time and notice the relationship between them. Ask them to work together to consider how to express this relationship as a formula.

Next, let them use the string to measure the circumferences as accurately as they can and find the relationship between these and the diameters. Once they have done this, give the children a calculator to investigate the relationship further.

Progress check: Visit the pairs to ensure they are taking accurate measurements. If necessary demonstrate how to find the circumference of a circle by measuring the string.

Review

Invite the pairs to share the relationships that they found. Agree that the formula for the radius and diameter could be $2r = d$. Call out some radius lengths and ask the children to tell you what the diameters would be. Include fraction and decimal radii such as $14\frac{2}{5}$in and 11.25cm. Ask the children to talk about what they noticed about their circumference measurements. Agree that the circumference is just over three diameter lengths. Invite those that divided their circumferences with calculators to share what they found. Confirm that the ratio of the circumference to the diameter of any circle is always about 3.14, and prompt the children to recall that this is known as pi.

Curriculum objectives

● To recognise, describe and build simple 3D shapes, including making nets.

Success criteria

● I can identify and make 3D shapes and describe their properties.

You will need

Photocopiable sheets

'3D shapes'

Equipment

3D shapes; plain paper; rulers; scissors

Differentiation

Less confident learners

Give children a selection of 3D shapes to help them with work on the photocopiable sheet.

More confident learners

When children have completed the photocopiable sheet, challenge them to make up nets for other 3D shapes, such as tetrahedron and pentagonal prism.

Main teaching activities

Whole-class work: Ask the children what kind of shapes they have been looking at so far this week. Prompt them towards *2D shapes*. Now ask: *What can you tell me about 3D shapes?* Agree that 3D shapes are three-dimensional, with a height, width and length. Ask the children to give examples, and write their ideas on the board. Ensure the list includes: sphere, cylinder, cone, cube, cuboid, square-based pyramid, tetrahedron, triangular and pentagonal prism, and any others the children suggest. Show physical examples of as many as possible. Discuss how the sphere, cylinder and cone, specifically, are different from the others. Prompt the children to notice that they have curved surfaces, whereas the others are made from flat surfaces. Point out that these shapes don't have vertices because no edges meet. Remind the children that the point on the cone is called an apex. Explore each shape, asking the children to identify their properties in terms of number of faces, edges, vertices, shapes of faces and whether they are prisms or not.

Now play a '10 questions' shape game. Think of a shape, for example a tetrahedron. Challenge the children to work out which shape you are thinking of by asking you a maximum of 10 questions to which you answer only yes or no. Then, invite one or two confident children to take on your role and let the rest of the class ask them questions.

Finally, draw a square on the board. Ask the children what 3D shape it could be. Elicit that it could be a cube, a cuboid or a square-based pyramid. Encourage the children to explain why, for example, all the faces on a cube are square, two of the faces on a cuboid could be square, and the base face on a pyramid is always square. Repeat the exercise for other shapes.

Paired work: Distribute photocopiable page '3D shapes' from the CD-ROM, spare paper, rulers and scissors, and explain to the children what they need to do.

Progress check: Visit pairs you particularly want to assess. Check they are able to draw the nets successfully. Ask questions such as: *What is a prism? How are the properties of a cube and cuboid the same? How are they different?*

Review

Invite children to say what 3D shapes they thought might be represented by the 2D shapes on the photocopiable sheet. Encourage them to explain their thinking. Invite volunteers to show the 3D shapes they made and to sketch the corresponding nets on the board.

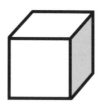

SCHOLASTIC

Curriculum objectives
● To recognise, describe and build simple 3D shapes, including making nets.

Success criteria
● I can draw different nets of a 3D shape and use them to make the actual shape.

You will need

Equipment

Paper; card; rulers; scissors; sticky tape

Differentiation

The children should work in small mixed-ability groups to investigate nets.

Lesson 4 — Oral and mental starter 26

Main teaching activities

Whole-class work: Recap the work from lesson 3 by asking the children to tell you the 3D shapes they looked at. List these on the board. Then ask the children to visualise each shape and tell you its properties. Remind them about the difference between curved surfaces and flat faces and what is meant by a vertex and an apex. Ask the children to tell you which shapes have each.

Group work: Organise the children into mixed-ability groups of four to investigate all the possible nets of a cube. There are 11 in total. Ask them to work together to discuss and then sketch on paper all the nets they think will form a cube. Then let them cut them out and fold them to see if they are correct. Once they have found as many as they can, ask them to make accurate nets on card and to cut out, fold and stick. If there is time, encourage them to explore all the possible nets of other 3D shapes.

Progress check: After about ten minutes, stop the children to see how they are getting on. Invite each group to sketch one of the nets that they have found on the board. Ensure these are all different. Then let the children continue, using those shared if they had not thought of them.

Review

Invite the groups to show the cubes they have made. Ask individuals to sketch one of the nets they drew. Have the class managed to find all 11?

Curriculum objectives
● To find unknown angles where they meet at a point.

Success criteria
● I can estimate and measure angles.
● I can calculate unknown angles from given information.

You will need

Photocopiable sheets

'Angle problems'

Equipment

Individual whiteboards; protractors

Differentiation

Less confident learners

Support children as they work on the photocopiable sheet.

More confident learners

When children have completed the photocopiable sheet, ask them to draw other quadrilaterals and explore the least number of angles needed in order to calculate the others.

Lesson 5 — Oral and mental starter 53

Main teaching activities

Whole-class work: Ask: *What can you tell me about angles?* Explain that there are two types of angle: *static* (difference in direction of two lines) and *dynamic* (rotation). Both are measured in degrees. Focus on static angles and establish these can be acute, right angle, obtuse or a straight line. Ask the children to draw two of each. (The right angle and straight line angles should be in different orientations.) Ask the children to swap their drawings with a neighbour and identify each type. Then ask the children how they identified the angles. Elicit that a right angle is 90°, an acute angle is < 90°, an obtuse is > 90° but < a straight line. A straight line can be made of two right angles and is therefore 180°.

Ask the children to tell you how many degrees there are in a triangle and a quadrilateral. Agree 180° and 360° respectively. Ask: *If we know there are 180° in any triangle, what are the sizes of the angles in an equilateral triangle?* Prompt the children to explain their answer. Repeat with similar questions for a square and a rectangle. *How can we check to see if we are correct?* Agree that they could measure the angles with a protractor.

Paired work: Distribute photocopiable page 249 'Angle problems' and protractors, and explain to the children what they need to do.

Progress check: Visit each pair to ensure they are estimating first, and then using a protractor correctly for the first part of the task.

Review

Invite pairs to share how they worked out the missing angles of the shapes.

Problems involving measures

Expected prior learning

Children should be able to:
- convert between units of measure
- solve problems involving measures.

Topic	Curriculum objectives	Expected outcomes
Measurement	**Lesson 1**	
	To solve problems involving the calculation and conversion of units of measure, using decimal notation up to three decimal places where appropriate.	Solving problems involving measures including money.
	Lesson 2	
	To solve problems involving the calculation and conversion of units of measure, using decimal notation up to three decimal places where appropriate.	Solving problems involving measures including money.
	Lesson 3	
	To solve problems involving the calculation and conversion of units of measure, using decimal notation up to three decimal places where appropriate. To use, read, write and convert between standard units, converting measurements of length, mass, volume and time from a smaller unit of measure to a larger unit, and vice versa, using decimal notation up to three decimal places.	Solving problems involving measures and money. Convert between standard units of measurement.
	Lesson 4	
	To solve problems involving the calculation and conversion of units of measure, using decimal notation up to three decimal places where appropriate. To use, read, write and convert between standard units, converting measurements of length, mass, volume and time from a smaller unit of measure to a larger unit, and vice versa, using decimal notation up to three decimal places.	Convert amounts between imperial and metric units.
	Lesson 5	
	To solve problems involving the calculation and conversion of units of measure, using decimal notation up to three decimal places where appropriate. To use, read, write and convert between standard units, converting measurements of length, mass, volume and time from a smaller unit of measure to a larger unit, and vice versa, using decimal notation up to three decimal places.	Solve problems involving time.

Preparation

Lesson 1: copy 'Party hotdogs' for each child

Lessons 2 and 3: arrange internet access for online 'shopping'

Lesson 3: collect a variety of furnishing catalogues with prices and dimensions

Lesson 4: write the conversions on the board

Lesson 5: find a time zone map resource that you can provide for each pair; copy 'Which flight?' for each pair

You will need

Photocopiable sheets

'Party hotdogs'; 'Which flight?'

General resource

Interactive activity 'What do we need?'

Equipment

Individual whiteboards; internet access; furniture and furnishings catalogues; time zone maps; analogue clocks

Further practice

Interactive activity 'What do we need?'

Oral and mental starters suggested for week 5

See the bank of starters on pages 246 and 247. Oral and mental starters are also on the CD-ROM.

66 Measuring time

69 Fractions

70 Reach the target!

72 Factors

Overview of progression

During this week the children will extend their knowledge and understanding of measures. Each lesson involves solving problems, so the children will have good practice of close reading and identifying the calculations in a text. The lessons cover length, capacity, mass, money and time, and converting from imperial units to metric.

> ### Watch out for
> Some children may have difficulty converting between units. Provide a table of unit equivalences as a guide for them so that they can access the activities.

Creative context

Ask the children to explore maps and find routes from city to city. Suggest that when they have established the routes they convert the centimetre lengths of their measurements to the scale on their map, and also work out how long the journeys would take by different forms of transport, investigating which transport would be available.

Children might also like to look into the history of clocks and the 'standardisation' of time.

Vocabulary

12-hour clock, 24-hour clock, centimetres, digital/analogue clock/watch, **feet**, **Greenwich Mean Time**, imperial units, **inches**, metres, metric units, **yards**

Curriculum objectives
- To solve problems involving the calculation and conversion of units of measure, using decimal notation.

Success criteria
- I can solve problems involving measures and money.

You will need
Photocopiable sheets
'Party hotdogs'
Equipment
Individual whiteboards

Differentiation
Adapt 'Party hotdogs' so that children work with numbers suitable to their attainment level.

Lesson 1   Oral and mental starter 69

Main teaching activities

Whole-class work: Explain to the children that over the next two lessons they will be planning and costing an end-of-term outdoor party including a barbecue. Consider what tasks might need to be undertaken, such as working out how much food is required, the costs of the food, a disco or band to play music, hire of a hall or marquee and perhaps even leaving presents.

Go on to say that in this particular lesson you will be working out quantities of food and drink to serve and the costs of these. Ask: *If we know that one bottle of lemonade will serve six people, how many bottles will we need to buy for 40 people?* (7.) Ask the children to show you their answer on their whiteboards. If there are any children who do not give the correct answer, ask another child to explain the reasoning. Point out that we divide 40 by 6, which gives 6.66, but this must be rounded up to 7, so we will need to buy seven bottles.

Independent/paired work: Organise the children to work individually or in pairs on the photocopiable sheet 'Party hotdogs' from the CD-ROM. Explain to the children that they should first work out the quantities needed, using the information given at the top of the sheet, and then calculate the costs. Encourage them to estimate their answers first, using rounding, and to check their calculations with an equivalent calculation.

Progress check: Pause the children at various times to make sure they are working systematically, referring to the information given. Help any who need support.

Review

Discuss any difficulties that have been encountered during the lesson, and compare the children's answers for question 2. Have they suggested realistic prices for their hotdogs?

Then give the children the quantities for a fruit punch recipe for the party:

1 l lemonade

¾ l orange juice

¼ l blackcurrant squash

3 oranges

2 apples

1 lemon.

Tell the children that the recipe serves 6 people.

Ask: *How much orange juice would be needed for 20 people?* (2½ litres.) Discuss how this is calculated, encouraging the children to explain their method. Ask: *How many oranges would be needed for 20 people?* (10.) For a further check, you could ask the children to calculate other quantities, such as how much blackcurrant squash is needed (⅚ of a litre).

Curriculum objectives

● To solve problems involving the calculation and conversion of units of measure, using decimal notation.

Success criteria

● I can solve problems involving measures and money.

You will need

General resources

Interactive activity 'What do we need?'

Equipment

Internet access

Differentiation

The children should work in mixed-ability groups of about four. Ensure everyone takes part. If a group finishes early, ask them to work together on the interactive activity 'What do we need?' on the CD-ROM.

Lesson 2 — Oral and mental starter

Main teaching activities

Group work: Organise the children to work in mixed-ability groups of about four, and ask them to consider how many people will be at their party. Is it just their year group, or are others invited? Then they should decide how much food they will need, make a shopping list and cost it for the amounts required. They will need price lists, if you have them, or they could use the internet to visit online shops to find out prices and delivery costs. Set an overall budget, such as £200, or a cost per head, for example £5. (Remind them to allow for delivery costs at the end, if applicable.)

Progress check: Visit the groups to ensure everyone is taking part, that the quantities and amounts are being noted down and calculated, and that there is no one dominating the proceedings.

Review

Invite the children to compare their shopping lists and, discuss what would be a reasonable cost per head. Have they managed to stay within their budgets? Ask the children to identify the mathematics involved in this activity. Emphasise how we use mathematics all the time in our day-to-day lives.

Invite one of the groups to demonstrate the interactive activity 'What do we need?' to the rest of the class.

Curriculum objectives

● To solve problems involving the calculation of units of measure, using decimal notation.
● To use, read, write and convert between standard units, converting measurements of length and using decimal notation.

Success criteria

● I can solve problems involving measures and money.
● I can convert units of measurement.

You will need

Equipment

Individual whiteboards, furnishing and carpet catalogues; internet access

Differentiation

Less confident learners

Work with children as a group. Encourage them to explain how they intend to solve the problem.

More confident learners

Challenge children to price furniture for the room from catalogues or from the internet.

Lesson 3 — Oral and mental starter 72

Main teaching activities

Whole-class work: Remind the children of the work they have done previously on decorating a bedroom with wallpaper and shelves (see Spring I Week 3 Lessons 4 and 5). Explain that, in this lesson, they will have the opportunity to plan and design their ideal bedroom. Discuss with the children what features they would like in their ideal bedroom, making a note of suggestions on the board. Consider things like carpeting, bedding, lighting, paint and wallpaper.

Independent work: Distribute catalogues and price lists for furniture. Explain to the children that they need to draw a plan of the new room. They should do this in centimetres and then scale the dimensions up to metres. Then they can decide on the furniture they would like and work out whether the sizes will fit in the room. This might also involve converting from imperial to metric units, depending on how the sizes are given in the catalogues. Explain that then they will need to position the furniture in the room, drawing the items to scale on their plans. Finally, ask them to work out how much it will cost to furnish their room.

Progress check: Visit the children periodically to talk about their designs and the costs. Ensure that they know how to cost each aspect of the design.

Review

Arrange for the children to compare their plans with a partner's. Encourage them to discuss improvements and consider how each other's suggestions will affect their costings. Then share designs and costings as a class.

Curriculum objectives

● To solve problems involving the calculation and conversion of units of measure.
● To use, read, write and convert between standard units, converting measurements of length, mass, volume and time from a smaller measure to a large unit and vice versa, using decimal notation to three-decimal places.

Success criteria

● I can convert measures from imperial units to metric, and vice versa.

You will need

Equipment

Individual whiteboards

Differentiation

Less confident learners

Support children when they are multiplying numbers and rounding off measurements.

More confident learners

Challenge children to make conversions between feet and metres, and vice versa.

Curriculum objectives

● As lesson 4.
Success criteria
● I can solve problems involving time.

You will need

Photocopiable sheets

'Which flight?'

Equipment

Individual whiteboards; time zone maps; clocks

Differentiation

Less confident learners

Ask children to calculate the journey time for option A on the photocopiable sheet.

More confident learners

Ask children to make up other options that have journey times of between 12 and 20 hours.

Lesson 4 — Oral and mental starter 66

Main teaching activities

Whole-class work: Ask the children: *What is an imperial measurement?* Establish that these are measurements introduced by Britain in 1824 and used by countries that were part of the British Empire. In the late twentieth century, many countries began using metric measurements. Some countries still use imperial measurements today, many use just metric measurements; others, including the UK, use a mixture (both miles and metres, for example). Display these approximate equivalences:

● A mile is a unit of distance, about 1.6km.
● An inch is a unit of length, about 2.5cm.
● A pint is a unit of volume, about 570ml.
● A gallon is a unit of volume, about 4.5 litres.
● An ounce is a unit of mass, about 28.3g.
● A pound is a unit of mass, about 0.45kg.

Ask the children to work out some approximate equivalences, for example: *How many pints in a litre? How many grams in 5 ounces? How many miles in 8km? How many centimetres in 8 inches?*

Group work: Organise small groups and set problems similar to this: *Carlos has just driven his car from Spain to the UK. The speedometer in his car is in kilometres per hour. He sees a speed restriction of 30mph. What speed does he need to travel at in kilometres to make sure he doesn't drive too fast?* Then ask the children to work together to write a problem for the class.

Progress check: Make sure the children can convert the measurements. Ask: *How many inches in 10cm? (4.) How many centimetres in 16 inches? (40.)*

Review

Check the group work and solve the children's problems.

Lesson 5 — Oral and mental starter 66

Main teaching activities

Whole-class work: Ask the children: *What can you tell me about times around the world?* Agree that the world is divided into time zones. These are based on Greenwich Mean Time (GMT), established in Greenwich in London in 1884.

Give pairs of children a time zone map. Ask them to find different countries, such as China, Argentina, Greenland, Madagascar and Ecuador, and to tell you how many hours they are ahead or behind the UK.

Then hand out analogue clocks. Give different GMT digital times and ask the children to show you on their clocks what the time would be in the countries above. For example: 12:35 in London, would be 25 to 4 in Madagascar. Ask also for the time in 24-hour digital format.

Paired work: Distribute photocopiable page 250 'Which flight?' and explain to the children what they need to do.

Progress check: After about five minutes, pause the children to work through one option together to check the children are approaching the problem correctly.

Review

Review 'Which flight?'. Ask children to share how they found out the journey times of the four options. Discuss whether the cities where Adam will have to change planes are relevant. Agree that the important times are the departure and arrival times. Did everyone remember to add on 7 hours? Agree that Adam should take option A, as it is the shortest journey time (10 hours 30 minutes).

 SCHOLASTIC

Using data

Expected prior learning

Children should be able to:

- interpret data shown on line graphs and bar charts
- create line graphs for a set of given data.

Topic	Curriculum objectives	Expected outcomes
Statistics	**Lesson 1**	
	To interpret and construct pie charts and line graphs and use these to solve problems.	Construct a line graph from given data.
	Lesson 2	
	To interpret and construct pie charts and line graphs and use these to solve problems.	Interpret pie charts. Connect pie charts to fractions and percentages.
	Lesson 3	
	To interpret and construct pie charts and line graphs and use these to solve problems.	Construct pie charts and relate them to angles.
	Lesson 4	
	To calculate and interpret the mean as an average.	Solve problems involving finding the mean of data.
	Lesson 5	
	To calculate and interpret the mean as an average.	Calculate and interpret the mean of a set of data. Write problems involving the mean.

Preparation

Lesson 1: draw the line graph on the board; copy 'Temperature change' for each pair

Lesson 2: draw or make available on the board an example pie chart; copy 'Pie charts' for each child

Lesson 3: write up a tally chart as suggested in the lesson

Lesson 4: copy 'Shoe size' for each pair

You will need

Photocopiable sheets
'Temperature change'; 'Pie charts'; 'Shoe size'

General resources
Interactive activity 'Island Paradisio rainfall'

Equipment
Individual whiteboards; squared paper; circular protractors; calculators

Further practice

Photocopiable sheets
'Line graph'

Oral and mental starters suggested for week 6

See the bank of starters on page 246. Oral and mental starters are also on the CD-ROM.

66 Measuring time

69 Fractions

70 Reach the target!

Overview of progression

During this week the children will revise their knowledge and understanding of data handling. The lessons require the children to interpret and construct line graphs and pie charts. They will be thinking about discrete, continuous and grouped data. They will also be finding the range, mode, mean and median of sets of data.

Watch out for

Children might have difficulty constructing pie charts, even if they can interpret them. Provide examples so that children can use fractions that they are familiar with, for example, halves, quarters and eighths.

Creative context

Ask the children to study line graphs and pie charts in newspapers and on food packaging to find out what information they are showing.
Children might also like to examine different averages in sports statistics, for example football, tennis and cricket.

Vocabulary

average, axis, continuous data, discrete data, frequency, grouped data, line graph, **mean**, **median**, pie chart, proportion, range

Lesson 1 Oral and mental starter 70

Main teaching activities

Whole-class work: Recall that a line graph shows something happening over a period of time. Ask the children to suggest such things that might be recorded in a line graph, such as the growth of a plant, some ice melting.

Display a line graph like the one below on the board and explain that it shows what happens to a water level at bath time. Share ideas about what is happening in the graph. Look at the times where there is no change in the level of water. How long do these periods last?

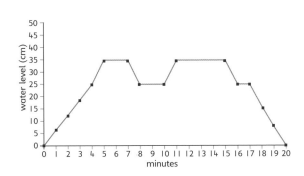

Paired work: Organise the children into mixed-ability pairs to work on photocopiable page 'Temperature change', drawing their graphs on squared paper.

Progress check: Visit pairs to check their understanding and success with transferring the data to a graph. Remind them to label axes.

Review

Ask the children to show the line graphs they made in their task. Invite pairs to ask the questions that they made up.

Lesson 2 Oral and mental starter 66

Main teaching activities

Whole-class work: Ask the children if they know what a pie chart is? Agree that it is data arranged in the form of a circle to show proportions of a whole value. Demonstrate by drawing this pie chart:

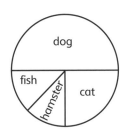

Tell the children that it shows the favourite animals of 40 children. Agree that the whole pie represents 40 children, therefore the half for dogs must represent 20 children. Discuss what fractions and/or percentages make up the number of children voting for cats (¼), hamsters and fish (about ⅛ each). Ask the children to write down how many children voted for these three animals on their whiteboards.

Now ask the children to suggest five other animals, and hold a class vote for each one. Draw a tally chart for the results. Then ask the children to draw a pie chart which approximately represents this information. Discuss the fractions and percentages for each animal using the tally and compare this with the pie chart. Are they similar?

Independent work: Distribute photocopiable page 251 'Pie charts' for the children to interpret.

Progress check: Monitor children to check they understand how to read the pie chart.

Review

Check the questions on the photocopiable sheet. Ask children to explain how they found their answers.

Curriculum objectives
- To interpret and construct pie charts and use these to solve problems.

Success criteria
- I can construct pie charts and relate them to angles.

You will need

Equipment

Individual whiteboards; circular protractors

Differentiation

This is a whole-class lesson where the children support each other.

Lesson 3 — Oral and mental starter 66

Main teaching activities

Whole-class work: Recap pie charts from lesson 2. Tell the children that they will be constructing their own today. Say: *I asked my friends what their favourite sport was. This tally shows what they said:*

Football	𝍸 II	Rugby	𝍸 𝍸
Tennis	𝍸	Athletics	III
Formula 1	𝍸 𝍸 I		

Ask: *How many friends did I ask? (36.)* Show the children a circular protractor. Ask: *How many degrees are there around this protractor?* Elicit 360. *How could we use this to construct a pie chart to show my information?* After some thinking time, establish that every 10 degrees could represent one person because 36 lots of ten make 360.

Give the children protractors and paper and ask them to construct a pie chart. Say: *Tell me what fraction of your friends like watching each sport. Now try to simplify those fractions if possible.*

Repeat the activity by asking the children to think of a 'vote' to tally. Ensure this totals a factor or multiple of 36. Discuss the value of each person or item on the tally. Then ask the children to make another pie chart. Again, ask them to write the relevant fractions, reducing as appropriate.

Progress check: Pause the children to ask questions such as: *How would you describe a pie chart? How are fractions linked to pie charts?*

Review

Use one or two of the children's examples to review pie chart percentages and fractions. Put questions such as: *What does ¼ look like on a pie chart?*

Curriculum objectives
- To calculate and interpret the mean as an average.

Success criteria
- I can solve a problem and find the mean of a set of data.

You will need

Photocopiable sheets

'Shoe size'

Equipment

Individual whiteboards; calculators; squared paper

Differentiation

Less confident learners

Give children squared paper to draw their graph on.

More confident learners

When children have finished, ask them to find the range, mode, median and mean of the heights of the children in the class.

Lesson 4 — Oral and mental starter 66

Main teaching activities

Whole-class work: Ask the children if they know: *What is meant by median and mean?* Establish they are *averages* or typical numbers in a set of data: median – the middle value; mean – the sum of all values divided by the number of values.

Say: *I think that in our class the mean shoe size is 6. How can I find out if I am right?* Agree that you need to tally everyone's shoe size. (Keep this information for the children's task.) Consider how to group the sizes together, known as *grouped data*. Group the sizes in a table, for example 11–12, 1–2, 3–4, 5–6, 7–8.

Now consider ways of showing this data; perhaps a bar chart. Ask the children to draw one on their whiteboards. Then discuss how to find the median and mean.

Paired work: Distribute photocopiable page 'Shoe size' from the CD-ROM. Tell the children that Mr Boot owns a shoe shop and would like to know how many children's shoes of different sizes he should order.

Progress check: Visit pairs you wish to assess. Ask: *What is the range of a set of data? How are median and mean similar? How are they different?*

Review

Share answers to 'Shoe size'. Invite children to explain how they found the range, median and mean, and compare these with their estimates.

Curriculum objectives
● To calculate and interpret the mean as an average.

Success criteria
● I can calculate and interpret the mean of a set of data.
● Write problems involving the mean as an average.

You will need

General resources
Interactive activity 'Island Paradisio rainfall'

Equipment
Individual whiteboards

Differentiation

Less confident learners
Ensure children start with four numbers that they can add and divide easily.

More confident learners
Encourage children to use up to 20 numbers in the problems they make up.

Lesson 5
Oral and mental starter 69

Main teaching activities

Whole-class work: Recap the learning about the mean of a set of data from lesson 4. Establish with the children that it is an average. Elicit that it can be calculated by adding up all the values of the data and then dividing this total by the number of values.

Write these numbers on the board: 13, 18, 13, 14, 13, 16, 14, 21, 13. Ask the children to work out the mean number on their whiteboards. Share answers and agree that the mean is 15 (135 ÷ 9). If anyone has a different answer, encourage a volunteer to help explain by demonstrating the calculation process on the board. Help the children to understand that the mean is a common result and therefore doesn't have to appear itself in the original list of numbers.

Now set this problem:

In a small village school, there is a class of 12 Year 4, 5 and 6 children. Three of the children are aged 8, five are 9, two are 10 and two are aged 11. What is the mean age of the class?

Give the children a little time to work this out on their whiteboards. Take feedback. Agree that the ages total 111 and when this is divided by 12 the answer is 9 $\frac{3}{12}$ or 9 $\frac{1}{4}$ (or 9.25). Discuss if this figure is useful information for a school to have and why or why not. *Does it matter that it is a fraction figure?* (It gives an accurate picture of the mean age as 9 years and 3 months.)

Then set another problem:

If a footballer scored two goals in one match, three in the next and one in the third game, what is his average goal score?

Share answers, and agree on 2. Again discuss how this is useful information. For example, it is helpful when considering the overall performance of the player.

Paired work: Organise the children to work in pairs to make up problems that involve finding the mean. For example:

These are the times it took some runners to complete 100m: Bud took 17 seconds, Jess took 23 seconds, Sam took 12 seconds and Tyrone took 18 seconds. What was the average time?

Progress check: Pause the children to ask questions such as: *How would you describe the mean? How can you find the mean of your numbers?*

Review

Ask the children to share the problems they have written. Ask the rest of the class to answer them on their whiteboards. Ask them to assess their confidence in working out the mean of a set of data.

Make time to work through the interactive activity 'Island Paradisio rainfall' with the class as this will consolidate their understanding of mean while giving practice in reading bar charts. Work together as a class, and invite volunteers to type the answers in the boxes on screen.

Curriculum objectives
● To express missing number problems algebraically.

You will need
1. Check
Oral and mental starter
73 Algebra practice

2. Assess
'Number cards 0–9'

3. Further practice
Photocopiable sheets
'Numbers and letters'

Algebra

Most children should be able to work out numbers that are represented by letters.

Some children will require additional practice at sentences with missing numbers, substituting text boxes or question marks with letters.

1. Check

73 Algebra practice

Put a variety of number sentences on the board of increasing complexity so that all of the children can answer at least some of them. Ask: *How can you find out what* n *is? What would be a sensible estimate of* n*? How will you begin to find out the value of* x*?*

2. Assess

Give each child a set of number cards. Ask them to make a two-digit number. Explain that this number represents the answer to a calculation. The children's task then is to make up an algebraic number sentence. For example: if the number made from the number cards is 47, their sentence might read $47 = 9x + 2$. They should then tell you what their letter represents. Ask the children to repeat this a few times. Record the outcomes.

3. Further practice

Photocopiable page 252 'Numbers and letters' provides the opportunity for the children to show their skills at finding the numerical value of letters. They should work on this independently.

Curriculum objectives
● To recall and use equivalences between simple fractions, decimals and percentages including in different contexts.

You will need
1. Check
Oral and mental starter
69 Fractions

2. Assess
'Dominoes'; individual whiteboards

3. Further practice
Oral and mental starter
59 Percentage bingo

Fractions, decimals and percentages

Most children should be able to find equivalences between simple fractions, decimals and percentages.

Some children will need to focus on finding basic equivalences such as decimals and percentages for ½, ¼, ¾ and tenths.

1. Check

69 Fractions

During this activity, ask the children to give their solutions as decimals and percentages as well as fractions. Ask: *How are fractions, decimals and percentages the same? How are they different? What is ¼ as a decimal? Can you explain why? What is ¾ as a percentage? How do you know?*

2. Assess

Give each child a set of 'Dominoes' from the CD-ROM. Ask them to pick one, make a proper fraction, write it on their whiteboard and then convert it to a decimal and then a percentage. For any that do not convert into a non-recurring decimal, for example ⅓, ask them to focus on rounding the denominator to the nearest tenth. Record the outcomes.

3. Further practice

Adapt oral and mental starter 'Percentage bingo' so that the children fill in their tables with a mixture of fractions, decimals and percentages. As bingo caller, call out one of the three. The children should then cross out any on their bingo cards that are the same or equivalent.

Curriculum objectives
● To solve problems involving the calculation of percentages and the use of percentages for comparison.

You will need
1. Check
Oral and mental starter
59 Percentage bingo

2. Assess
Individual whiteboards

3. Further practice
Photocopiable sheets
'What percentage?'

Comparing percentages

Most children should be able find percentages of simple amounts.

Some children will not have made such progress and might need to focus on multiples of 10%.

1. Check

59 Percentage bingo

Use 'Percentage bingo' to assess how well the children can find percentages of simple numbers. Ask: *What is a percentage? What else can you tell me? Where would you see these in real life? How would you work out 15% of 40?*

2. Assess

Write on the board: *100% is £280.* Ask the children to work out on their whiteboards as many other percentages of this amount as they can. Observe how they do this. Do they find 10% and then use doubling and halving, addition and subtraction, multiplying and dividing by 10? Record the outcomes.

3. Further practice

Photocopiable page 253 'What percentage' is designed to assess the children's understanding of sets of percentages totalling 100% and how to compare them.

Curriculum objectives
● To interpret and construct pie charts and line graphs and use these to solve problems.
● To calculate and interpret the mean as an average.

You will need
1. Check
53 Get the point
Individual whiteboards

2. Assess
Individual whiteboards

3. Further practice
Photocopiable sheets
'Line graph'

Data handling: pie charts and line graphs

Most children should be able to interpret and draw graphs and charts.

Some children will need frameworks for making simplified line graphs and pie charts.

1. Check

53 Get the point

Use this starter to check the children's understanding of how to interpret line graphs.

Then write a series of simple numbers on the board, for example: 2, 4, 7, 4, 4, 3. Ask the children to write the mean. Repeat this a few times. Ask: *How do you find the mean of a set of data? What does it tell us?*

2. Assess

Tell the children that 40 people were surveyed about their favourite flavour of ice cream. Write the results on the board:

Vanilla 5
Chocolate 20
Strawberry 10
Banana 5

Ask the children to draw a pie chart to show this information and then to express the results as fractions in their lowest forms. Record the outcomes.

3. Further practice

Photocopiable page 254 'Line graph' is an activity that allows you to assess how confident the children are at creating line graphs.

Oral and mental starters

Addition, subtraction, multiplication and division

64 Dividing by 9

Ask the children to suggest how to find out if a number can be divided by 9. Agree that if the sum of the number's digits adds up to 9, then the number is divisible by 9. For example: 135: 1 + 3 + 5 = 9, 891: 8 + 9 + 1 = 18, 1 + 8 = 9. Put some large numbers on the board, such as 549, 289, 369 and 108, for the children to investigate if this method is accurate.

65 Tables bingo (2)

Ask the children to draw a 3 × 2 table on their whiteboards and, in each section, write a different multiple of 8 (so, six multiples in total). Call out different multiplication questions from the eight times table. If the answer is one of the numbers on a child's bingo card, they should cross through it. The winner is the first to cross out all six numbers. Check the winner's card. Then repeat for other multiplication tables.

66 Measuring time

Call out pairs of 24-hour times, for example, 0940 and 1350 and ask the children to work out the difference between the two times. Encourage them to draw a number line on their whiteboards and count on, in minutes and hours, from the earliest time to the latest.

67 Operation problems

Pose this question: *I think of a number, add 12 then divide by 9. My answer is 6. What was my starting number?* Ask the children to solve this and explain how they would work it out. Elicit that they needed to use inverse operations: (6 × 9) −12 = 54 − 12 = 42. Pose similar problems such as: *I think of a number, subtract 17, then multiply by 4. My answer is 320. I think of a number, add 10 and multiply by 6. My answer is 156.*

68 Multiplying by 7

Together chant the 7-times table. Tell the children that in pairs they are going to use their knowledge of this times table to find answers in other tables. Ask them to write down on their whiteboards the ×70 table (1 × 70 = 70, 2 × 70 = 140, and so on). Once they have done this, ask them to work on the ×0.7 table and then the ×700 table. Ask the pairs to feed back their answers.

Fractions and decimals

69 Fractions

Write pairs of simple fractions on the board and ask the children to add, then subtract and finally multiply them. Remind the children that they need to find common denominators to add and subtract. Elicit that multiplying both the numerator and denominator by the same number will give a fraction that is equivalent to the original. Remind the children that they need to multiply the numerators and denominators when multiplying fractions. Prompt them to reduce the answer to its simplest form if possible.

Extension
Challenge the children to add, subtract and, if they can, multiply three or four sets of fractions.

70 Reach the target!

Give the children a target number such as 353 and explain that the aim is to find a product of two numbers that is as close as possible to the target number, for example 50 × 7 = 350 or 71 × 5 = 355. You might want to allow some children to use a calculator. Let the children compare their suggestions to see which is the closest, and ask them to explain the mental calculations they used. Repeat with other three-digit numbers.

■SCHOLASTIC

71 Decimal ordering

Write a set of mixed decimal numbers on the board, such as: 4.37, 14.2, 6.97 and 6.9. Ask the children to order them in descending order. Repeat for other sets of numbers, including some with similar digits and up to three decimal places, such as: 6.665, 6.656, 6.566 and 6.576. This time ask the children to order them in *ascending* order.

72 Factors

Recap the meaning of *factor*, then write the following numbers on the board: 30, 48, 96, 16, 40, 25, 50 and 81. Ask the children to list the factors for each number on their whiteboards. Check their answers and ask: *What do you notice about the number of factors for 16, 25 and 81?* Agree that these are square numbers because they have an odd number of factors. Try another square number, such as 49, to check this statement.

Algebra

73 Algebra practice

Write this sentence on the board: $3n - 2 = 10$. Ask: *What is the value of n?* Establish that $n = 4$. Repeat the activity with similar examples, including additions.

Remind the children that they can use simple expressions involving letters to record formulae. Say, for example: *If pencil-top erasers cost 20p, I can use the expression 20n pence to find out the cost of however many I wish to buy. If I buy five erasers, n would be 5, so 20 × 5 = 100p.* Ask the children to convert the following statements to simple formulae expressions:

- *The cost of n erasers at 9p each.*
- *The cost of n apples at 26p each.*
- *The cost of n bananas at 17p each.*

Ask the children to work out the cost of 13 erasers, 7 apples, 6 bananas if *n* is the number bought.

Percentage problems

1. In a cinema, there were 300 people. 40% of them were adults, $\frac{1}{4}$ were girls, and the rest were boys.

a. What percentage were boys?

b. Were most of the people adults, girls or boys?

c. How many adults were there?

d. How many boys were there?

e. How many were girls?

2. At the wildlife park, there were 200 primates. 12% were gorillas, $\frac{2}{5}$ were chimpanzees. The rest were lemurs.

a. What percentage were lemurs?

b. Were the animals mostly gorillas, chimpanzees or lemurs?

c. How many gorillas were there?

d. How many chimpanzees were there?

e. How many were lemurs?

3. In a circus, there were 300 performers. 24% were acrobats, $\frac{2}{3}$ were clowns, and the rest were jugglers.

a. What percentage were jugglers?

b. Were most of the performers acrobats, clowns or jugglers?

c. How many acrobats were there?

d. How many clowns were there?

e. How many jugglers?

I can solve problems and compare amounts using percentages.

How did you do?

Angle problems

- Estimate the sizes of the angles drawn below.
- Then measure them.
- How close were your estimates?

- Abigail needs to work out the missing angles in these shapes. Can you help her?

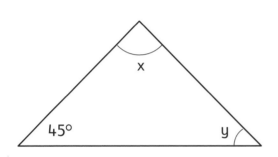

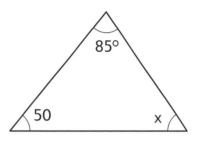

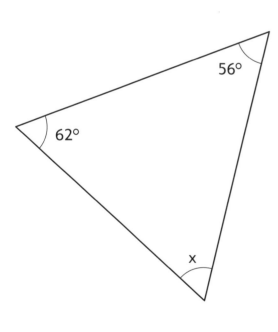

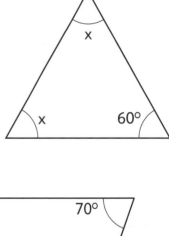

I can estimate, measure and calculate unknown angles.

How did you do?

Name: _____   Date: _____

Which flight?

- Use the information below to work out the best flight for Adam to take from London Heathrow (UK) to Austin Texas (US).
- He wants the shortest journey time.
- There is no direct flight to Austin, so he has to change planes.
- All times in the flight tables are local times.
- The time in Austin is 7 hours behind the time in London.

Here are Adam's flight options:

Option	Departs Heathrow	Arrives	Departs	Arrives Austin
A	07:45	Dallas: 08:45	Dallas: 10:15	11:15
B	09:45	Detroit: 11:45	Detroit: 14:50	19:50
C	10:35	Houston: 11:40	Houston: 12:40	15:40
D	12:40	Dallas: 14:40	Dallas: 15:40	16:40

- Fill in this table to show your working and the total journey times:

Options	Show your working here:	Journey length
A		
B		
C		
D		

- On the back of this sheet, write which flight should Adam choose, and why?

I can solve problems involving time.

How did you do?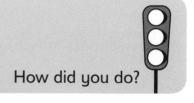

PHOTOCOPIABLE   ■SCHOLASTIC
                                                                              www.scholastic.co.uk

Pie charts

This pie chart show the ages of the people in a village. The population of the village is 3600.

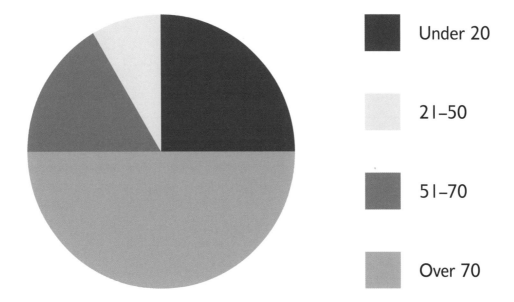

Under 20

21–50

51–70

Over 70

■ Use the pie chart to answer these questions:

1. What fraction of the population is under 20? _____

2. What is this as a percentage? _____

3. How many people are between 21 and 50? _____

4. What fraction of the population is over 70? _____

5. What percentage of the population is over 70? _____

6. How many people are between 51 and 70? _____

■ Now make up your own questions to ask about this pie chart.

_____

_____

_____

I can interpret pie charts and relate them to fractions and percentages.

How did you do?

Numbers and letters

- Work out the values of the letters in these number statements.

1. $3x + 9 = 54$

  $x =$

2. $140 = 89 + y$

  $y =$

3. $21 = 3y$

  $y =$

4. $14 + 3z = 41$

  $z =$

5. $36 - 2z = 16$

  $z =$

6. $2x + 29 = 81$

  $x =$

7. $60 - 4x = 12$

  $x =$

8. $4n - 11 = 13$

  $n =$

9. $6x + 24 = 30$

  $x =$

10. $3y + 6 = 12$

  $y =$

I can solve missing number problems algebraically.

How did you do?

PHOTOCOPIABLE

What percentage?

- Find the missing percentages in these number sentences.

1. 20% + ⬚ + 15% = 100%

Which is the largest percentage? _____ Which is the smallest? _____

2. ⬚ + 39% + 42% = 100%

Which is the largest percentage? _____ Which is the smallest? _____

3. 16% + 54% + ⬚ = 100%

Which is the largest percentage? _____ Which is the smallest? _____

4. 8% + ⬚ + 24% + 35% = 100%

Which is the largest percentage? _____ Which is the smallest? _____

5. 62.5% + 12% + ⬚ = 100%

Which is the largest percentage? _____ Which is the smallest? _____

6. 7.5% + 36% + ⬚ = 100%

Which is the largest percentage? _____ Which is the smallest? _____

7. ⬚ + 22% + 38% + 26% = 100%

Which percentage is closest to $\frac{2}{5}$? _____ Which is closest to $\frac{3}{8}$? _____

8. ⬚ + 41.75% = 100%

Which percentage is closest to $\frac{1}{3}$? _____ Which is closest to $\frac{1}{10}$? _____

I can solve percentage problems.

How did you do?

Line graph

- Draw a line graph to show these average temperatures for a year in an African country.
- Decide on the best scale to use for the vertical axis.
- Don't forget to label the axes and give your graph a title.

Jan	Feb	Mar	Apr	May	June	July	Aug	Sept	Oct	Nov	Dec
14°C	16°C	22°C	25°C	30°C	34°C	34°C	39°C	30°C	27°C	21°C	16°C

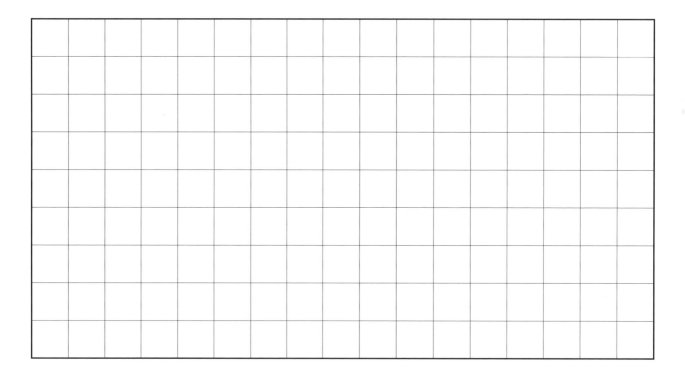

- Now make up four statements from your graph:

1. _____

2. _____

3. _____

4. _____

I can draw a line graph and use it to find information.

How did you do?

PHOTOCOPIABLE **SCHOLASTIC** www.scholastic.co.uk

Vocabulary list

Number, place value and rounding

approximately, approximating, compare, decimal, difference, digit, estimating, expanded notation, hundred, hundreds, hundred thousand, hundreds of thousands, index notation, million, millions, minus, nearest, nearly, negative, numeral, ones, order, place-holder, place value, positive, £ (pound), roughly, rounding, tens, ten million, ten thousand, tens of thousands, thousand, thousands

Addition, subtraction, multiplication and division

addition, approximate, calculate, calculation, carry, carrying, common multiple, **complimentary addition,** consecutive, decimal number, decimal place, decimal point, decomposition, decrease, difference, digit, dividend, division, divisor, double, estimate, factor, factorise, fraction, halve, increase, index, indices, integer, inverse, jotting, less than, long division, long multiplication, mental calculation method, mental method, method, minus, more than, multiple, multiplication, multiplier, number bonds, numeral, operation, partition, partitioning, pattern, plus, power, predict, prime factor, prime number, problem, **product, quotient,** reason, reduce, relationship, remainder, rounding, round down, round up, sequence, **sequencing,** solution, solving, square number, strategy, subtraction, sum total, unit, whole number

Fractions, decimals and percentages

cancelling down, **common denominator,** decimal, decimal fraction, decimal place, decimal point, denominator, discount, division, eighth, equivalent, equivalent fraction, factor, fraction, half, highest common factor, hundredth, improper fraction, increase, infinite decimal number, inverse, long multiplication, **lowest common denominator,** lowest terms, mixed number, numerator, operation, per cent (%), percentage, product, proper fraction, quarter, recurring, recurring decimal number, reduced, rounding, round down, round up, sharing, tenth, terminating decimal number

Ratio and proportion

fraction, one for every, proportion, ratio, scale

Algebra

algebra, ascending order, commutative property, descending order, equation, expression, formula, formulae, integer, linear, pattern, puzzle, rule, sequence, symbol, term, triangular number, unknown, variable

Measurement

12-hour clock, 24-hour clock, about, approximate, approximately, area, axis, centilitre (cl), centimetre (cm), centimetres, cm², cm³, constant proportion, conversion, cubic centimetre, cubic metres, cylinder, digital/analogue clock/watch, dimension, division, estimate, **feet,** foot (ft), gallon, gram (g), **Greenwich Mean Time,** imperial, imperial units, inch (in), **inches,** interval, kilogram (kg), kilometre (km), length, litre (l), mass, measure, metre (m), metres, metric, metric units, mile, millilitre (ml), millimetre (mm), ounce, perimeter, pint, pound, scale, scales, table, tonne (t), volume, width, yard (yd), **yards**

Geometry: properties of shapes

2D, 3D, acute, acute angle, angle, apex, arc, centre, chord, circle, circumference, cone, cube, cuboid, cylinder, degree, diameter, dodecahedron, dynamic angle, equilateral triangle, hemi-sphere, heptagon, hexagon, intersecting, irregular, isosceles triangle, **kite,** oblong, obtuse, obtuse angle, octahedron, octagon, parallel, **parallelogram,** pentagon, perpendicular, pi, polygon, polyhedron, prism, protractor, pyramid, quadrant, quadrilateral, radius, reflex, regular, revolution, rhombus, right angle, scalene triangle, sector, segment, semicircle, sphere, straight line, static angle, tetrahedron, three-dimensional, **trapezium,** two-dimensional, vertices

Geometry: position and direction

axes, coordinate, origin, **quadrant, reflection, rotation,** translation, x axis, y axis

Statistics

average, axis, chart, constant proportion, continuous data, conversion graph, data, discrete data, division, frequency, graph, grouped data, horizontal axis, interval, line graph, **mean, median,** origin, pie chart, proportion, range, scale, table, vertical axis

Equipment list

Number and place value

Abacus charts; atlases; counting blocks; dice; individual whiteboards; internet access; notation cards showing columns up to ten million; number cards (positive (0–20) and negative (−20 to 0)); number flip books; number lines

Addition, subtraction, multiplication and division

Blank paper triangles; charts; highlighter pens; individual whiteboards; internet access holiday brochures; number cards with a decimal point card; key words display chart (multiplication and division words); squared paper; tables squares

Fractions (including decimals and percentages)

Blank number lines; calculators; dice; decimal point cards; digit cards; fraction sets; individual whiteboards; fractions blocks or similar; fraction boards; rulers; squared paper; strips of A4 paper

Ratio and proportion

10p and 1p coins; amounts cards (40, 50, 150 and so on); calculators; counters (blue and red); food packaging; individual whiteboards; marker pens; on-screen calculator; percentage cards; paints (red and yellow); plain paper; paintbrushes (small); water

Algebra

Matchsticks or similar; counters, squared paper or interlocking cubes; individual whiteboards

Measurement

analogue clocks; calculators; centimetre cubes; centimetre-squared paper; dice (6- and 12-sided); furniture and furnishings catalogues; individual whiteboards; internet access; jug; large squared paper or squared whiteboard screen; measuring cylinders; measuring jugs, metre sticks rulers; metric abbreviations and conversions poster; place value charts; plastic cups; selection of cuboids; shopping till receipts; small plastic containers; tape measures; time zone maps; trundle wheels; unit cards: cm, m and km; water; weighing scales

Geometry: properties of shapes

2cm-squared paper; 2D shapes (including hexagons, octagons and trapezia) and 3D shapes; 3D objects; art straws; calculators; card; classroom protractor; coloured pencils; compasses; construction equipment (such as Polydron and Clixi); dotty paper; felt-tipped pens; glue; individual whiteboards; large flashcards (real or digital) showing angles about a point, on a straight line and opposite each other; large flashcards (real or digital) showing different kinds of angles; large paper or card, triangle and quadrilateral; selection of small round objects; maths dictionaries; pair of compasses; plain paper; poster of 2D drawings of 3D shapes; cardboard boxes; nail boards and elastic bands; protractors; rulers; scissors; sharp pencils; squared paper; string; sticky tack; sticky tape; string; tape measures; thin card

Geometry: position and direction

Grid paper; individual whiteboards

Statistics

360° protractors; circular protractors; calculators; coloured pencils or crayons; individual whiteboards; large paper circles divided into eight sectors; compasses; list of exchange rates; plain paper; rulers; squared paper